The authors have set out to characterize electrochemical reactions at an electrode by means of current-potential curves, and systematically to apply this method to the solution of diverse electrochemical problems. The electrochemical methods of analysis have been described in an entirely new way. Their book includes chapters devoted to recently developed techniques, electrodes, instrumentation, electrochemical reactions in various solvents including molten salts, reducing properties of metals, heterogeneous catalysis, and separation and preparation by electrolysis.

ELECTROCHEMICAL REACTIONS

Library of Congress Catalog Card Number 61-8849

With 174 illustrations and 118 tables

PRINTED IN THE NETHERLANDS BY J. B. WOLTERS, GRONINGEN

ELECTROCHEMICAL REACTIONS

THE ELECTROCHEMICAL METHODS OF ANALYSIS

by

G. CHARLOT

Professor of Analytical Chemistry, Faculté des Sciences, Paris

J. BADOZ-LAMBLING

Maître de Recherches, Centre National de la Recherche Scientifique, Paris

B. TRÉMILLON

Docteur des Sciences, École de Physique et de Chimie Industrielles, Paris, France

ELSEVIER PUBLISHING COMPANY

AMSTERDAM – NEW YORK

1962

CONTENTS

CHAPTER IV

CURRENT–POTENTIAL CURVES DURING CHEMICAL REACTIONS.
SLOW ELECTROCHEMICAL REACTIONS

CHAPTER V

INFLUENCE OF PHYSICAL FACTORS ON THE ELECTROCHEMICAL PHENOMENA

CHAPTER VI

EXPERIMENTAL DETERMINATION OF THE CURRENT–POTENTIAL CURVES

CHAPTER VII

POTENTIOMETRY

CHAPTER VIII

AMPEROMETRY

CHAPTER IX

THE RELATIONSHIP BETWEEN POTENTIOMETRY AND AMPEROMETRY

CONTENTS

CHAPTER XIII

NON-AQUEOUS SOLVENTS

Electrochemical properties of the solvent. Limitations on the range of electro-activity, 337 – Influence of the solvent on electrochemical reactions, 339 – The effect of the temperature, 341 – Problems peculiar to the use of non-aqueous solvents, 341 – Types of non-aqueous solvents, 343

APPENDIX

DEFINITIONS, SYMBOLS AND UNITS

INTRODUCTION

This book is written for chemists, especially analytical chemists.

Our aim has been the essentially practical one of showing the way in which electrochemical reactions can help the chemist to solve his problems. We have therefore not dealt with the real physical chemistry of this subject (thermodynamics, mechanisms, etc.); this is treated in many text-books of physical chemistry and electrochemistry. Nor, on the other hand, have we discussed industrial electrochemistry, where the reaction conditions are often far from the ideal conditions which are generally realised in electrochemical methods of analysis.

Most of the tools which a chemist has at his disposal when dealing with solutions consist of chemical or electrochemical reactions. We know how to deal with a large number of chemical reactions theoretically, and how to bring them about and prevent them in practice, thanks to our knowledge of the various chemical species involved and of the equilibrium constants for the reactions. It is possible to use a similar systematic approach when dealing with electrochemical reactions. A simple means of classifying many of them, and at the same time of giving a measure of their rates, is the use of current–potential curves at a given electrode. We have also a number of means at our disposal for influencing electrochemical reactions in a predictable way: altering the nature of the electrode, various chemical reactions, etc. This systematic approach is developed in the first part of the book.

The applications may then be treated, often in a novel way. On the one hand we have discussed the electrochemical methods of analysis: potentiometry, amperometry, coulometry, electrolytic separations, etc. The use of current–potential curves has proved of great help here. Among other things, it throws a clearer light on the significance of classical potentiometric determinations with zero current; and it allows the other methods to be treated in the clearest way. It also leads to a classification of the various electrochemical methods of analysis.

On the other hand we have given the principles of a number of more general applications, such as reduction by metals, catalysis and electrochemical preparations.

One chapter is devoted to non-aqueous solvents including fused salts, and another to recent electrochemical methods such as chronopotentiometry, chronoamperometry oscillographic polarography and a.c.-polarography.

We would beg the readers' pardon for often having used idealized curves in our explanations when no experimental curves were available, without taking into account such possible complicating factors as the existence of slow reactions, parasitic chemical reactions, and adsorption. We have often supposed that ideal conditions can be realised. We have indicated such curces as 'ideal curves' or 'theoretical curves' and have given the reference for all experimental curves.

We have generally cited the paper which is the most useful for our purposes, without taking any account of priority, and we also ask to be excused for this.

We have given as complete a list of references as possible for the more recent applications, and have classified them as best we could.

We thank herewith all collaborators who by their research have personally partaken in the preparation of this work.

We will always be glad to receive criticisms of this book from readers.

École Supérieure de Physique et de Chimie

Paris, January 1959.

Chapter I

ELECTROCHEMICAL REACTIONS
QUALITATIVE TREATMENT

It is known that an oxidation or a reduction corresponds to an exchange of electrons

$$\text{Oxidizing agent} + ne \underset{(2)}{\overset{(1)}{\rightleftharpoons}} \text{Reducing agent}$$

In the direction (1), the substance which accepts the electrons plays the part of an oxidizing agent or oxidant, and it is said to be reduced. In the direction (2), the substance which gives up the electrons plays the part of a reducing agent or reductant, and it is oxidized.

The exchange of electrons can take place in two ways:

1. To a solution of an oxidizing agent 1

$$\text{Oxidant}_1 + ne \rightleftharpoons \text{Reductant}_1$$

a reducing agent 2 is added

$$\text{Reductant}_2 - ne \rightleftharpoons \text{Oxidant}_2$$

and the net result is an exchange of electrons

$$\text{Oxidant}_1 + \text{Reductant}_2 \rightleftharpoons \text{Reductant}_1 + \text{Oxidant}_2$$

This is a *chemical reaction*.

2. Under suitable conditions, the electrons can be given up by a conductor which dips into the solution of the oxidizing agent 1, or accepted from the solution of the reducing agent 1. The electrons are exchanged between an electrode and the dissolved substance.

This is an *electrochemical reaction*.

An electrochemical reaction is thus an electron-exchange reaction, an oxidation or a reduction, at an electrode. It is this latter class of phenomena which is considered in this book.

We will begin by giving three successive descriptions of these phenomena, starting with a simplified theory and passing to theories more in agreement with the facts. Each of these theories has the preceding one as a special case under certain conditions.

In the first section we will suppose that the phenomena encountered, *viz.* oxidation reactions at the electrode (electrochemical reactions) on the one hand, and displacement of ions and molecules (transport phenomena) on the other hand, proceed with infinite velocities. The reactions which take place may then be treated by the use of oxidation potentials (equilibrium potentials), as is the case with rapid chemical oxidation–reduction reactions (redox reactions).

In the second section we will still suppose that the transport phenomena are infinitely rapid, but we will make allowance for the fact that the exchange of electrons usually takes place at a finite rate. The electrolytic phenomena can no longer be treated by means of equilibrium potentials, and a knowledge of the current–potential curves becomes of fundamental importance.

Finally, the velocity of displacement of ions and molecules in the solution is also finite. This gives rise to the phenomena of migration, diffusion and convection which are studied in the third section.

I. SIMPLIFIED THEORY OF ELECTROLYSIS

As stated above, the hypotheses which are supposed to hold in this section are: that the velocities of all reactions taking place, including the exchange of electrons, are infinite; and that the velocities of displacement of the ions or the molecules in solution are also infinite.

Rapid electrochemical reactions. Equilibrium potential

Consider a solution containing the redox system Oxidant $+ ne \rightleftharpoons$ Reductant. If a chemically inert conducting wire, for example a platinum wire, is dipped into the solution a continual exchange of electrons takes place between the wire and the oxidizing and reducing substances which come into contact with the electrode. An equilibrium is finally established in which the reaction

Oxidizing agent $+ ne \rightarrow$ Reducing agent

takes place at the same rate as the reverse reaction

Reducing agent $- ne \rightarrow$ Oxidizing agent.

The composition of the solution near the electrode then remains constant, and the wire has an equilibrium potential given by Nernst's equation

$$E_{eq} = E_0 + \frac{RT}{nF} \ln \frac{|Ox|}{|Red|}$$

where E_0 is a constant characteristic of the redox system considered, which is called the standard potential, R is the gas constant, T the absolute temperature, n the number of electrons involved, F the faraday and $|Ox|$ and $|Red|$ the activities of the oxidizing and reducing agents. All the potentials are given with respect to an arbitrary zero, for example the potential of the standard hydrogen electrode. Replacing these symbols by their value at a temperature of 20° C and transforming the natural logarithms into logarithms to base ten, we obtain

$$E_{eq} = E_0 + \frac{0.058}{n} \log \frac{|Ox|}{|Red|}$$

In the general case, where the redox system can be represented as

$$aA + bB\downarrow + cC + \ldots + ne \rightleftharpoons mM + pP + \ldots$$

where $\downarrow$ indicates that the substance in question is present in the solid state, the equation becomes

$$E_{eq} = E_0 + \frac{0.058}{n} \log \frac{|A|^a|C|^c \cdots}{|M|^m |P|^p \cdots} \qquad \text{(Nernst's equation).}$$

The activity of the substance B, which saturates the solution, does not appear in the equation.

This potential is called the oxidation potential of the system in question, and may be used in the theoretical treatment of reactions.

Let us suppose that the solution contains ferrous and ferric ions; the potential of the chemically inert wire with respect to the solution is given by

$$E_{eq} = E_0 + 0.058 \log \frac{|Fe^{3+}|}{|Fe^{2+}|}$$

If the electrode is given a potential of $E' > E_{eq}$, the wire is no longer in equilibrium with the solution, and electrons are therefore exchanged between the solution and the electrode until the potential of the solution reaches the same value as that of the electrode. Some ferrous iron is oxidized

$$Fe^{2+} - e \rightarrow Fe^{3+}$$

and the value of the ratio $\dfrac{|Fe^{3+}|}{|Fe^{2+}|}$ increases until E_{eq} becomes equal to E'. The system is then again at equilibrium.

If, on the other hand, the electrode is given a potential of $E' < E_{eq}$, some reduction takes place.

In brief, if a potential other than that of the solution is applied to the electrode, an oxidation or reduction reaction is produced.

The principle of electrolysis

Let us consider two conductors A and C, which will be assumed for the sake of simplicity to be chemically inert, dipping into a solution; and let us suppose that these two electrodes are connected to a source of electrical current.

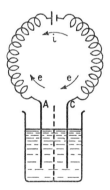

Fig. 1. Electrolysis.

A current i will now pass in the direction of the arrow shown in Fig. 1; i.e. electrons will pass in the opposite direction in the metallic conductor, leaving the electrode A and arriving in the same number at the electrode C. But electrons cannot exist as such in solution; the electrons supplied by A must therefore have come from an oxidation reaction

$$Red_1 - ne \rightarrow Ox_1$$

while the electrons arriving at C will be used up by a reduction reaction

$$Ox_2 + ne \rightarrow Red_2$$

The passage of current in the body of the solution therefore corresponds to the movement of the charges carried by the ions. This phenomenon is known as *migration.*

The passage of current from the electrode where the electrons exist in the free state, to the solution where the charges are carried by ions takes place at the surface of the electrode by means of electrochemical reactions.

The electrode where oxidation takes place is called the *anode,* that where reduction takes place the *cathode,* and the electrons pass from the anode to the cathode along the metallic conductor.

Example. Let us consider a solution of ferric chloride; and let us suppose that it contains only Fe^{3+} and Cl^- ions (neglecting the presence of ferrichloride complexes, for the sake of simplicity). Two electrodes are now placed in the solution, and a voltage V applied between them. The following reduction can occur at the cathode

$$Fe^{3+} + e \rightarrow Fe^{2+} \tag{1}$$

and the following oxidation at the anode

$$Cl^- - e \rightarrow \tfrac{1}{2} Cl_2 \tag{2}$$

The voltage applied between the two electrodes may be split up into two parts: $V = E_A - E_C$, where E_A and E_C are the potentials applied to the anode and the cathode.

We can also define the oxidation potential of the Fe^{3+}/Fe^{2+} system in the solution; it is the potential E_{Fe} of an electrode in equilibrium with the system

$$E_{Fe} = E_0 + 0.058 \log \frac{|Fe^{3+}|}{|Fe^{2+}|}$$

If the cathode is given a potential $E_C < E_{Fe}$, the system is not in equilibrium; the reaction which is thus spontaneously produced tends to re-establish this equilibrium, *i.e.* to increase E_C and to decrease E_{Fe}. In this case, this is the reaction (1), which cause electrons to disappear from the cathode ($E_C \nearrow$) and produces Fe^{2+} ions at the expense of Fe^{3+} ions ($E_{Fe} \searrow$).

Conversely, if reaction (1) is to take place at the cathode, E_C must be smaller than E_{Fe}. Similar reasoning shows that E_A must be greater than E_{Cl}, the oxidation potential of the Cl^-/Cl_2 system in solution, if the anodic reaction is to take place.

If electrolysis, *i.e.* passage of current, is to take place, these conditions must be simultaneously fulfilled

$$E_C < E_{Fe} \text{ and } E_A > E_{Cl}, \text{ whence } V = E_A - E_C > E_{Cl} - E_{Fe}$$

Remarks. 1. The above condition is necessary, but not sufficient, since the exchange of electrons may be infinitely slow. This will be discussed further in the second section.

2. V may be positive, zero or negative. Oxidation–reduction phenomena can still occur in the special case $V = 0$. The system is then said to function as a galvanic cell; it may be seen that this is not a different phenomenon, but a special case of electrolysis.

3. If V is negative, the potential of the anode is less than that of the cathode. The use of the signs + and − to designate the electrodes may thus lead to confusion.

The prediction of the reactions which will occur at the electrodes

In general, several oxidation reactions and several reduction reactions will be possible. But, if we keep our initial hypotheses, we may predict which reactions will actually take place at the electrodes. The following rules may be stated:

1. Any substance capable of being oxidized can react at the anode, and any substance capable of being reduced can react at the cathode. It may be noted that the charge is of no importance in this connection: anions, cations and molecules can all react at the anode, and also at the cathode.

2. Of the oxidizable substances, that with the lowest oxidation potential will be oxidized first at the anode; and the reducible substance with the highest oxidation potential will be the first to be reduced at the cathode.

Example. Consider a solution of copper sulphate (0.1 M) and silver sulphate (0.05 M) in molar perchloric acid. The possible reduction reactions are

$$Cu^{2+} + 2e \rightarrow Cu \downarrow \qquad E_{eq} = 0.34 + 0.029 \log |Cu^{2+}| = 0.31V$$
$$Ag^+ + \ e \rightarrow Ag \downarrow \qquad E_{eq} = 0.80 + 0.058 \log |Ag^+| \ = 0.74V$$
$$2 H^+ + 2e \rightarrow H_2 \uparrow \qquad E_{eq} = 0.00 + 0.058 \log |H^+| \ = 0.00V$$

and the possible oxidation reactions

$$2 SO_4^{2-} - 2e \rightarrow S_2O_8^{2-} \qquad E_0 = 2.0V$$
$$Ag^+ - \ e \rightarrow Ag^{2+} \qquad E_0 = 2.0V$$
$$2 H_2O - 4e \rightarrow O_2 \uparrow + 4 H^+ \qquad E \ = 1.23 + 0.058 \log |H^+| = 1,23V$$

If electrolysis takes place, then Ag^+ ions will be reduced at the cathode and water will be oxidized at the anode. The condition for electrolysis to take place is

$$E_A - E_C \geq 1.23 - 0.74 = 0.49V$$

Remarks. 1. The substances which disappear in the course of electrolytic reactions may be dissolved ions or molecules, or the metal of the electrode itself, *e.g.*

$$Cu \downarrow - 2e = Cu^{2+}$$

or the solvent, *e.g.*

$$2 H_2O - 4e \rightarrow O_2 \uparrow + 4 H^+$$
or $$4 OH^- - 4e \rightarrow O_2 \uparrow + 2 H_2O \quad \text{if the medium is alkaline enough}$$

$$2 H_2O + 2e \rightarrow H_2 \uparrow + 2 OH^-$$
or $$2 H^+ \ + 2e \rightarrow H_2 \uparrow \qquad \text{if the medium is acid enough}$$

2. The substances which are formed can pass into solution, can be evolved as gases, or be precipitated. In the last case, if the substance formed is a metal it will in general be deposited on the electrode.

3. The concentration of a substance which takes part in an electrolytic reaction will in general diminish as the reaction proceeds; in the example given above, this is so for the Ag^+ ions which are reduced to give the metal. The equilibrium potential of the system therefore varies, decreasing if an oxidizing agent disappears and increasing

References p. 30

if a reducing agent is affected. Again considering the example given above, when the concentration of Ag^+ ions falls to 3×10^{-9} the oxidation potential of the system is

$$E = 0.80 + 0.058 \log |Ag^+| = 0.31 V$$

It will then not be possible to go on reducing Ag^+ ($E_C < 0.31$ V) without reducing Cu^{2+} at the same time.

4. The substances formed at the anode by oxidation may pass through the solution to the cathode and be reduced there, and vice versa. Such phenomena may be prevented by separating the anode from the cathode, *e.g.* by a porous diaphragm.

II. THEORY OF ELECTROLYSIS INVOLVING CURRENT–POTENTIAL CURVES

The phenomena are in fact more complicated than described above. They do not proceed at an infinite rate, for two reasons:

1. The electrochemical reactions have a finite velocity which varies considerably from case to case.

2. The electrochemical reactions can only continue in so far as the substances which are used up as a result of the electrolysis are replaced at the surface of the electrode. The transport of matter to the surface of the electrode also proceeds at a finite rate.

For the present, we will still assume that the second process takes place infinitely quickly, and can thus be neglected. It follows that the composition of the solution at any moment is the same near the electrode as in the body of the solution.

We will restrict ourselves to considering phenomena at a single electrode, until mention is made to the contrary.

Current–potential curves

A. Reducing agent or oxidizing agent alone

Let us suppose, for example, that an oxidation reaction such as

$$Red - ne \rightarrow Ox$$

is taking place.

If the anode potential E_A is progressively increased, it is found that the electrolysis current also increases as soon as E_A exceeds the equilibrium potential. The current may be plotted as a function of the potential, as in Fig. 2. It may be seen from this figure that the current attains a mesasurable value (for an arbitrarily chosen measuring device) at a potential ε_A, and continues to increase thereafter.

When considering a cathode reaction, it is convenient to regard the currents as negative. Examining a plot of current as a function of cathode potential (Fig. 3) shows that the absolute value of i increases as E_C falls below the equilibrium potential.

Now the current is proportional to the number of electrons exchanged per unit time; it is thus a measure of the rate of the reaction in question. A knowledge of the current–potential curves thus allows the rate of the electrochemical reaction to be determined for each value of the electrode potential.

For a given oxidizing or reducing agent, the form of the current–potential curve depends on the chemical and physical nature of the electrode, also on its shape and

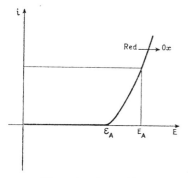

Fig. 2. Anode reaction.

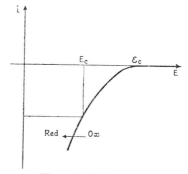

Fig. 3. Cathode reaction.

size; it also varies with the activity of the oxidizing or reducing agent in solution. Moreover, chemical factors such as the pH, complex formation and precipitation which can influence the oxidation–reduction reactions taking place will also have an effect on the curve.

B. Oxidizing–reducing couple

If the oxidizing and reducing agents chosen are the two components of the same oxidizing–reducing system

$$Red - ne \rightleftarrows Ox$$

the current–potential curves can still be drawn separately for each component. These curves can occupy different positions relative to each other, for a fixed scale along the voltage axis (Fig. 4 and Fig. 5). Let us suppose that both the oxidized and reduced forms are present simultaneously. In the case shown in Fig. 4 it will be seen that at no value of the potential do both reactions take place at the same time with an appreciable velocity. In the case shown in Fig. 5, however, for a potential such as E_1 the oxidation of Red occurs with a finite velocity i_1, while at the same time Ox is reduced at a finite rate i_2. The equilibrium potential corresponds to a zero net current $i = i_1 + i_2 = 0$. This is the potential which will be assumed by an isolated electrode dipping into the solution; at this potential the composition of the solution does not

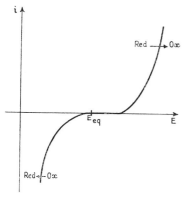

Fig. 4. Slow system.

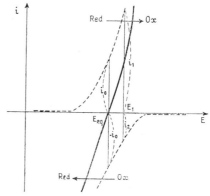

Fig. 5. Fast system.

change, since the rate of oxidation is equal to the rate of reduction. Knowing the
form of the two current–potential curves in Fig. 5, it is possible to determine the value
of the equilibrium potential E_{eq} and the form of the curve of net current i as a function of E (full line). There is also an equilibrium potential for the case shown in Fig. 4,
but it is not possible to determine its exact value from the form of the curves.

'*Slow*' *and* '*fast*' *systems.* We propose the term 'slow system' for a redox system for
which the current–potential curves are as shown in Fig. 4, and the anode and cathode
currents are thus small for a potential E_{eq}. Similarly, we will call a system corresponding to the case shown in Fig. 5 a 'fast system'.

    If it is desired to oxidize the reducing agent of a slow system at a given finite
rate, the potential must be increased to a value E which is much larger than E_{eq}.
This potential $E - E_{eq}$ is known as the overpotential at the anode, and is an important
quantity in such a system. Under such conditions, the oxidizing agent is reduced at
a rate very close to zero (Fig. 4).

    In a fast system, the potential must only be very little more than E_{eq} in order to
oxidize the reducing agent at the same rate as above; the overpotential is thus very
low (Fig. 5). In such a case, it is possible to carry out an oxidation (or reduction) at
a finite rate under conditions which are very nearly reversible. This is why such systems are often called 'reversible systems' while others are called 'irreversible systems'.
In our opinion, however, it is not proper to apply the adjectives 'reversible' or 'irreversible' to a system, as only a reaction can be described as being reversible or irreversible.

    A very fast system gives a curve of net current against potential which is nearly
a vertical line throught the point E_{eq} (Fig. 6). Oxidation can be carried out very rapidly

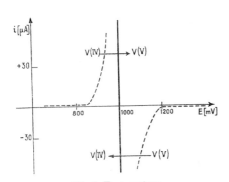

Fig. 6. Fast system.

0.1 M V(V)/V(IV) in molar $HClO_4$. Platinized
platinum electrode (after Coursier [1]).

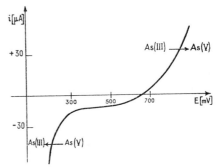

Fig. 7. Slow system.

0.1 M As(V)/As(III) in molar $HClO_4$. Platinized platinum electrode (after Coursier [1]).

indeed by raising the potential very slightly above E_{eq}. Such a system will show all
the characteristics predicted by the simplified theory of Section I. The form of the
curves naturally depends on the current scale chosen. We have generally chosen to
represent i as negligibly small on the graph for a residual current due to the electrolysis of impurities of concentration $10^{-6} - 5 \cdot 10^{-6}$ (M). Slow and fast systems can be
given a precise definition in terms of quantitative relationships (see Chapter II).

C. Several oxidizable and reducible substances present. Additivity of the currents

In general, several oxidizable and reducible substances will be present in solution. The current–potential curve can then be traced separately for each component.

In most cases, in the absence of any chemical reactions between the substances present in solution, the resulting current due to the oxidation and reduction of the various compounds is the algebraic sum of the currents resulting from the oxidation or reduction of each substance taken separately.

Example. Typical current–potential curves for the two compounds when one oxidizing agent and one reducing agent are present are shown in Fig. 8. At a potential E_1 it may be seen that Red_1 is oxidized at a rate given by i_1, while the rate of reduction of Ox_2 is given by i_2. The net current is then $i = i_1 + i_2$ (full line).

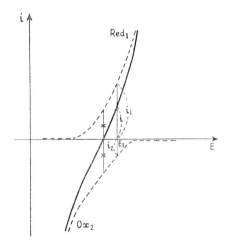

Fig. 8. Additivity of the currents.

In the example we have chosen, the absolute value of i_1 is greater than that of i_2, so that the net current is positive and oxidation predominates. The electrode thus behaves as an anode, but this does not prevent a reduction from taking place at this electrode at the same time.

D. Two electrodes

Both an anode and a cathode are necessary for electrolysis, and the same current passes through both electrodes.

1. The electrodes are placed in two solutions which are separated by e.g. a porous diaphragm. The current–potential curves for the two solutions may then be plotted together on the same graph (Fig. 9).

   (a) If a voltage ΔE is applied between the two electrodes 1 and 2, a segment of length ΔE must be marked on the E axis so that the corresponding currents are equal and opposite. The value of the current i_1 and of the electrode potentials E_A and E_C may then be read off from the curves.

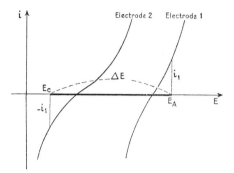

Fig. 9. Electrolysis with a constant voltage.   Fig. 10. Electrolysis with a constant current.

(b) If instead of the voltage the current I due to the electrolysis is fixed, then the electrode potentials can be determined (Fig. 10). If the direction of the current is such that electrode 1 acts as an anode, the electrode potentials are found to be E_A and E_C. If, however, the current has the same magnitude but the opposite direction the electrode potentials are found to be E'_A and E'_C.

2. Two identical electrodes are placed in the same solution. Each electrode then has the same current–potential curve. Let us suppose for the sake of simplicity that the solution contains one oxidant and one reductant. We can then draw the two current–potential curves and hence the curve of net current i against E (Fig. 11).

(a) If the electrolysis current is fixed at say I, then since we know that the anode and cathode currents must be equal and opposite, we can deduce the values of the anode and cathode potentials E_A and E_C. It can also be seen that at the anode the reductant is oxidized at a rate i_1 and the oxidant is reduced at a rate i_2, while at the cathode the rate of oxidation is i_3 and the rate of reduction i_4 (Fig. 11).

(b) If the voltage is fixed at ΔE, a segment of length ΔE must be found along the E axis such that the corresponding currents are equal and opposite (Fig. 12).

3. If the two electrodes are of a different material or if they have a different surface, they will have two separate currents–potential curves. The two curves can be plotted on the same graph, and the same method as in the first case (Fig. 9 and 10) can be used.

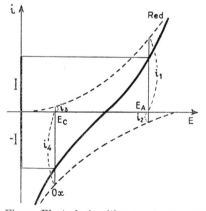
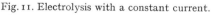
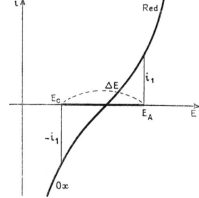

Fig. 11. Electrolysis with a constant current.   Fig. 12. Electrolysis with a constant voltage.

Oxidation and reduction of the solvent

The solvent can in general be oxidized or reduced. Water or its ions can be oxidized according to the overall equations

$$2 H_2O - 4e \rightarrow O_2\uparrow + 4 H^+$$

and

$$4 OH^- - 4e \rightarrow O_2\uparrow + 2 H_2O$$

and reduced according to

$$2 H_2O + 2e \rightarrow H_2\uparrow + 2 OH^-$$

and

$$2 H^+ + 2e \rightarrow H_2\uparrow$$

The current–potential curves for these reactions are shown in Fig. 13.

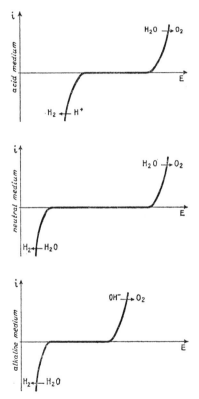

Fig. 13. Oxidation and reduction of water and its ions.

We shall see that the nature of the solvent limits the voltage range in which oxidations and reductions can be carried out.

Treatment of the electrode reactions. Examples

Once the current–potential curves are known, we can predict the electrochemical reactions which will take place.

Example 1. Electrolysis of an acid solution containing ferric iron and persulphate (graphite electrodes).

The current–potential curves at the start of electrolysis are shown in Fig. 14.

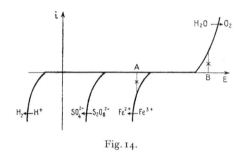

Fig. 14.

The only possible oxidation is that of water

$$2\ H_2O - 4e \rightarrow O_2\uparrow + 4\ H^+$$

If a voltage equal to the distance AB (Fig. 14) is applied between the two electrodes, ferric iron will be reduced to ferrous at the cathode at the same rate as water is oxidized at the anode.

1. The composition of the solution changes as the reaction proceeds, *e.g.* Fe^{2+} appears.

2. The equilibrium potentials of the systems

$$S_2O_8{}^{2-}/SO_4{}^{2-} \qquad E_0 = 2.0V$$

and

$$Fe^{3+}/Fe^{2+} \qquad E_0 = 0.78V$$

are such that the simplified theory would predict that persulphate would be reduced before ferric iron. If, however, the rate of the reaction is taken into account by using current–potential curves, it is found that ferric iron is reduced first.

Example 2. Electrolysis of a solution of sodium chloride, with separate anode and cathode compartments.

1st case: graphite anode, iron cathode. Since the two electrodes are different, a separate current–potential graph must be drawn for each one.

The reactions theoretically possible at the graphite electrode (Fig. 15) are

oxidations: $2\ Cl^- - 2e \rightarrow Cl_2\uparrow$

$\qquad\qquad\ 2\ H_2O - 4e \rightarrow O_2\uparrow + 4\ H^+$

reductions: $2\ H_2O + 2e \rightarrow H_2\uparrow + 2\ OH^-$

$\qquad\qquad\ Na^+ + e \rightarrow Na\downarrow$

Fig. 15 shows that the easiest oxidation is the reaction of chloride ion to give chlorine gas.

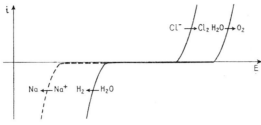

Fig. 15.

The reactions possible in theory at the iron electrode (Fig. 16) are

oxidations: $2 \text{Cl}^- - 2e \rightarrow \text{Cl}_2 \uparrow$

$\qquad\qquad 2 \text{H}_2\text{O} - 4e \rightarrow \text{O}_2 \uparrow + 4 \text{H}^+$

$\qquad\qquad \text{Fe} \downarrow - 2e \rightarrow \text{Fe}^{2+}$

reductions: $\quad \text{H}_2\text{O} + 2e \rightarrow \text{H}_2 \uparrow + 2 \text{OH}^-$

$\qquad\qquad \text{Na}^+ + e \rightarrow \text{Na} \downarrow$

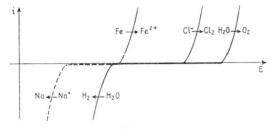

Fig. 16.

According to Fig. 16, the only possible reaction is the evolution of hydrogen. Plotting the curves which interest us on the same graph (Fig. 17) we find that for a voltage ΔE applied so that $E_{\text{graphite}} > E_{\text{iron}}$, the electrolysis current is i, chlorine and hydrogen being evolved.

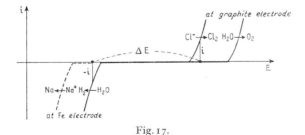

Fig. 17.

2nd case: Graphite anode, mercury cathode. The curves for the anode remain the same, but the replacement of iron by mercury for the cathode has a double effect: the curve for the system $\text{H}_2\text{O} \rightarrow \text{H}_2 \uparrow$ is displaced to the left (the overpotential of

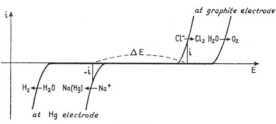

Fig. 18.

hydrogen on mercury is greater than that on iron by about 0.4 V), while the curve for the system $Na^+ \rightarrow Na\downarrow$ is shifted to the right, because of the formation of sodium amalgam (Fig. 18). In fact, the relative positions of the two curves are reversed, so that sodium amalgam is formed at the cathode.

III. THEORY OF ELECTROLYSIS TAKING INTO ACCOUNT
THE TRANSPORT OF MATTER IN SOLUTION

In this section we will consider the second effect limiting the velocity of electrolytic reactions: the transport of matter in solution, which proceeds with a finite velocity.

Modes of transport

We may distinguish three ways in which matter may be transported in solution:

1. *Migration.* The current passing through the electrolysis circuit is the same at all points of that circuit at any given moment. If we suppose that in a given space of time n elements of charge (electrons) pass a given point in the metallic circuit, then n electrons must be exchanged at the surface of each electrode in the same space of time; and the system must be balanced by the passage of n elements of charge through the solution. These charges can only be carried by ions. Ions are thus moving through the solution: the anions (negatively charged) move in the same sense as the electrons in that part of the circuit outside the solution, while the cations (positively charged) move in the opposite sense. The overall movements of charges, which is called migration, corresponds to 'the passage of current' in the solution.

2. *Diffusion.* During electrolysis, the electrochemical reaction produces a change in the concentration of the electrolyzed substances near the electrode. A concentration gradient is thus set up between the surface of the electrode and the body of the solution, and this leads to a movement of these substances from regions of high concentration to regions of low concentration. This phenomenon is called diffusion.

Diffusion occurs around the electrode and can only affect a part of the solution (unlike migration).

3. *Convection.* Substances can move through the solution for a variety of other reasons: differences in density or temperature, vibrations and shocks, etc., or of course by stirring. We will include all such phenomena under the name of convection; mechanical agitation of the solution is the most important form of motion by convection.

Stationary state

The solution is generally homogeneous at the start of the electrolysis. An electrode placed in such a solution will take up an equilibrium potential E_{eq}. If a potential E, different from E_{eq}, is applied to the electrode, an electrochemical reaction occurs at its surface, tending to establish other equilibrium concentrations near the electrode corresponding to the applied potential E. This gives rise to an electrolysis current. If no transport of matter took place, or if it were infinitely slow, the current would cease as soon as the concentrations at the surface of the electrode had reached values satisfying the relationship between concentration and potential. But transport does occur, tending to keep the concentrations near the electrode constant, so the current decreases much more slowly.

If the electrochemical reaction is instantaneous, the rate of electrolysis is determined by the rate of transport towards the electrode (or from the electrode), which exactly balances the disappearance (or formation) of matter caused by the electrolysis. Since the transport takes place at an finite rate, a finite current is set up. If the rate of transport does not vary with time, a constant current determined only by the rate of transport is produced. At the start of the electrolysis, a transition period is observed during which the rate of transport varies, after which a stationary state is reached.

In the more realistic case where the rate of the electrochemical reaction is also finite, a transition period is again observed at the start of the electrolysis. During this period (i) the concentrations at the electrodes adjust themselves slowly, tending to a new state of equilibrium corresponding to the applied potential; (ii) the rate of transport of the electrolyzed substances changes until it attains a constant value to the rate of electrolysis. A steady state is reached after this initial period.

It has been found by experiment that such a steady state can be attained fairly rapidly if the transport of matter in the solution is much accelerated by convection (*e.g.* vigourous stirring of the solution), and if it is held at a constant value by regulating the physical factors which cause it. The existence of a stationary state implies that the concentrations in the electrolytic cell remain constant. This implies in its turn that the amount of material electrolyzed during the period of measurement is negligible compared to the total amount present in the cell. It is convenient to assume that a diffusion layer exists at the surface of the electrode during the stationary state. The reacting substances are brought to this layer by convection (*e.g.* stirring) and are transported across it by diffusion. While the stationary state lasts, the diffusion layer will have a constant thickness.

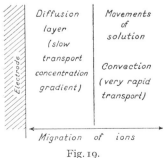

Fig. 19.

This hypothesis, suggested by Nernst, is only an approximation to the facts; but it simplifies calculations and is based on experimental results.

We have assumed above that the electrode potential E is fixed. If the current i is fixed instead, it will similarly be seen that the current can only be kept constant by transport of matter to replace that used up by the electrolysis. After some time, as above, a stationary state may be reached. If an electrode potential E_1 is applied, the current will reach a stable value i_1 after a certain transition period; and if the electrode current is kept at i_1, the potential will reach the same value E_1 after a different transition period. The current–potential curve is independent of time in the stationary state.

We will assume in all that follows (unless stated to the contrary) that a stationary state exists. We will give the name 'diffusion current' to that part of the electrolysis current due to substances transported by diffusion near the electrode, always remembering that the diffusion is accelerated by convection processes in the body of the solution.

Migration current and diffusion current

It is interesting to see how much of the transport occuring during electrolysis is due to migration, and how much is due to diffusion near the electrode.

In the stationary (or steady) state, the overall rate of electrolysis is equal to the rate of transport of the electrolytes. The electrolysis current may thus be expressed as the sum of the current due to the electrolysis of ions transported by migration and that due to the electrolysis of substances transported by diffusion

$$i = i_d \pm i_m \tag{1}$$

where i is the overall electrolysis current, i_m that part of the current due to migration and i_d that part due to diffusion.

Conventions

For an oxidation, i is taken as positive and for a reduction negative, and the same sign convention is used for i_d and i_m. The positive sign is taken in Eq. (1) if the transport by migration takes place in the same direction as that by diffusion (reduction of a cation or oxidation of an anion): $i = i_d + i_m$. The negative sign is taken if the transports occur in opposite directions (oxidation of a cation or reduction of an anion, e.g. $Fe(CN)_6{}^{3-}$): $i = i_d - i_m$. If the substances electrolyzed are molecules, $i_m = 0$.

Similar equations may be written for the substances formed by electrolysis, which diffuse away from the electrode. The sign of i_d must therefore be changed in this case.

In the body of the solution, on the other hand, the current i is equal to the charges transported by migration per unit time and is named 'migration current'. The fraction of the total migration current i carried by one ion is given by $t.i$, where t is the transport number of the ion, i.e. the fraction of the charges which it carries

$$t = \frac{l \cdot z \cdot C}{\Sigma\, l_i \cdot z_i \cdot C_i}$$

Here z represents the ionic charge, C the concentration of the ion, and l a constant called the equivalent conductivity of the ion in question. If this ion is electrolyzed, the above equation allows the current due to its electrolysis, i_m, to be calculated (i_m is *not* the 'migration current'). Since the number of charges carried by the ion per unit time is $t.i$, the number of migrating ions of this species is $t.i/z$; and if n is the number of electrons involved in the electrolysis of the ion, then i_m, the fraction of the electrolysis current due to its migration, is

$$i_m = \frac{n.t.i}{z}$$

If $n = z$, it follows that i_m, the migration current of the electrolyzed ion, is equal to $t.i$. If several ions are electrolyzed simultaneously

$$\Sigma\, i_m = \Sigma\, \frac{n.t.i}{z}$$

It follows that the fraction of the electrolysis current due to substances transported by the diffusion is

$$i_d = i\left(1 \pm \frac{n.t.}{z}\right)$$

Example. Consider the electrolysis of a solution of hydrochloric acid. The following electrochemical reactions occur at the electrodes:

$$Cl^- - e \rightleftarrows \tfrac{1}{2}Cl_2$$

at the cathode

$$H^+ + e \rightleftarrows \tfrac{1}{2}H_2$$

The migration current is provided by the movement of H^+ and Cl^-. The transport numbers of H^+ and Cl^- are given by

$$t_{H^+} = \frac{l_{H^+}.C_{H^+}}{l_{H^+}.C_{H^+} + l_{Cl^-}.C_{Cl^-}} = \frac{l_{H^+}}{l_{H^+} + l_{Cl^-}}$$

and

$$t_{Cl^-} = 1 - t_{H^+}$$

since $l_{H^+} \approx 4\, l_{Cl^-}$, $t_{H^+} = \tfrac{4}{5}$ and $t_{Cl^-} = \tfrac{1}{5}$. For every 5 electrons exchanged at the electrodes, therefore, $4\,H^+$ migrate towards the cathode and one Cl^- towards the anode. At the anode (Cl^-): $i = i_d + i_m$, so $i_d = i - i_m = 5 - 1 = 4$, *i.e.* $4\,Cl^-$ arrive at the anode by diffusion. At the cathode (H^+): $i = i_d + i_m$, so $i_d = i - i_m = -5 + 4 = -1$, *i.e.* $1\,H^+$ arrives at the cathode by diffusion.

The 'balance sheet' for the transport may be represented as shown below (after COURSIER [1]).

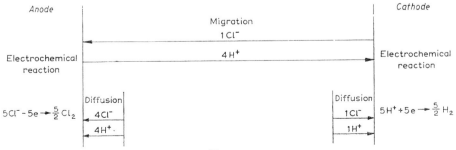

Fig. 19a.

1. *Balance of the Cl^- ions.* At the anode: $5\,Cl^-$ disappear by electrolysis; $1\,Cl^-$ arrives by migration, so $4\,Cl^-$ arrive by diffusion.

At the cathode: $1\,Cl^-$ migrates from the cathode. so $1\,Cl^-$ arrives by diffusion.

2. *Balance of the H^+ ions.* At the cathode: $5\,H^+$ are used by electrolysis; $4\,H^+$ arrive by migration, so $1\,H^+$ arrives by diffusion.

At the anode: $4\,H^+$ migrate away, so $4\,H^+$ diffuse to the anode.

The diffusion of $4\,HCl$ towards the anode and of $1\,HCl$ towards the cathode makes up the losses caused by electrolysis and migration.

Another example. Consider a solution containing equal concentrations C of ferrous and ferric perchlorate. The electrochemical reactions are:
At the anode

$$Fe^{2+} - e \rightarrow Fe^{3+}$$

At the cathode

$$Fe^{3+} + e \rightarrow Fe^{2+}$$

The transport numbers of the ions are

$$t_{Fe^{2+}} = \frac{l_{Fe^{2+}} \cdot 2\,C}{l_{Fe^{2+}} \cdot 2\,C + l_{Fe^{3+}} \cdot 3\,C + l_{ClO_4^-} \cdot 5\,C} \text{ etc.}$$

If we take $l_{Fe^{2+}}$, $l_{Fe^{3+}}$ and $l_{ClO_4^-}$ as all having about the same value, then

$$t_{Fe^{2+}} = \tfrac{2}{10}, \quad t_{Fe^{3+}} = \tfrac{3}{10}, \quad t_{ClO_4^-} = \tfrac{5}{10}$$

For every 10 electrons exchanged at each electrode, $1\,Fe^{3+}$ (3 charges out of 10) and $1\,Fe^{2+}$ (2 charges) migrate towards the cathode, and $5\,ClO_4^-$ (5 charges) migrate towards the anode. At the anode: $i = i_d - i_m$ for Fe^{2+}, i.e. $10 = 11 - 1$. $1\,Fe^{2+}$ migrates away from the anode, so $11\,Fe^{2+}$ diffuse towards it. At the cathode, $i = i_d + i_m$ for Fe^{3+}, i.e. $-10 = -9 - 1$. $1\,Fe^{3+}$ arrives by migration, so 9 arrive by diffusion.

The ionic balance may be represented as in the previous example

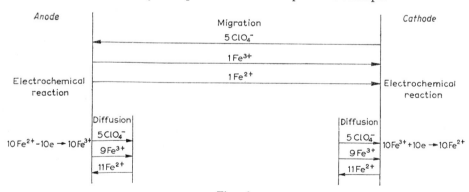

Fig. 19b.

Presence of an excess of an indifferent electrolyte

In many cases a simplification is achieved by adding a large excess of an indifferent electrolyte to the solution; this takes part in the production of the migration current, but not in the electrolysis.

The part played by the electrolyzed ions in the migration current then becomes negligible, and nearly all the electrolysis current arises from the oxidation and reduction of ions which arrive at the electrodes by diffusion.

Example. Let us consider a solution containing equal concentrations of ferrous and ferric perchlorate (*e.g.* 10^{-3} *M*). Let us suppose that sodium perchlorate, $Na^+ClO_4^-$, is added to the solution to give a concentration of 0.1 *M*.

The migration current is provided by the following ions

$$Na^+(10^{-1}), \quad ClO_4^-(10^{-1} + 5 \cdot 10^{-3}), \quad Fe^{3+}(10^{-3}), \quad Fe^{2+}(10^{-3})$$

If we suppose that all the ions have roughly the same equivalent conductivity, we have for the transport numbers

$$t_{Fe^{3+}} = \frac{3 \cdot 10^{-3}}{10^{-1} + 10^{-1} + 5 \cdot 10^{-3} + 3 \cdot 10^{-3} + 2 \cdot 10^{-3}} = \frac{3}{210} = 0.014$$

$$t_{Fe^{2+}} = \frac{2}{210} = 0.009, \qquad t_{ClO_4^-} = 0.500, \qquad t_{Na^+} = 0.477$$

The number of Fe^{3+} and Fe^{2+} ions arriving at the cathode by migration is negligible, giving rise to a migration current of the order of 1% of the total migration current, the remainder being provided by those ions present in very high concentrations.

Under these conditions the situation may be represented as follows

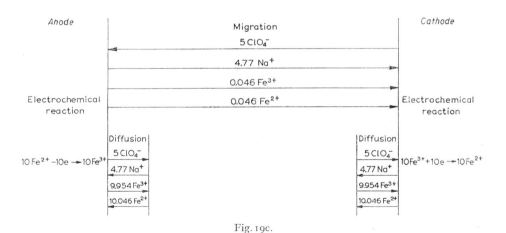

Fig. 19c.

In this example, where the migration current is almost entirely provided by the sodium perchlorate, the electrolysis current is equal to the diffusion current of Fe^{2+} in the one direction, and of Fe^{3+} in the other, to within about 0.5%.

Nearly all the electrochemical analytical methods described in this book are carried out in the presence of indifferent electrolyte, so that the electrolysis current is practically equal to the diffusion current of the electrolyzed substance.

Nevertheless, migration cannot always be ignored, even in the presence of an excess of indifferent electrolyte, as will be seen below (p. 27).

Expression for the diffusion current. Limiting diffusion current

We will assume that in the stationary state Nernst's hypothesis holds, *i.e.* the diffusion is limited to a layer of constant thickness δ_0 around the electrode. According to Fick's law, the rate of transport of the electrolyzed substances by diffusion is proportional to the concentration gradient. We will suppose that the concentration varies linearly with the distance from the electrode within the diffusion layer (constant gradient). If we call the concentration in the body of the solution C_s and the concentration at the surface of the electrode C_e, then the diffusion current is proportional to the difference $(C_s - C_e)$

$$i_d = k_d(C_s - C_e)$$

where k_d is the constant of proportionality.

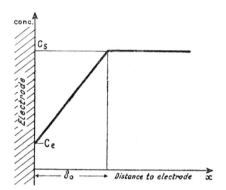

Fig. 20. Diffusion phenomena.

We have seen that in the presence of an excess of an indifferent electrolyte $i \approx i_d$, and taking the sign into account we may write

$$i = \pm k_d(C_s - C_e)$$

For an oxidation current, the positive sign is taken for all those substances arriving at the electrode, and the negative sign for all those leaving it, while for a reduction current the opposite sign convention is used. In other words, if the electrochemical reactions are written $Ox + ne \rightarrow Red$, the current may be expressed as

$$i = k_{red}(|Red|_s - |Red|_e) = -k_{ox}(|Ox|_s - |Ox|_e)$$

It will be seen that the diffusion current, and thus also the electrolysis current under the chosen conditions, tends to a limit as C_e tends to zero: $i_{lim} = \pm k_d C_s$. This limiting current is known as the limiting diffusion current.

We can derive the following expression for k_d. According to Fick's law, the rate of diffusion per unit surface area is $D_0 \dfrac{\delta C}{\delta x}$ (where D_0 is the diffusion constant for the substance in question).

The current density resulting from the electrolysis of the diffusion substance is then $nFD_0 \dfrac{\delta C}{\delta x}$ (where $n =$ number of electrons involved and F the faraday unit). The diffusion current is

$$i_d = nFSD_0 \frac{C_s - C_e}{\delta_0}$$

where S is the surface area of electrode.
According to Nernst's hypothesis

$$\frac{\delta C}{\delta x} = \frac{C_s - C_e}{\delta_0}$$

whence

$$i_d = nFSD_0 \frac{C_s - C_e}{\delta_0}$$

The value of k_d is therefore

$$k_d = \frac{nFSD_0}{\delta_0}$$

k_d is thus inversely proportional to the thickness of the diffusion layer, and directly proportional to the diffusion constant D_0 (which is of the same order of magnitude for most substances) and to the number of electrons involved in the electrochemical reaction. For example, in the reaction of the hypoiodite ion to give iodide

$$IO^- + 2\,H^+ + 2e \rightarrow I^- + H_2O$$

two electrons are consumed per molecule of hypoiodite; while in the reduction of iodate to iodide

$$IO_3^- + 6\,H^+ + 6e \rightarrow I^- + 3\,H_2O$$

six electrons are involved per iodate molecule.

Iodate can also be formed by the disproportionation of hypoiodite in an alkaline medium, according to the equation

$$3\,IO^- \rightarrow IO_3^- + 2\,I^-$$

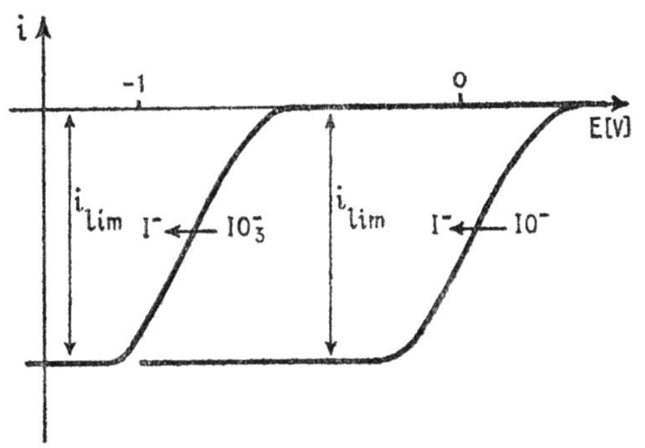

Fig. 21. Reduction curves of hypoiodite and of the iodate formed by the disproportionation of the hypoiodite (after Souchay[2]).

This reaction is slow enough to allow the current–potential curve to be determined for IO^-. A limiting current i_{lim} is found. If the solution is allowed to stand until all the hypoiodite has dismutated into iodate, the limiting current is still practically i_{lim} (see Fig. 21). Although n is three times as big for the reduction of IO_3^- as for that of

IO^-, this is compensated for by the fact that three IO^- ions give only one IO_3^- ion by disproportionation.

General case

In the general case of an electrochemical reaction involving several substances

$$aA + bB + \ldots + ne \rightleftharpoons mM + pP + \ldots$$

the same reasoning may be applied to all the substances appearing at the electrode. The rate of diffusion of each substance may still be expressed as $D_0\,(C_s - C_e)/\delta_0$. The substances A, B, etc., must arrive simultaneously at the electrode if the reduction reaction is to take place; while the substances formed, M, P, etc., move in the opposite direction. The current is given by

$$i = -\,k_A(|A|_s - |A|_e) = -\,k_B(|B|_s - |B|_e) = \ldots$$
$$= \;\; k_M(|M|_s - |M|_e) = \;\; k_P(|P|_s - |P|_e) = \ldots$$

This equation holds whatever the sign of the current: the expressions for the substances taking part in the reduction reaction (A, B, etc.) are preceded by a negative sign, while the expressions for those substances which participate in the oxidation reaction (M, P, etc.) are preceded by a positive sign.

The expression for the proportionality constant for each substance, k_d, is now slightly modified. During oxidation, the passage of n electrons is effected by the reaction of m molecules of M, p molecules of P, etc., at the electrode. The constants k_M, k_P, etc., are then proportional to n/m, n/p, etc.

Current–potential curves

Quantitative expressions for the current–potential curves are given in the next chapter. It may be remarked qualitatively here that when e.g. Fe^{2+} is oxidized, the diffusion current, given by

$$i = k_{Fe^{2+}}(|Fe^{2+}|_s - |Fe^{2+}|_e)$$

increases as $|Fe^{2+}|_e$ decreases. When the electrolysis is sufficiently fast, $|Fe^{2+}|_e$ tends to zero, and the rate of arrival of Fe^{2+} at the electrode reaches a limit; the electrolysis current is then limited by the maximum rate of diffusion of Fe^{2+}. The current may then be expressed as $i_{lim} = k_{Fe^{2+}}|Fe^{2+}|_s$. This is the limiting diffusion current of Fe^{2+} (see Fig. 22).

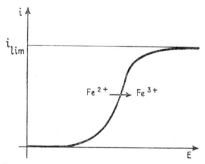

Fig. 22. Current–potential curve for the oxidation of Fe^{2+}.

The addivity of currents

When several electrolyzable substances, both oxidants and reductants, are present in a solution, the phenomena may be treated in terms of the individual properties of the substances. In the absence of chemical reactions the currents may be added algebraically, and the overall current–potential curve may be plotted given a knowledge of the current–potential curves for the individual substances.

For example, when Ag^+ and H^+ ions are reduced separately at a silver electrode, the current–potential curves marked 1 and 2 in Fig. 23 are obtained. When a mixture of Ag^+ and H^+ ions is reduced, the curve for the reduction of the Ag^+ ions (curve 1) remains unchanged, but the reduction of H^+ ions is accompanied by that of Ag^+ ions, so the current produced in this case is the sum of the currents for the reduction of each ion separately (curve 3).

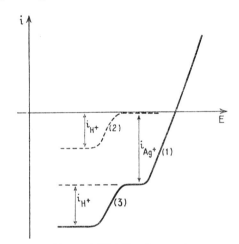

Fig. 23. Additivity of currents.

The treatment of reactions

As we have already seen (page 13), a qualitative treatment of reactions may be made if their current–potential curves are known.

The curves for the two electrodes may in certain cases be plotted on the same graph; but if the electrodes are made of different materials, or if their surface areas are different, or if they are placed in two separate compartments, each curve must be plotted on a separate graph.

When the substance reacting at the electrode is present in high concentration, its limiting rate of diffusion will not be reached with normal current densities.

When the reacting substance is present at the electrode in the solid state, there are no diffusion phenomena. This is the case when a silver electrode is oxidized (Fig. 24), or when a conducting oxide or salt precipitated on the electrode is oxidized or reduced.

In the case of a mercury electrode with a metal dissolved in it, the diffusion of the metal in the mercury towards the solution has a limiting effect on the anodic dissolution of the amalgamated metal (see pag. 41 and Fig. 25).

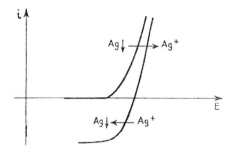
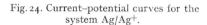

Fig. 24. Current–potential curves for the
system Ag/Ag⁺.

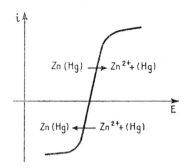

Fig. 25. Current–potential curve
for an amalgam.

Everything which was said on current–potential curves in Section II, page 8 *et seq.*, also holds here as long as allowance is made for the diffusion phenomena. Figures 26 and 27 show the current-potential curves for the slow system $H_3AsO_4/HAsO_2$ and the fast system Fe^{3+}/Fe^{2+}.

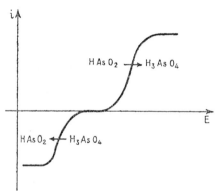

Fig. 26. Slow system.

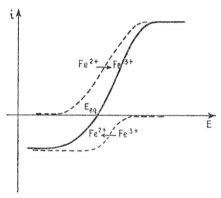

Fig. 27. Fast system.

The limitations imposed by the solvent

Fig. 13 showed the current–potential curves for the oxidation and reduction of water and its ions. In a neutral aqueous solution the oxidation and reduction of water form two barriers, since the water is present in such concentration that the limiting rates of diffusion are not reached (Fig. 28).

Oxidants and reductants dissolved in water may therefore be classed according to the position of their currents–potential curves with respect to those of water. Thus all the oxidants whose curves lie to the right of that for H_2O can be reduced in water; $Fe(CN)_6^{3-}$ falls into this class, for example. Those oxidants for which the curve lies to the left of that of water, on the other hand (shaded portion, Fig. 28), can only be reduced after H_2O. The SO_4^{2-} ion, for example, cannot be reduced in aqueous solution as the water is reduced first.

Members of the first class are often called 'electroactive', and those of the second class 'non-electroactive' or 'indifferent'. Similar remarks may be made about reducing agents.

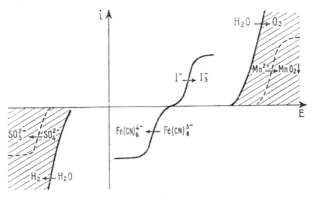

Fig. 28.

Importance of migration phenomena

Let us consider an acid solution (pH = 0) of a copper salt; the current–potential curves for this system, *e.g.* in a sulphuric acid medium, are shown in Fig. 29.

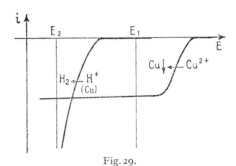

Fig. 29.

The concentration of indifferent electrolyte (H^+ and HSO_4^-) is about 100 times that of copper (II) in the solution. Applying the equations given on page 18 *et seq.*, we have

$$i_{Cu^{2+}} = i_{d\ Cu^{2+}} + i_{m\ Cu^{2+}}$$

i.e. the current due to the deposition of copper, $i_{Cu^{2+}}$, is equal to the sum of the limiting diffusion current of Cu^{2+} and the migration current of Cu^{2+}.

Now

$$i_{m\ Cu^{2+}} = \frac{n \cdot i \cdot t_{Cu^{2+}}}{z}$$

where i is the total current and $t_{Cu^{2+}}$ is the transport number of the Cu^{2+} ions. Since n (number of electrons exchanged in the reduction) $= z$ (charge on the ion)

$$i_{Cu^{2+}} = i_{d\ Cu^{2+}} + i \cdot t_{Cu^{2+}}$$

The transport number $t_{Cu^{2+}}$ is approximately equal to $\frac{1}{500}$, so if the deposition of copper is carried out at a potential E_1, $i_{Cu^{2+}} \approx i_{d\ Cu^{2+}}$; *i.e.* the current for the deposition of copper is approximately equal to the diffusion current of the Cu^{2+} ions.

If however the electrolysis is carried out at a potential E_2, i becomes very large because of the evolution of a large amount of hydrogen. If $i = 1000\ i_{Cu^{2+}}$, the migration current of the Cu^{2+} ions also becomes 1000 times greater, and thus ceases to be negligible compared to the diffusion current. In this case, the migration current is twice as big as the diffusion, so the rate of deposition of copper is tripled.

The rate of deposition of copper is thus increased when the electrolysis is carried out with a large current which is caused by the reduction of another substance. This phenomenon is called 'exaltation of the migration current' by simultanious electrolysis of another substance.

Ohmic voltage drop

The voltage to be applied in a given case is given by the sum of the potential difference $E_A - E_C$ and the ohmic voltage drop through the solution, Ri. The latter term is always important when i becomes large, even in the presence of an indifferent electrolyte.

Examples

1. Electrolysis of a solution containing As(III) and As(V). Two identical electrodes

The current–potential curves are shown in Fig. 30. A positive value of the current corresponds to the oxidation of As(III) to As(V), which is limited by the rate of diffusion of As(III); if the potential is made sufficiently high, simultaneous oxidation of As(III) and of H_2O occurs. Similarly, a low negative current indicates the reduction of As(V) only; while a sufficiently low potential results in the simultaneous reduction of As(V) and H^+.

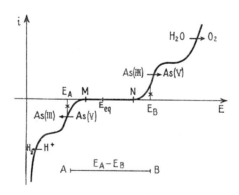

Fig. 30.

(*a*) If a voltage corresponding to the segment AB (Fig. 30) is applied to the electrodes, they will assume potentials E_A and E_B such that the anode and cathode currents are equal and opposite. As(III) is oxidized at the anode, and As(V) is reduced at the cathode. If the potential difference is less than MN, practically no current flows.

(*b*) If the current is fixed at i_1 (Fig. 31), the anode potential becomes E_B and As(III) is oxidized at this electrode. The corresponding cathode potential is E_A, and As(V) is reduced here. If the value of the current is raised to i_2, the anode potential becomes

E'_B, and As(III) is oxidized at a rate corresponding to i_3 while H_2O is simultaneously oxidized at a rate corresponding to $i_2 - i_3$. At the cathode, the potential is E'_A and As(V) and H^+ are reduced simultaneously.

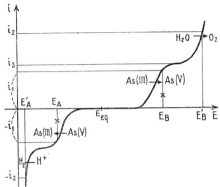

Fig. 31.

2. Electrolysis of an acid solution of ferrous and ferric sulphate. Platinized platinum electrodes

The possible oxidation reactions are

$$Fe^{2+} - e \rightarrow Fe^{3+}$$
$$2 H_2O - 4e \rightarrow O_2\uparrow + 4 H^+$$
$$2 SO_4^{2+} - 2e \rightarrow S_2O_8^{2-}$$

and the possible reduction reactions

$$Fe^{3+} + e \rightarrow Fe^{2+}$$
$$2 H^+ + 2e \rightarrow H_2\uparrow$$

The reduction of sulphate does not occur; and it is supposed that the solution is free from dissolved oxygen.

The current–potential curves are given in Fig. 32. It may be seen that the potential difference for a current i is E_{AC} (which is very small); at the anode Fe^{2+} is oxi-

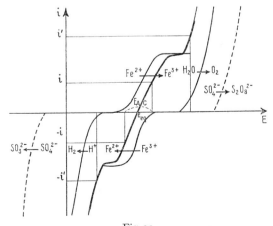

Fig. 32.

dized rapidly and Fe^{3+} is reduced more slowly, while the conditions are reversed at the cathode. The phenomena observed here are typical of the electrolysis of a 'fast' system (in this case, the system Fe^{3+}/Fe^{2+}). The total effect in this case is zero from a chemical point of view. If however the current is increased sufficiently, *e.g.* to i', oxygen is also evolved at the anode and hydrogen at the cathode.

3. Electrolysis of a solution of thiocyanate and a solution of dichromate, separated by a porous diaphragm

The reactions may be considered with the aid of the current–potential curves shown in Fig. 33 for each of the electrodes. It may be seen from this figure that if a

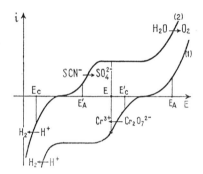

Fig. 33.

sufficiently large positive voltage $E_A - E_C$ is applied between the electrodes 1 and 2, electrode 1 acts as an anode, and the reaction

$$2\,H_2O - 4e \rightarrow O_2\uparrow + 4\,H^+$$

takes place here at potential E_A, while electrode 2 acts as a cathode

$$2\,H^+ + 2e \rightarrow H_2\uparrow$$

at potential E_C.

If the two electrodes are short-circuited, the system functions as a galvanic cell, both electrodes having the potential E; electrode 1 now acts as a cathode, and the reaction

$$Cr_2O_7{}^{2-} + 14\,H^+ + 6e \rightarrow 2\,Cr^{3+} + 7\,H_2O$$

takes place here. At electrode 2 the reaction is

$$SCN^- + 4\,H_2O - 6e \rightarrow SO_4{}^{2-} + HCN + 7\,H^+$$

If on the other hand a negative potential difference $E'_A - E'_C$ is applied between electrodes 1 and 2, electrode 2 acts as the anode, where SCN^- is oxidized at a potential E'_A, and electrode 1 as the cathode where $Cr_2O_7{}^{2-}$ is reduced at a potential E'_C.

REFERENCES

[1] J. COURSIER, *Thesis*, Masson, Paris, 1954.
[2] P. SOUCHAY, *Anal. Chim. Acta*, 2 (1948) 17.

Chapter II

THE EQUATIONS OF THE CURRENT–POTENTIAL CURVES
QUANTITATIVE TREATMENT OF ELECTROCHEMICAL REACTIONS

In this chapter we will give the equations for the current–potential curves for the simplest cases; when these curves are known it is often possible to make quantitative calculations about the reactions.

We will suppose throughout that the solution contains an excess of an indifferent electrolyte and that the simple diffusion laws (for a steady state) are obeyed; these assumptions constitute a very useful first approximation.

We assume further that the difference between activities and concentrations is negligible.

I. THE SYSTEM: OXIDANT $+ ne \rightleftharpoons$ REDUCTANT

We will first consider the simple case of the oxidation–reduction system

$$Ox + ne \rightleftharpoons Red$$

at one electrode. Two things happen during the course of this electrochemical reaction: (1) electrons are exchanged at a certain rate which depends on the electrode potential; (2) the substances to be electrolyzed arrive by diffusion at the electrode at a certain rate; which determines the steady-state conditions.

Velocity of the electron exchange reaction

The rate of the electron exchange reaction at the surface of the electrode may be expressed as molecules reacting per unit time per unit surface area. If we suppose that the process is of the first order, this rate will be proportional to the concentration of the reactants

rate of reduction $\qquad\qquad v_1 = k_1 |Ox|_e$

rate of oxidation $\qquad\qquad v_2 = k_2 |Red|_e$

where k_1 and k_2 are the velocity constants of the reduction and oxidation reactions respectively, and $|Ox|_e$ and $|Red|_e$ are the concentrations at the surface of the electrode.

It has been shown that these velocity constants can be expressed as functions of the difference $E - E_0$ between the potential of the electrode E and the standard oxidation potential (E_0) of the redox system in question

$$k_1 = k_0 \exp\left[\frac{-\alpha n F}{RT}(E - E_0)\right]$$

$$k_2 = k_0 \exp\left[\frac{\beta n F}{RT}(E - E_0)\right]$$

where α and β are called 'transfer coefficients', and must satisfy the equation

$\alpha + \beta = 1$. The oxidation and reduction current densities, *i.e.* the rates of electron exchange per unit surface of the electrodes, may then be expressed as

$$I_{cat} = -nF v_1 = -nF \,|\mathrm{Ox}|_e\, k_0 \exp\left[\frac{-\alpha nF}{RT}(E-E_0)\right] = -I_0\,|\mathrm{Ox}|_e \exp\left[\frac{-\alpha nF}{RT}(E-E_0)\right]$$

$$I_{an} = +nF v_2 = +nF \,|\mathrm{Red}|_e\, k_0 \exp\left[\frac{\beta nF}{RT}(E-E_0)\right] = I_0\,|\mathrm{Red}|_e \exp\left[\frac{\beta nF}{RT}(E-E_0)\right]$$

remembering the sign convention $I_{cat} < 0$, $I_{an} > 0$. The total current density is the sum of the reduction current density and the oxidation current density, and the total current i is the product of this and the surface area of the electrode

$$i = i_{cat} + i_{an} = S(I_{cat} + I_{an})$$

$$i = i_0\left\{|\mathrm{Red}|_e \exp\left[\frac{\beta nF}{RT}(E-E_0)\right] - |\mathrm{Ox}|_e \exp\left[\frac{-\alpha nF}{RT}(E-E_0)\right]\right\}$$

where S is the surface area of the electrode and $i_0 = nFSk_0$ is the absolute value of the current at the standard oxidation potential E_0 when $|\mathrm{Red}|_e = 1$ and $|\mathrm{Ox}|_e = 0$ or when $|\mathrm{Red}|_e = 0$ and $|\mathrm{Ox}|_e = 1$. This quantity is proportional to k_0, and is thus a specific rate constant for the redox system in question.

It is supposed in the above argument that the reduction of the oxidant Ox gives Red directly, and vice versa.

Fast systems

The velocity constant k_0 is very large for such a system, and therefore i_0 is very large too. Since i has a finite value, and hence i/i_0 is small, the two terms in the braces must be of the same order of magnitude, *i.e.*

$$\exp\left[\frac{(\alpha + \beta)nF}{RT}(E-E_0)\right] \approx \frac{|\mathrm{Ox}|_e}{|\mathrm{Red}|_e}$$

whence

$$E = E_0 + \frac{RT}{(\alpha + \beta)nF}\ln\frac{|\mathrm{Ox}|_e}{|\mathrm{Red}|_e}$$

Since $\alpha + \beta = 1$, we see that this is Nernst's equation applied to the concentrations at the surface of the electrode

$$E = E_0 + \frac{0.058}{n}\log\frac{|\mathrm{Ox}|_e}{|\mathrm{Red}|_e} \quad \text{(at 20° C)} \tag{1}$$

Slow systems

The rate constant, and therefore i_0, is very small. In order for i to attain an appreciable value, one of the terms in the braces must become large, *i.e.* E must differ considerably from E_0.

If $E \ll E_0$

$$|i| \approx -i_0\,|\mathrm{Ox}|_e \exp\left[\frac{-\alpha nF}{RT}(E-E_0)\right]$$

or

$$E = E_0 + \frac{RT}{\alpha nF}\ln i_0 + \frac{RT}{\alpha nF}\ln\frac{|\mathrm{Ox}|_e}{|i|}$$

where $|i|$ is the absolute value of the current. At 20° C, then

$$E = E_0 + \frac{0.058}{\alpha n} \log i_0 + \frac{0.058}{\alpha n} \log \frac{|\mathrm{Ox}|_e}{|i|} \tag{2}$$

If $E \gg E_0$ and at 20° C

$$i \approx i_0 |\mathrm{Red}|_e \exp\left[\frac{\beta n F}{RT} (E - E_0)\right]$$

or

$$E = E_0 - \frac{0.058}{\beta n} \log i_0 + \frac{0.058}{\beta n} \log \frac{i}{|\mathrm{Red}|_e} \tag{3}$$

In a fast system, oxidation and reduction occur simultaneously at appreciable rates at each electrode while the potential is a little different from the equilibrium potential. In a slow reaction on the other hand either reduction or oxidation takes place, according to the sign of $E - E_0$.

A steady-state diffusion system

When a steady state is reached the concentration of the electrolyzed substance at the surface of the electrode is constant, *i.e.* the formation or disappearance of substances at the electrode is exactly balanced by diffusion. The electrolysis current may then be expressed as a diffusion current (*cf.* page 22)

$$i_d = k_d (C_s - C_e)$$

where C_s is the concentration of a substance in the body of the solution and C_e is the concentration at the surface of the electrode. If the system may be represented as $\mathrm{Ox} + ne \rightarrow \mathrm{Red}$, the oxidation current is given by

$$i = k_{red} (|\mathrm{Red}|_s - |\mathrm{Red}|_e)$$

and the reduction current by

$$i = - k_{ox} (|\mathrm{Ox}|_s - |\mathrm{Ox}|_e)$$

where $|\mathrm{Red}|_s$ and $|\mathrm{Ox}|_s$ are the concentrations of the reductant and the oxidant in the body of the solution.

A limiting reduction current is reached when $|\mathrm{Ox}|_e = 0$, and a limiting oxidation current when $|\mathrm{Red}|_e = 0$. If we call the two limiting currents i_{ox} and i_{red} respectively, then

$$i_{ox} = - k_{ox} |\mathrm{Ox}|_s \qquad i_{red} = k_{red} |\mathrm{Red}|_s$$

The concentrations at the surface of the electrode may thus be expressed as

$$|\mathrm{Ox}|_e = \frac{i - i_{ox}}{k_{ox}} \qquad |\mathrm{Red}|_e = \frac{i_{red} - i}{k_{red}}$$

These values can now be substituted in equations (1), (2) and (3), giving for

Fast systems

oxidant and reductant

$$E = E_0 + \frac{0.058}{n} \log \frac{k_{red}}{k_{ox}} + \frac{0.058}{n} \log \frac{i - i_{ox}}{i_{red} - i} \tag{4}$$

This is the equation of the current–potential curve for a fast system.

Half-wave potential: this is the potential $E_{\frac{1}{2}}$ at wich the total current is equal to the mean of the two limiting diffusion currents. It follows from Eq. (4) that

$$E_{\frac{1}{2}} = E_0 + \frac{0.058}{n} \log \frac{k_{red}}{k_{ox}} \tag{5}$$

whence

$$\boxed{E = E_{\frac{1}{2}} + \frac{0.058}{n} \log \frac{i - i_{ox}}{i_{red} - i}} \tag{6}$$

Since the diffusion constants k_{red} and k_{ox} are generally of the same order of magnitude, $E_{\frac{1}{2}}$ lies very near to the standard oxidation potential E_0 of the system. It does not depend on the concentrations (Fig. 34 and 35).

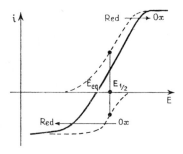

Fig. 34.
The fast system $Ox + ne \rightleftharpoons Red$.

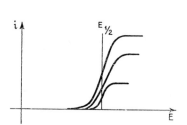

Fig. 35. $E_{\frac{1}{2}}$ is independent of the concentration ($Ox + ne \rightleftharpoons Red$).

When only the oxidant is present, a 'reduction wave' is produced, having the equation

$$E_{cat} = E_0 + \frac{0.058}{n} \log \frac{k_{red}}{k_{ox}} + \frac{0.058}{n} \log \frac{i_{ox} - i}{i}$$

The half-wave potential as defined above, in this case, is equal to the potential at which the current is equal to half the limiting current i_{ox}

$$E_{\frac{1}{2}} = E_0 + \frac{0.058}{n} \log \frac{k_{red}}{k_{ox}}$$

giving for

oxidant only

$$\boxed{E_{cat} = E_{\frac{1}{2}} + \frac{0.058}{n} \log \frac{i_{ox} - i}{i}} \tag{7}$$

When only the reductant is present, an 'oxidation wave' is produced, with the equation

$$E_{an} = E_0 + \frac{0.058}{n} \log \frac{k_{red}}{k_{ox}} + \frac{0.058}{n} \log \frac{i}{i_{red} - i}$$

The half-wave potential has the same value for the two corresponding anodic and cathodic waves (see Fig. 34), giving for

reductant only

$$E_{an} = E_{\frac{1}{2}} + \frac{0.058}{n} \log \frac{i}{i_{red} - i} \tag{8}$$

Slow systems

If $E \ll E_0$

$$E_{cat} = E_0 - \frac{0.058}{\alpha n} \log \frac{k_{ox}}{i_0} + \frac{0.058}{\alpha n} \log \frac{i_{ox} - i}{i} \tag{9}$$

If $E \gg E_0$

$$E_{an} = E_0 + \frac{0.058}{\beta n} \log \frac{k_{red}}{i_0} + \frac{0.058}{\beta n} \log \frac{i}{i_{red} - i} \tag{10}$$

Eq. (9) represents the cathodic wave (reduction) and Eq. (10) the anodic wave (oxidation). The half-wave potential for each wave is the potential at which the current is equal to half the limiting current. It follows from Eq. (9) and (10) that

$$E_{\frac{1}{2} cat} = E_0 - \frac{0.058}{\alpha n} \log \frac{k_{ox}}{i_0} \tag{11}$$

$$E_{\frac{1}{2} an} = E_0 + \frac{0.058}{\beta n} \log \frac{k_{red}}{i_0} \tag{12}$$

whence

$$E_{cat} = E_{\frac{1}{2} cat} + \frac{0.058}{\alpha n} \log \frac{i_{ox} - i}{i} \tag{13}$$

and

$$E_{an} = E_{\frac{1}{2} an} + \frac{0.058}{\beta n} \log \frac{i}{i_{red} - i} \tag{14}$$

Unlike the fast systems, slow systems have a different half-wave potential for the anodic and cathodic waves (Fig. 36), and the lower the value of i_0, *i.e.* the slower the system, the greater the difference between $E_{\frac{1}{2} cat}$ and $E_{\frac{1}{2} an}$; this is thus a criterion of

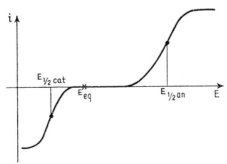

Fig. 36. Slow system.

the speed of the system. The half-wave potentials are still independent of the concentrations. In general $k_{ox} \approx k_{red}$. It may be shown that if this is so, then for a slow system

$$E_0 = \tfrac{1}{2}(\alpha \, E_{\frac{1}{2}\,cat} + \beta \, E_{\frac{1}{2}\,an})$$

Systems which are neither fast nor slow

For these systems, the equation of the current–potential curve may be found in the same way

$$i = \frac{|\mathrm{Red}|_s \cdot \exp\left[\dfrac{\beta n \mathrm{F}}{RT}(E-E_0)\right] - |\mathrm{Ox}|_s \exp\left[\dfrac{-\alpha n \mathrm{F}}{RT}(E-E_0)\right]}{\dfrac{1}{i_0} + \dfrac{1}{k_{red}}\exp\left[\dfrac{\beta n \mathrm{F}}{RT}(E-E_0)\right] + \dfrac{1}{k_{ox}}\exp\left[\dfrac{-\alpha n \mathrm{F}}{RT}(E-E_0)\right]}$$

but E cannot be expressed simply as a function of i.

Oxidation and reduction waves are still obtained, limited by $i_{r\,d} = k_{red}\,|\mathrm{Red}|_s$ and $i_{ox} = -k_{ox}\,|\mathrm{Ox}|_s$ respectively.

II. THE GENERAL CASE

Consider the system

$$a\mathrm{A} + b\mathrm{B} + \ldots + n e \rightleftharpoons m\mathrm{M} + p\mathrm{P} + \ldots$$

with an equilibrium potential given by

$$E_{eq} = E_0 + \frac{0.058}{n}\log\frac{|\mathrm{A}|^a\,|\mathrm{B}|^b\,\ldots}{|\mathrm{M}|^m|\mathrm{P}|^p\,\ldots}$$

If the system is a fast one, we may derive the equation

$$E = E_0 + \frac{0.058}{n}\log\frac{|\mathrm{A}|_e^a\,|\mathrm{B}|_e^b\,\ldots}{|\mathrm{M}|_e^m|\mathrm{P}|_e^p\,\ldots}$$

and expressing the concentrations in terms of currents, with the aid of Nernst's hypothesis

$$E = E_0 + \frac{0.058}{n}\log\frac{k_M^m k_P^p\,\ldots}{k_A^a\, k_B^b\,\ldots} + \frac{0.058}{n}\log\frac{(i - i_\mathrm{A})^a\,(i - i_\mathrm{B})^b\,\ldots}{(i_\mathrm{M} - i)^m\,(i_\mathrm{P} - i)^p\,\ldots} \tag{15}$$

where $i_\mathrm{A}, i_\mathrm{B}, \ldots, i_\mathrm{M}, i_\mathrm{P}, \ldots$ represent the limiting diffusion currents due to the reduction of A, B, ... and the (simultaneous) oxidation of M, P, ..., and where k_A, $k_\mathrm{B}, \ldots, k_\mathrm{M}, k_\mathrm{P}, \ldots$ are the constants of proportionality according to Nernst's hypothesis.

If the system is slow, the oxidation of M, P, ... and the reduction of A, B, ... occur independently at potentials which differ considerably from each other. We may define the anodic wave with the equation

$$E \gg E_0 \qquad E_{an} = E_0 + \frac{0.058}{\beta n}\log\frac{k_M^m k_P^p\,\ldots}{i_0} + \frac{0.058}{\beta n}\log\frac{i}{(i_\mathrm{M}-i)^m\,(i_\mathrm{P}-i)^p\,\ldots}$$

and a cathodic wave with the equation

$$E \ll E_0 \qquad \boxed{E_{cat} = E_0 - \frac{0.058}{\alpha n} \log \frac{k_A^a k_B^b \cdots}{i_0} + \frac{0.058}{\alpha n} \log \frac{(i - i_A)^a (i - i_B)^b \cdots}{i}}$$

In all cases, the height of the cathodic wave is determined by the rate of diffusion of the most slowly moving of the oxidants A, B, C, etc., which is in general the substance present in the lowest concentration. Similarly, the height of the anodic wave is limited by the rate of diffusion of the reductant which is present in the lowest concentration (see Fig. 37).

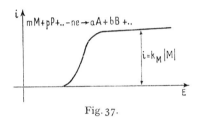

Fig. 37.

If one substance, *e.g.* M, is present in a high concentration, i become negligible compared to i_M, and Eq. (15) can be rewritten

$$E = E_0 + \frac{0.058}{n} \log \frac{k_P^p \cdots}{k_A^a k_B^b \cdots} + \frac{0.058}{n} \log \frac{(i - i_A)^a (i - i_B)^b \cdots}{(i_P - i)^p \cdots} - \frac{0.058}{n} \log |M|$$

The case where two substances are present in high concentrations, forming a buffer solution, will be discussed in Chapter III.

We have supposed in deriving the above that there are no intermediate reactions, *i.e.* that the rates of exchange of electrons are proportional to $|A|^a$, $|B|^b$, ... in the oxidation reactions and to $|M|^m$, $|P|^p$, ... in the reduction reactions.

It may be seen from the above equations that the half-wave potential for a fast system is in general considerably different from E_0, even when the diffusion coefficients of the various substances are of the same order of magnitude. Moreover, $E_{\frac{1}{2}}$ depends on the concentrations of the dissolved ions, for fast systems as well as for slow ones.

$$AB + e \rightleftharpoons C + B$$

Let us suppose that this is a fast redox system. The equilibrium potential is given by

$$E_{eq} = E_0 + 0.058 \log \frac{|AB|}{|C| |B|}$$

and the equation for the current–potential curve may be found from the general equation (15) to be

$$E = E_0 + 0.058 \log \frac{k_B \cdot k_C}{k_{AB}} + 0.058 \log \frac{i - i_{AB}}{(i_B - i)(i_C - i)}$$

(1) If only AB is present in the solution, the equation of the cathodic wave is

$$E = E_0 + 0.058 \log \frac{k_B k_C}{k_{AB}} + 0.058 \log \frac{i - i_{AB}}{i^2}$$

$$E_{\frac{1}{2}\ cat} = E_0 + 0.058 \log \frac{k_B k_C}{k_{AB}^2} + 0.017 - 0.058 \log |AB|$$

As in the general case, $E_{\frac{1}{2}}$ depends on the concentration, in this case that of AB.

(2) If only B and C are present, the equation of the anodic wave is given by

$$E = E_0 + 0.058 \log \frac{k_B k_C}{k_{AB}} + 0.058 \log \frac{i}{(i_B - i)(i_C - i)} \qquad (17)$$

The current is limited by whichever of the concentrations $|B|$ and $|C|$ is the smaller (Fig. 38).

(3) When B, C and AB are present, the equation of the current–potential curve is given by Eq. (16). The cathode current is limited by $|AB|$, and the anode current by $|B|$ or $|C|$, whichever is smaller. $E_{\frac{1}{2}}$ can no longer be expressed in a simple way.

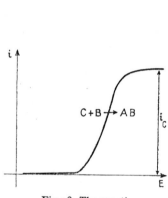

Fig. 38. The reaction

$C + B - e \rightarrow AB, \quad |B| > |C|$

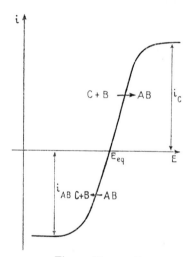

Fig. 39. The reaction

$C + B - e \rightleftharpoons AB, \quad |B| > |C|$

(4) If $|B|$ is large, the equation becomes that of a simple system with the addition of one term

$$E = E_0 + 0.058 \log \frac{k_C}{k_{AB}} + 0.058 \log \frac{i - i_{AB}}{i_C - i} - 0.058 \log |B|$$

and $E_{\frac{1}{2}}$ may be defined for each value of $|B|$

$$E_{\frac{1}{2}} = E_0 + 0.058 \log \frac{k_C}{k_{AB}} - 0.058 \log |B|$$

This is also true if the concentration of B is kept constant, by a buffer solution, even if the actual value of $|B|$ is low.

More than one molecule of a kind is involved in the reaction

Examples of such reactions are

$$2\,\text{Hg}^{2+} + 2e \rightleftharpoons \text{Hg}_2^{2+}, \qquad E_{eq} = E_0 + 0.029 \log \frac{|\text{Hg}^{2+}|^2}{|\text{Hg}_2^{2+}|}$$

and

$$2\,\text{H}^+ + 2e \rightleftharpoons \text{H}_2, \qquad E_{eq} = E_0 + 0.029 \log \frac{|\text{H}^+|^2}{|\text{H}_2|}$$

Let us consider the second example. This system is fast at a platinized platinum electrode. The current–potential curve is given by Eq. (15)

$$E = E_0 + 0.029 \log \frac{k_{\text{H}_2}}{k_{\text{H}^+}^2} + 0.029 \log \frac{(i - i_{\text{H}^+})^2}{i_{\text{H}_2} - i}$$

The half-wave potential, *i.e.* the potential at which $i = \tfrac{1}{2}(i_{\text{H}^+} + i_{\text{H}_2})$, is given by

$$E_{\frac{1}{2}} = E_0 + 0.029 \log \frac{k_{\text{H}_2}}{k_{\text{H}^+}^2} + 0.029 \log \frac{i_{\text{H}_2} - i_{\text{H}^+}}{2}$$

It depends on the concentration of dissolved hydrogen and on that of the H+ ions. If there is no hydrogen in the solution, it varies as -0.029 pH. This example is discussed further in Chapter III.

Some of the substances forming part of the system are present in the solid state

When the activity of one of the reactants at the electrode is constant, the diffusion of this substance has no effect on the system. This is the case with the solvent (water, mercury, etc.), and also with sparingly soluble substances (indicated by $\downarrow$), *i.e.* metals, oxides, and salts deposited on the electrode.

Nernst's equation still holds, the constant activities forming part of the constant E'_0. Let us consider the case

$$aA + bB\downarrow + cC + \ldots + ne \rightleftharpoons mM\downarrow + pP + \ldots$$

$$E = E'_0 + \frac{0.058}{n} \log \frac{|A|_e^a \, |C|_e^c \ldots}{|P|_e^p \ldots}$$

The diffusion of B and M does not appear in the final form of Eq. (15), which becomes

$$E = E'_0 + \frac{0.058}{n} \log \frac{k_P^p \ldots}{k_A^a k_C^c \ldots} + \frac{0.058}{n} \log \frac{(i - i_A)^a \, (i - i_C)^c \ldots}{(i_P - i)^p} \qquad (18)$$

The system $Ag\downarrow / Ag^+$

We will take as an example the fast system

$$\text{Ag}^+ + e \rightleftharpoons \text{Ag}\downarrow \qquad (A + e \rightleftharpoons C\downarrow)$$

The equilibrium potential is given by

$$E_{eq} = E_0 + 0.058 \log |\text{Ag}^+|$$

Eq. (18) gives the equation for the current–potential curve

$$E = E_0 - 0.058 \log k_{\text{Ag}^+} + 0.058 \log (i - i_{\text{Ag}^+}) \qquad (19)$$

(a) When only the silver electrode is present, with no Ag⁺, the equation becomes

$$E = E_0 - 0.058 \log k_{Ag^+} + 0.058 \log i$$

This is an exponential, shown as curve 1 in Fig. 40.

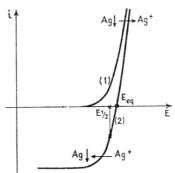

Fig. 40. The system $Ag^+ + e \rightleftharpoons Ag\downarrow$ (fast).

(b) It is not possible to reduce Ag⁺ without there being some metallic silver on the surface of the electrode. The reduction curve for Ag⁺ alone does not exist in practice. When both Ag⁺ and Ag↓ are present, Eq. (19) gives curve 2 of Fig. 40.

$$E_{\frac{1}{2}} = E_0 - 0.018 + 0.058 \log |Ag^+|$$

The slow system $M\downarrow/M^{n+}$

The current–potential curve is composed of two separate branches, an anodic wave and a cathodic wave. For $M\downarrow - ne \rightarrow M^{n+}$

$$E_{an} = E_0 + \frac{0.058}{\beta n} \log \frac{i}{i_0}$$

and for $M^{n+} + ne \rightarrow M\downarrow$

$$E_{cat} = E_0 + \frac{0.058}{\alpha n} \log \frac{i_0}{k_{M^{n+}}} + \frac{0.058}{\alpha n} \log \frac{i - i_{M^{n+}}}{i}$$

The half-wave potential for the reaction at the cathode may be defined as

$$E_{\frac{1}{2}\ cat} = E_0 + \frac{0.058}{\alpha n} \log \frac{i_0}{k_{M^{n+}}}$$

Such a system differs from the corresponding fast system in that $E_{\frac{1}{2}\ cat}$ is independent of the concentration of the cation (Fig. 41).

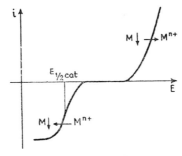

Fig. 41. The slow system $M^{n+} + ne \rightleftharpoons M\downarrow$.

This behaviour is found with a large number of metals, *e.g.* Ni, Co, Fe, etc., if the cathode consists of the metal itself, platinum, or mercury as long as no amalgam is formed.

Further examples

Reduction at a mercury cathode $(C + B\downarrow + e \rightarrow AB)$

During reduction at a mercury cathode, the metals produced can either dissolve in the mercury as such, dissolve forming a compound (amalgam), or be deposited on the surface of the electrode. Note that when a dropping mercury electrode is used, the mercury is constantly renewed (see Chapter VI). When the metal diffuses in the mercury, this diffusion must be taken into account as well as that of the compounds in the solution. The diffusion coefficients in mercury and in aqueous solution are of the same order of magnitude. For example, thallium (I) salts are reduced at a mercury electrode according to the equation

$$Tl^+ + Hg\downarrow + e \rightleftharpoons Tl(Hg), \qquad E_{eq} = E'_0 + 0.058 \log \frac{|Tl^+|}{|Tl(Hg)|}$$

where Tl(Hg) represents thallium amalgam.

Eq. (18) may be used, as this is a fast system

$$E = E'_0 + 0.058 \log \frac{k_{(TlHg)}}{k_{Tl^+}} + 0.058 \log \frac{i - i_{Tl^+}}{-i}$$

$i_{Tl(Hg)} = 0$, since the concentration of thallium in the mercury is zero. The equation of the cathode curve is thus

$$E = E_{\frac{1}{2}} + 0.058 \log \frac{i_{Tl^+} - i}{i}$$

The expression for $E_{\frac{1}{2}}$ contains the constants of proportionality k_{Tl^+} and $k_{Tl(Hg)}$ for the diffusion of thallium ions in solution and of thallium metal in mercury.

The complex of mercury with EDTA $(AB + ne \rightarrow C\downarrow + B)$

We will represent EDTA (ethylene diamine tetracetic acid and its ions) by the symbol Y^{4-}. Mercury (II) forms a complex with this substance

$$HgY^{2-} \rightleftharpoons Hg^{2+} + Y^{4-}$$

where $$\frac{|Hg^{2+}| \, |Y^{4-}|}{|HgY^{2-}|} = K$$

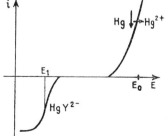

Fig. 42. Solution of HgY²⁻, mercury electrode.

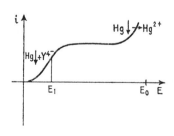

Fig. 43. Solution of Y⁴⁻, mercury electrode.

K is a conditional constant being determined at a given pH (see Definitions, Symbols, Units, p.oo). Let us consider the redox system

$$HgY^{2-} + 2e \rightleftharpoons Hg\downarrow + Y^{4-}$$

in which the Hg^{2+}-EDTA complex and a mercury electrode are involved.

The equilibrium potential of this system is given by

$$E_{eq} = E_1 + 0.029 \log \frac{|HgY^{2-}|}{|Y^{4-}|}$$

and the equation of the current–potential curve is

$$E = E_1 + 0.029 \log \frac{k_{Y^{4-}}}{k_{HgY^{2-}}} + 0.029 \log \frac{i - i_{HgY^{2-}}}{i_{Y^{4-}} - i}$$

This is completely analogous to what we have seen for the system $A + e \rightleftharpoons C$, since in the complex system $AB + e \rightleftharpoons C\downarrow + B$ the activity of one of the components, the mercury, is constant. The current–potential curves and the corresponding values of $E_{\frac{1}{2}}$ are given in Fig. 42, 43 and 44 (cf. Fig. 34).

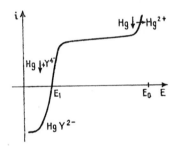

Fig. 44. Solution of HgY^{2-} and Y^{4-}, mercury electrode.

The system $Ag\downarrow/AgCl\downarrow$ $(AB\downarrow + e \rightleftharpoons C + B\downarrow)$

We have the redox system

$$Ag\downarrow + Cl^- - e \rightleftharpoons AgCl\downarrow$$

$$E_{eq} = E_1 - 0.058 \log |Cl^-|$$

The general equation gives

$$E = E_1 + 0.058 \log k_{Cl^-} - 0.058 \log (i_{Cl^-} - i) \tag{20}$$

(a) Reduction of silver chloride deposited on an electrode. This is an exponential, as shown in Fig. 45.

(b) Oxidation of silver in the presence of dissolved chloride. AgCl is formed immediately, covering the electrode. All the components of the redox system are now present, and the equation of the current-potential curve is therefore given by Eq. (20). It may be seen that the oxidation current is limited by the diffusion of chloride; but at higher potentials, the electrode may be oxidized according to

$$Ag\downarrow - e \rightarrow Ag^+$$

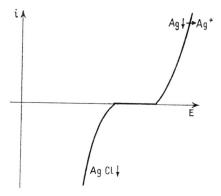

Fig. 45. The reduction of AgCl↓.

The half-wave potential of the anodic wave depends on the concentration of Cl^- (see Fig. 46)

$$E_{\frac{1}{2}} \, an = E_1 + 0.018 - 0.058 \log |Cl^-|$$

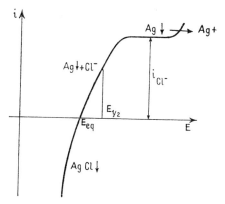

Fig. 46. The system $Ag\downarrow + Cl^- - e \rightleftharpoons AgCl\downarrow$.

Reduction of a mixture of iodate and cadmium (II) ions

Let us first consider the reduction of Cd^{2+} only (in a neutral medium, $1 \, M$ KCl). The electrochemical reaction at the mercury electrode is

$$Cd^{2+} + Hg\downarrow + 2e \rightarrow Cd(Hg) \tag{21}$$

which is a fast reaction, $E_{\frac{1}{2}} \approx E_0 = -0.40$ V (curve 1, Fig. 47).

The reduction of IO_3^- in the same medium and at the same electrode gives the electrochemical reaction

$$IO_3^- + 3 \, H_2O + 6e \rightarrow I^- + 6 \, OH^- \tag{22}$$

which is a slow reaction, $E_{\frac{1}{2}} \approx -1.0$ V, $E_0 = 0.48$ V. The value of $E_{\frac{1}{2}}$ is independent of the pH in neutral or basic media (curve 2, Fig. 47).

Now let us consider the reduction of a mixture of IO_3^- and Cd^{2+} at a mercury electrode. The two above-mentioned electrochemical reactions (21) and (22) are both possible. But if iodate is reduced and the pH of the solution is not controlled, OH^- ions will appear and undergo a chemical reaction with the Cd^{2+} arriving at the electrode

$$Cd^{2+} + 2\ OH^- \rightarrow Cd(OH)_2 \downarrow$$

The overall reaction is thus

$$IO_3^- + 3\ Cd^{2+} + 3\ H_2O + 6e \rightarrow I^- + 3\ Cd(OH)_2 \downarrow \qquad (23)$$

We may treat the overall reaction (23) as if it occurred directly at the electrode, and apply the usual reasoning to this reaction also. This reaction produces a wave whose height is limited by the diffusion of either iodate or cadmium. But the reduction of Cd^{2+} occurs at considerably higher potentials than those for reaction (23).

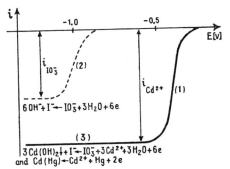

Fig. 47. Reduction of a mixture of IO_3^- and Cd^{2+}.
Curve (1): Cd^{2+} only.
Curve (2): IO_3^- only.
Curve (3): mixture of Cd^{2+} and IO_3^-, $i_{Cd^{2+}} > i_{IO_3^-}$ (theoretical curves).

We thus have two cases to consider:

1. The concentration of Cd^{2+} is sufficiently great for the limiting diffusion current of Cd^{2+} for reaction (21), $i_{Cd^{2+}}$, to be greater than the limiting current $i_{IO_3^-}$ for reaction (22). The limiting current due to the sum of the reactions (21) and (23) is therefore determined by the rate of arrival of the Cd^{2+} ions which participate in both reactions; thus only one wave will be produced (curve 3, Fig. 47).

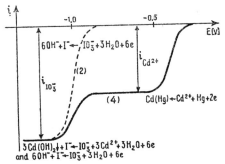

Fig. 48. Reduction of a mixture of IO_3^- and Cd^{2+}.
Curve (2): IO_3^- only.
Curve (4): mixture of Cd^{2+} and IO_3^-, $i_{IO_3^-} > i_{Cd^{2+}}$ (theoretical curves).

2. The concentration of iodate ions is high, so that $i_{IO_3^-}$ is greater than $i_{Cd^{2+}}$. The first wave produced corresponds to reaction (21) followed by reactions (21) and (23), and the second wave to reaction (22) which now takes place in addition to the first two reactions (curve 4, Fig. 48).

Fig. 49 shows an experimental curve. The small wave at $E < -1.0$ V is due to the fact that the solubility of cadmium hydroxide is not completely negligible.

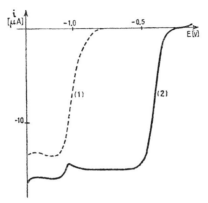

Fig. 49. Reduction of a mixture of 1.89×10^{-3} M Cd^{2+} and 0.5×10^{-3} M IO_3^- in 0.1 M KCl at a dropping mercury electrode.
Curve (1): reduction of IO_3^- only.
Curve (2): reduction of the mixture after Kolthoff and Lingane [2, 3].

If the Cd^{2+} ions are replaced by thallium ions Tl^+, a reaction like (23) cannot be produced so there are always two waves, one due to the reduction of Tl^+ with a limiting current of i_{Tl^+} and the other due to the reduction of IO_3^- according to Eq. (22), the total limiting current being $i_{Tl^+} + i_{IO_3^-}$.

REFERENCES

[1] J. J. Lingane, *Ph. D. Thesis*, University of Minnesota, USA, 1938.
[2] I. M. Kolthoff and J. J. Lingane, *Polarography*, Interscience, New York, 2nd Ed., 1952, p. 105.
[3] I. M. Kolthoff and J. J. Lingane, *Polarography*, 2nd Ed., Interscience, New York, 1952, p. 108–116.

Chapter III

CURRENT–POTENTIAL CURVES DURING CHEMICAL REACTIONS

FAST ELECTROCHEMICAL REACTIONS

Current–potential curves give a quantitative description of the electrochemical behaviour of substances, and a number of simple cases have already been discussed.

We will now consider the case where a reactant is added little by little to the
solution, and we will use the current–potential curves to characterize the state of the
solution during the chemical reaction.

We will consider only a limited number of examples, but similar arguments can
be applied to a wide range of related reactions. Chemical oxidation–reduction reactions will be treated separately.

Throughout this chapter we will suppose that the electrochemical reactions are
fast and also that the chemical reactions are fast enough for equilibrium to be obtained in the body of the solution in a reasonable time. It may be remarked here that
when the electrochemical reactions are fast the current–potential curves are independent of the kinetics of the chemical reactions when equilibrium has been reached in
the body of the solution. This is not so when the electrochemical reactions are slow:
this case will be discussed in the next chapter.

I. ELECTROCHEMICAL REACTION $A + e \rightleftharpoons C$

CHEMICAL REACTION $A + B \rightleftharpoons AB$

Let us consider a solution containing a redox system

$$A + e \rightleftharpoons C, \qquad E_{eq} = E_0 + 0.058 \log \frac{|A|}{|C|}$$

and let us imagine that a substance B, which is not electroactive when alone in the
solution, but which reacts chemically with A according to the equation

$$A + B \rightleftharpoons AB, \qquad \frac{|A| |B|}{|AB|} = K$$

is added to the solution little by little. A second redox system is now produced

$$AB + e \rightleftharpoons C + B, \qquad E_{eq} = E_1 + 0.058 \log \frac{|AB|}{|B| |C|}$$

The standard potentials E_0 and E_1 (which are the equilibrium potentials when all the
activities are equal to 1) are related by the equation

$$\boxed{E_1 = E_0 + 0.058 \log K}$$

This relation is independent of the rates of the electrochemical and chemical reactions.
It is therefore valid in all cases.

We shall see how the addition of B to a solution already containing A and C displaces the cathodic waves (A + e → C) on the one hand and the anodic waves (C − e → A) on the other. We will suppose in what follows that the chemical reaction is practically quantitative, *i.e.* that the constant $K = \dfrac{|A||B|}{|AB|}$ is small, say $K \leqslant 10^{-8}$. Under these conditions the concentration of B is negligible until the equivalence point is reached. We will also suppose that there is no other chemical reaction.

Cathodic curves

We will start by considering the case where only A is present in the solution to begin with:

(a) Initially, as stated, the solution contains A only, and the current–potential curve has the following characteristics (see Chapter II)

$$E = E_{\frac{1}{2}} + 0.058 \log \frac{i_A - i}{i}$$

$$E_{\frac{1}{2}} = E_0 + 0.058 \log \frac{k_C}{k_A} \approx E_0$$

$$i_A = - k_A |A|_s$$

where i_A is the limiting diffusion current of A (that of C is zero since $|C|_s = 0$) and k_A and k_C are the constants of proportionality relating the limiting current to the concentrations of A and C respectively.

(b) The reactant B is now added to the solution of A. As long as B is not in excess, we have a mixture of A and AB.

The possible electrochemical reactions are now the reduction of A, with a half-wave potential very near to E_0, and the reduction of AB with half-wave potential near to E_1. If we denote the initial concentration of A by C_0, and the concentration of AB formed by addition of B by xC_0, then the concentration of A remaining in solution is $(1 - x)C_0$. The reduction curve of A will have a step whose height is proportional to the limiting diffusion current of A

$$i_A = - k_A (1 - x) C_0$$

Its equation will otherwise be identical with the one given above for the solution of A alone. This will be followed by the reduction curve of AB, the step height being given by $i_{AB} = - k_{AB} x C_0$. If we suppose that $k_{AB} \approx k_A$, the sum of the limiting diffusion currents will remain equal to $- k_A C_0$ during the addition of B to A (Fig. 50). The equation of the reduction curve of AB is

$$E = E_1 + 0.058 \log \frac{k_B \cdot k_C}{k_{AB}} + 0.058 \log \frac{i - i_{AB}}{(i_B - i)(i_C - i)} \tag{1}$$

where $i_C = 0$, since C does not exist in solution. When $x < 1$, i_B is negligible, and we may write

$$E = E_1 + 0.058 \log \frac{k_B \cdot k_C}{k_{AB}} + 0.058 \log \frac{i - i_{AB}}{i^2}$$

$$E_{\frac{1}{2}}' = E_1 + 0.058 \log \frac{k_B \cdot k_C}{k_{AB}} - 0.058 \log \tfrac{1}{2} x C_0$$

$E_{\frac{1}{2}}'$ varies with x and C_0.

References p. 89

(c) Near the equivalence point ($x \approx 1$), the concentration of A becomes very small and i_A becomes negligible compared to i_{AB}. Only the reduction curve of AB is then observed. The conditions may now be described by the equations given above, with $x = 1$. If we suppose that the diffusion coefficients are equal, we have

$$E_{\frac{1}{2}}' \approx E_0 + 0.058 \log K - 0.058 \log \tfrac{1}{2}C_0$$

at $x = 1$.

(d) If still more B is added, the solution will contain a constant concentration C_0 of AB, and an excess $(x - 1)C_0$ of B. Only one curve is observed, the curve for the reduction of AB, the limiting diffusion current being given by $i_{AB} = -k_{AB}C_0$ as B alone is not electroactive. Its equation can be derived starting from Eq. (1). If the excess of B is so large that i is negligible compared to i_B, then

$$E = E_1 + 0.058 \log \frac{k_C}{k_{AB}} + 0.058 \log \frac{i - i_{AB}}{-i} - 0.058 \log |B|_s$$

where $i_B = +k_B |B|_s$, even if B alone is not electroactive, and $|B|_s = (x - 1)C_0$. If we suppose that $k_C = k_{AB}$, then

$$E_{\frac{1}{2}}' \approx E_0 + 0.058 \log K - 0.058 \log |B|_s \approx$$
$$\approx E_0 + 0.058 \log K - 0.058 \log C_0 - 0.058 \log (x - 1)$$

The reduction curve is thus displaced as the excess of B increases (Fig. 50).

Thus, *to sum up*, during the addition of a reactant B to a solution of a reducible substance A:

(a) Before the equivalence point ($0 < x < 1$)

$$|A|_s \approx (1 - x)C_0, \qquad |B|_s \approx 0, \qquad |AB|_s \approx xC_0$$

Two reduction waves are observed, one corresponding to the reduction of free A, the half-wave potential and limiting diffusion current being given by

$$E_{\frac{1}{2}} \approx E_0, \qquad i_A = -k_A(1 - x)C_0$$

the other corresponding to the reduction of AB, with

$$E_{\frac{1}{2}}' \approx E_0 + 0.058 \log K - 0.058 \log \tfrac{1}{2}xC_0, \qquad i_{AB} = -k_{AB}xC_0 \approx -k_A xC_0$$

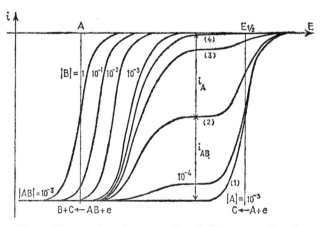

Fig. 50. The reactions $A + e \rightarrow C$ and $AB + e \rightarrow B + C$.

The total diffusion current is

$$i_A + i_{AB} = - k_A(1 - x)C_0 - k_{AB}xC_0 \approx - k_A C_0 = \text{constant}$$

(b) At the equivalence point $(x = 1)$

$$|A|_s \approx 0, \qquad |B|_s \approx 0, \qquad |AB|_s \approx C_0$$

Only one wave is produced, corresponding to the reduction of the AB formed, with a half-wave potential

$$E'_{\frac{1}{2}} \approx E_0 + 0.058 \log K - 0.058 \log \tfrac{1}{2}C_0$$

and a limiting diffusion current

$$i_{AB} \approx - k_{AB}C_0 \approx - k_A C_0$$

(c) After the equivalence point $(x > 1)$

$$|A|_s \approx 0, \qquad |B|_s \approx (x - 1)C_0, \qquad |AB|_s \approx C_0$$

A single wave is observed, corresponding to the reduction of AB, with a half-wave potential

$$E'_{\frac{1}{2}} \approx E_0 + 0.058 \log K - 0.058 \log (x - 1)C_0$$

if B is present in a large enough excess. The limiting diffusion current is still

$$i_{AB} = - k_{AB}C_0 \approx - k_A C_0$$

The family of curves described above is shown in Fig. 50 for an initial concentration of A, $|A|_s = 10^{-3}$. The right-hand curve, curve (1), represents the reduction of A alone. As B is added, $|A|_s$ decreases and the limiting diffusion current falls, curve (2). At a sufficiently low potential AB is reduced in its turn. As k_{AB} does not generally differ much from k_A, the total limiting current remains approximately constant. In curve (3), $|A|_s$ has decreased still further, and $|AB|_s$ has increased. When $|A|_s$ becomes very small ($\leq 10^{-5}$), curve (4) is obtained. Here we have only one wave, that for the reduction of AB. The remaining curves show the behaviour of the system when B is in excess, $|B|_s = 10^{-2}, 10^{-1}, 1$.

When A forms a complex as described here, its reduction is made more difficult. The difficulty of reduction increases with the stability of the complex and with the excess of the complexing agent, as in chemical reactions.

When $x < 1$, the result may be derived in another way: as long as A is present at the electrode in appreciable amounts, $i.e.$ as long as $i < i_A$, the amount of AB which dissociates at the surface of the electrode is negligible; its concentration remains constant and only A diffuses. The reduction takes place at a potential near E_0, and the reduction current is $i = - k_A (|A|_s - |A|_e)$. As the potential is lowered a point is reached at which the corresponding concentration $|A|_e$ is so low that AB starts to dissociate in appreciable amounts, thus reducing its concentration at the surface of the electrode. AB then diffuses towards the electrode, thus increasing the rate of tranport of A. The current will thus increase by an amount $- k_{AB} (|AB|_s - |AB|_e)$. It is possible, however, that as the potential is lowered AB is reduced directly at the electrode according to AB $+ e \rightleftharpoons C + B$, instead of by the successive reactions AB $\rightleftharpoons A + B$ and A $+ e \rightleftharpoons C$. The disappearance of AB corresponds to the same diffusion laws and the same potentials in both cases, since the direct reduction of AB gives the equation

$$E = E_1 + 0.058 \log \frac{|AB|_e}{|B|_e \, |C|_e}$$

while the reduction of A following the dissociation of AB gives

$$E = E_0 + 0.058 \log \frac{|A|_e}{|C|_e}$$

and as

$$K = \frac{|A|_e \, |B|_e}{|AB|_e}$$

$$E = E_0 + 0.058 \log K + 0.058 \log \frac{|AB|_e}{|B|_e \, |C|_e}$$

However, this second line of reasoning supposes that the chemical reaction is instantaneous and is thus less general than the argument we have used, which also holds for slow chemical reactions as long as the electrochemical reactions are fast.

Anodic curves

Now let us suppose that the solution initially contains the reductant C only, at a concentration of C_1. C may be oxidized to A by the fast electrochemical reaction which is the reverse of the one discussed above. The current–potential curve for this solution is defined by

$$E = E_{\frac{1}{2}} + 0.058 \log \frac{i}{i_C - i}, \qquad E_{\frac{1}{2}} = E_0 + 0.058 \log \frac{k_C}{k_A} \approx E_0, \qquad i_C = k_C |C|_s = k_C C_1$$

where i_C is the limiting diffusion current of C (Fig. 51). If some B is then added to the solution of C, the latter may more easily be oxidized by the reaction

$$B + C - e \rightarrow AB$$

which has a standard potential E_1 less than E_0. It is also possible to suppose that C is first oxidized to A, which is then removed by the chemical reaction $A + B \rightleftharpoons AB$. This mechanism leads to the same result as the other if the chemical reaction is instantaneous.

The redox systems involved are the same as in the previous case. The equation of the curve may be obtained from Eq. (1), with $i_{AB} = 0$

$$E = E_1 + 0.058 \log \frac{k_C k_B}{k_{AB}} + 0.058 \log \frac{i}{(i_C - i)(i_B - i)}$$

The anodic current may be limited by the diffusion of C or by B. As long as the solution contains an excess of C the diffusion of B is limiting. If, on the other hand, $|B|_s$ is greater than $|C|_s$, the diffusion of C limits the current.

If we denote the concentration of B added by $x C_1$, and the original concentration of C by C_1, then we may distinguish the following cases:

(a) $x = 0$ (*i.e.* C only), a single oxidation wave is produced. The equations for this curve have already been given.

(b) $0 < x < 1$; ($|C|_s > |B|_s$), two oxidation waves are produced. The first is limited by the diffusion of B, and its half-wave potential is given by

$$E_{\frac{1}{2}}'' + 0.058 \log \frac{k_C k_B}{k_{AB}} - 0.058 \log (i_C - \tfrac{1}{2} i_B) \approx E_1 - 0.058 \log C_1 (1 - \tfrac{1}{2} x)$$

as long as the constants k_C, k_B and k_{AB} are more or less equal to each other. The limiting current of this wave is $i_B = k_B |B|_s = k_B x C_1 \approx k_C x C_1$.

The second wave is limited by the diffusion of C. $|B|_e = 0$ for this wave, so $E_{\frac{1}{2}} = E_0$ as for the oxidation of C alone, and $i_C = k_C (1 - x) C_1$.

The total limiting current $i_B + i_C$ is practically constant.

(c) $x \geq 1$; $(|C|_s \leq |B|_s)$. There is only one oxidation wave, limited by the diffusion of C. The half-wave potential is

$$E_{\frac{1}{2}}'' = E_0 + 0.058 \log K + 0.058 \log \frac{k_C k_B}{k_{AB}} - 0.058 \log (i_B - \tfrac{1}{2}i_C)$$

$$\approx E_0 + 0.058 \log K - 0.058 \log C_1(x - \tfrac{1}{2})$$

The limiting current is $i_C = k_C |C|_s = k_C C_1$.

As the excess of B increases, the oxidation curve is displaced, since the oxidation becomes easier and easier. If $i_B \gg \tfrac{1}{2}i_C$, $E_{\frac{1}{2}}''$ varies with $- 0.058 \log |B|_s$.

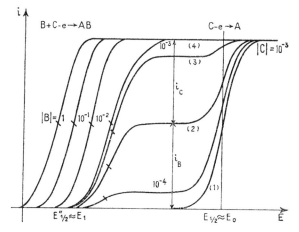

Fig. 51. The reactions $C - e \rightarrow A$ and $B + C - e \rightarrow AB$.

These results are shown in Fig. 51. Curve (1) represents the electrochemical reaction $C - e \rightarrow A$. Curve (2) shows two waves, the first corresponding to $B + C - e \rightarrow AB$, the second to $C - e \rightarrow A$. The height of the first step is determined by $|B|_s$, and the height of the second by $|C|_s$. Curve (4) represents the reaction $B + C - e \rightarrow AB$, where the amount of B added is enough to transform all the C into AB. There is therefore only one wave, limited by C. The remaining curves, corresponding to an excess of B, are similar to curve (4), the oxidation potentials of C in the presence of B become lower as the excess of B increases.

The combined anodic and cathodic curves

Let us finally suppose that the solution initially contains the oxidant A at a concentration C_0 and the reductant C at a concentration C_1.

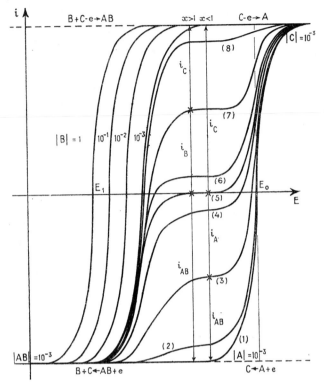

Fig. 52. The reactions $C - e \rightleftharpoons A$ and $B + C - e \rightleftharpoons AB$.
Curve (1), $x = 0$ Curve (5), $x = 1.0$
Curve (2), $x = 0.1$ Curve (6), $x = 1.1$
Curve (3), $x = 0.5$ Curve (7), $x = 1.5$
Curve (4), $x = 0.9$ Curve (8), $x = 1.9$

This solution gives a current–potential curve defined by

$$E = E_{\frac{1}{2}} + 0.058 \log \frac{i - i_A}{i_C - i}, \qquad E_{\frac{1}{2}} = E_0 + 0.058 \log \frac{k_C}{k_A} \approx E_0$$

$$i_A = - k_A |A|_s = - k_A C_0 \qquad i_C = k_C |C|_s = k_C C_1$$

where i_A and i_C are the limiting diffusion currents of A (reduction) and C (oxidation) respectively. Naturally, when $x = 0$, the equilibrium potential is

$$E = E_{eq} = E_0 + 0.058 \log \frac{|A|_s}{|C|_s} = E_0 + 0.058 \log \frac{C_0}{C_1}$$

If B is slowly added to this solution, the chemical reaction $A + B \rightleftharpoons AB$ takes place. We will call the concentration of B added (existing in the form of free B or AB) $x C_0$.

(a) Before the equivalence point ($x < 1$): B is totally consumed by reaction with A. The solution contains C, the remaining A and the AB formed. Two waves are observed, the first with $E_{\frac{1}{2}} \approx E_0$ and limited in oxidation by $i_C = k_C C_1$ and in reduction by $i_A = - k_A (1 - x) C_0$, and the second caused by the reduction of AB at lower potentials and having a limiting current given by

$$i_{AB} = - k_{AB} x C_0 \approx - k_A x C_0 \qquad i_A + i_{AB} \approx - k_A C_0$$

(cf. Fig. 52 and 53).

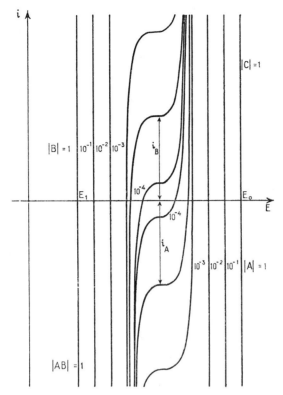

Fig. 53. The reactions $C - e \rightleftharpoons A$ and $B + C - e \rightleftharpoons AB$.

(b) At the equivalence point ($x = 1$): A is quantitatively combined with the added B, so the solution contains AB and C only. A wave due to the oxidation of C is observed, with $E_{\frac{1}{2}} \approx E_0$ and limiting current $i_C = k_C C_1$, followed at lower potentials by a wave due to the reduction of AB (the equation for this curve has already been given on page 47), with a limiting current

$$i_{AB} = - k_{AB} C_0 \approx - k_A C_0$$

(c) After the equivalence point ($x > 1$): the solution contains C, AB at a concentration of C_0 and excess B at a concentration of $(x-1)C_0$. As long as the concentration of B is less than that of C, i.e. $(x-1)C_0 < C_1$, two steps in the anodic wave will be observed, one corresponding to the reaction $B + C - e \rightarrow AB$ and limited by the diffusion of B, $i_B = k_B(x-1)C_0$, and the other corresponding to the reaction $C - e \rightarrow A$ with a height such that $i_B + i_C \approx k_C C_1$, and with $E_{\frac{1}{2}} \approx E_0$. There will also be a cathodic wave corresponding to $AB + e \rightarrow B + C$, with the current limited by the diffusion of AB. When the concentration of B is greater than that of C, the anodic current is only limited by the diffusion of C. Only one wave is observed, with $E_{\frac{1}{2}}$ becoming more and more negative as x increases, and the cathodic current having a limiting value of $i_{AB} \approx - k_A C_0$ and the anodic current of $i_C = k_C C_1$. The first part of the curve is defined by Eq. (1), and when $|B|_s$ becomes large

$$E = E_1 + 0.058 \log \frac{k_C}{k_{AB}} + 0.058 \log \frac{i - i_{AB}}{i_C - i} - 0.058 \log |B|_s$$

The anode and cathode curves for this system are plotted in Fig. 52 for $C_0 = C_1 = 10^{-3}$, and in Fig. 53 for $C_0 = C_1 = 1$.

Equilibrium potential. The equilibrium potential $(i = 0)$ is given by the equations

$$x < 1, \quad E_{eq} = E_0 + 0.058 \log \frac{C_0}{C_1} + 0.058 \log (1 - x)$$

$$x > 1, \quad E_{eq} = E_1 + 0.058 \log \frac{C_0}{C_1} - 0.058 \log (x - 1)C_0$$

$$x = 1, \quad E_{eq} = E_0 + 0.058 \log \frac{\sqrt{KC_0}}{C_1} = E_1 + 0.058 \log \frac{C_0}{C_1 \sqrt{KC_0}}$$

where $E_1 = E_0 + 0.058 \log K$. These curves are given in Fig. 54.

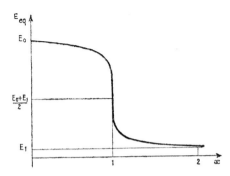

Fig. 54. Variation of the equilibrium potential during the reaction A + B → AB $(C_0 = C_1 = 1)$.

Solution buffered with respect to A

Let us suppose that the solution contains B and AB in large concentrations; the concentration of A is given by $|A| = K \dfrac{|AB|}{|B|}$, and will be small if K is small. Apart from this it will be constant for given values of $|AB|$ and $|B|$, and will vary very little if A is added or withdrawn in concentrations which are small compared to $|AB|$ and $|B|$: if a quantity of A is added to the solution which is sufficient to cause a concentration change $\Delta|A|$ in an unbuffered solution, the concentration of A in the buffered solution will change from $|A|$ to $|A|' = K \dfrac{|AB| + \Delta|A|}{|B| - \Delta|A|}$ as the reaction A + B → AB occurs.

$$|A|' = K \frac{|AB|}{|B|} \left\{ \frac{1 + \dfrac{\Delta|A|}{|AB|}}{1 - \dfrac{\Delta|A|}{|B|}} \right\} \approx |A|$$

The mixture of B and AB is thus a buffer for A, fixing the concentration of the latter at a constant value throughout the solution, including the neighbourhood of the electrodes.

If the solution contains C, AB and B, the last two in large concentrations, the current cannot be limited by AB or B under normal working conditions, but only by C (Fig. 55). The equation of the current–potential curve is

$$E = E_0 + 0.058 \log K + 0.058 \log \frac{k_B k_C}{k_{AB}} + 0.058 \log \frac{i - i_{AB}}{(i_B - i)(i_C - i)}$$

but i is negligible compared to i_B and i_{AB}, and if $|AB|_s = |B|_s$, then $K = |A|_s$ and the equation becomes

$$E = E_0 + 0.058 \log k_C - 0.058 \log (i_C - i) + 0.058 \log |A|_s$$

This is the equation of the curve for the system $C - e \rightleftharpoons A$ when $|A|_s$ is large. Thanks to the buffer solution, the same equation is obtained when $|A|_s$ is small but unchanged by addition or withdrawal of A.

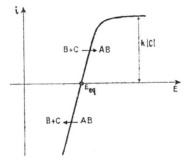

Fig. 55. The reaction $AB + e \rightleftharpoons B + C$, with AB and B present in large concentrations.

II. ELECTROCHEMICAL REACTION A + e ⇌ C

CHEMICAL REACTIONS A + B ⇌ AB, M + B ⇌ MB

The chemical reactions are

$$A + B \rightleftharpoons AB \qquad K = \frac{|A||B|}{|AB|}$$

$$M + B \rightleftharpoons MB \qquad K' = \frac{|M||B|}{|MB|}$$

We will suppose that $K \ll K'$, *i.e.* that the complex AB is more stable than the complex MB. The equilibrium

$$MB + A \rightleftharpoons AB + M$$

is thus far over to the right, and the reaction from right to left is negligible. The possible electrochemical reactions are

$$A + e \rightleftharpoons C, \qquad E_{eq} = E_0 + 0.058 \log \frac{|A|}{|C|}$$

$$AB + e \rightleftharpoons B + C$$

$$E_{eq} = E_1 + 0.058 \log \frac{|AB|}{|B||C|} \quad \text{with} \quad E_1 = E_0 + 0.058 \log K$$

$$AB + M + e \rightleftharpoons MB + C$$

$$E_{eq} = E_2 = 0.058 \log \frac{|AB||M|}{|MB||C|} \quad \text{with} \quad E_2 = E_0 + 0.058 \log K - 0.058 \log K'$$

We will consider two cases

(1) The reaction $B + M \rightarrow MB$ is carried out in the presence of such substances as A, C or AB (electrochemical indicators).

(2) M and MB are present in large concentrations (solution buffered with respect to B).

Electrochemical indicators

We have seen that although the substance B is not in itself electroactive its presence can influence current–potential curves since it forms part of the redox system

$$B + C - e \rightleftharpoons AB \tag{2}$$

(a) If an excess of C is added to a solution of B the presence of B is indicated by the occurrence of the electrochemical reaction (2). The current–potential curve

$$E = E_1 + 0.058 \log \frac{k c_k B}{k_{AB}} + 0.058 \log \frac{i}{(i_B - i)(i_C - i)}$$

is limited by the diffusion of B.

(b) In the presence of C and AB, the equilibrium potential depends on B

$$E_{eq} = E_1 + 0.058 \log \frac{|AB|}{|C|} - 0.058 \log |B|_s$$

and the diffusion of B again limits the anode current

$$E = E_1 + 0.058 \log \frac{k c_k B}{k_{AB}} + 0.058 \log \frac{i - i_{AB}}{(i_B - i)(i_C - i)}$$

If a reaction occurs involving B and other non-electroactive substance, *e.g.*

$$B + M \rightleftharpoons MB$$

the changes of concentration taking place can be followed by the addition of C, or AB and C, to the solution, thanks to the electrochemical reactions in which they take part; *i.e.* C can be used as an indicator to follow the reaction of M with B. We will suppose that C does not react with any of the substances present, and that M and MB are not electroactive on their own.

The chemical reaction $M + B \rightarrow MB$

B is added gradually to a solution containing M.

(a) In the presence of C, the following electrochemical reactions are possible

$$C - e \rightarrow A \tag{3}$$

$$C + MB - e \rightarrow AB + M \tag{4}$$

$$C + B - e \rightarrow AB \tag{5}$$

The curves corresponding to the course of the chemical reaction are shown in Fig. 56. The current is limited by two factors: first by the diffusion of MB, according to electrochemical reaction (4), and when the chemical reaction is complete and B is present in excess by the diffusion of B, according to electrochemical reaction (5).

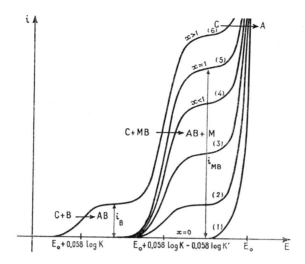

Fig. 56. The reactions C + B − e → AB,   C + MB − e → AB + M,   C − e → A.

(b) In the presence of AB, which we suppose to be a more stable complex than MB, the possible electrochemical reactions are

$$AB + e \rightarrow C + B$$

$$AB + M + e \rightarrow C + MB$$

The corresponding current–potential curves are given by Fig. 57, curves 1–5. The wave height is limited by diffusion of M.

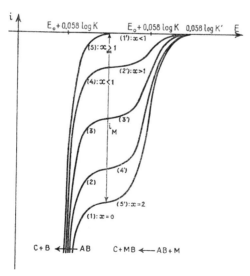

Fig. 57. The reactions AB + e → C + B,   AB + M + e → C + MB.
Chemical reaction M + B → MB: curves 1 to 5 ;
Chemical reaction B + M → MB: curves 1′ to 5′.

(c) In the presence of AB and C, the possible electrochemical reactions are

$$C - e \rightarrow A$$
$$C + B - e \rightleftharpoons AB$$
$$C + MB - e \rightleftharpoons AB + M$$

The current–potential curves are given in Fig. 58. Anodic waves are limited by MB, and also by B after the equivalence point, and cathodic waves are limited by M.

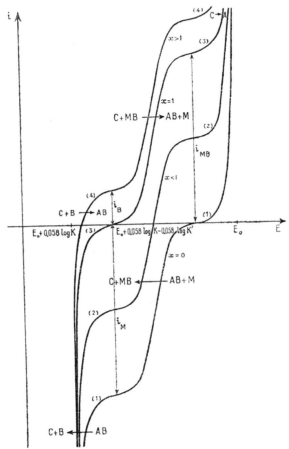

Fig. 58. The reactions $C - e \rightarrow A$, $C + MB - e \rightleftharpoons AB + M$, $C + B - e \rightleftharpoons AB$.

The equilibrium potentials are then given by

$$x < 1, \quad E_{eq} = E_0 + 0.058 \log \frac{K}{K'} + 0.058 \log \frac{|AB|}{|C|} + 0.058 \log \frac{1-x}{x}$$

$$x > 1, \quad E_{eq} = E_0 + 0.058 \log K + 0.058 \log \frac{|AB|}{|C|} - 0.058 \log (x - 1)$$

(see Fig. 59).

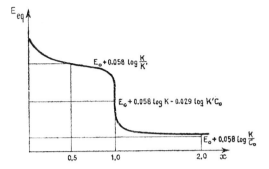

Fig. 59. Variation of the equilibrium potential of AB + e ⇌ C + B during the chemical
reaction M + B → MB.

Initial solution: $|AB| = |C|$ in excess of M, $x = \dfrac{B_{added}}{M_{initial}}$

$$M_{initial} = C_0$$

The reverse chemical reaction, $B + M \to MB$

The reverse reactions, when M is added gradually to a solution containing B,

$$B + M \to MB$$

may be followed in an entirely analogous way.

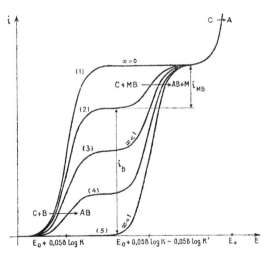

Fig. 60. The reactions $C + B - e \to AB$, $C + MB - e \to AB + M$, $C - e \to A$.

(a) An excess of C is added as indicator, (Fig. 60).

(b) AB is added in excess (Fig. 57, curves 1′–5′).

(c) AB and C are added together as indicators (Fig. 61).

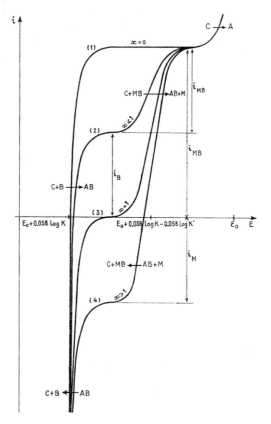

Fig. 61. The reactions $C + B - e \rightleftharpoons AB$, $C + MB - e \rightleftharpoons AB + M$, $C - e \rightarrow A$.

Chemical back-reactions

It may be desirable to follow a back-reaction, *e.g.* during a titration. For example a known excess of B is added to a solution of A

$$A + B \rightarrow AB$$

and then a substance M which reacts with the excess of B is added

$$B + M \rightarrow MB$$

This second reaction may also be followed. This is very like the previous case.

Various examples of the use of electrochemical indicators will be given in the chapters on potentiometry and amperometry.

A buffer solution for B

We suppose that, as in the previous case, the solution contains large concentrations of M and MB; C and AB may also be present, but not A, which reacts with MB

$$A + MB \rightarrow AB + M$$

MB/M forms a buffer solution for B, with $|B| = K' \dfrac{|MB|}{|M|}$. If the solution contains AB and C, the possible electrochemical reactions are

$$C - e \rightarrow A \tag{6}$$

$$C + B - e \rightleftharpoons AB \tag{7}$$

$$C + MB - e \rightleftharpoons AB + M \tag{8}$$

But $|B|$ is very small, so the reaction $C + B - e \rightarrow AB$ does not occur to an appreciable extent. The other reactions are limited by AB and C; the system is thus represented by Fig. 62.

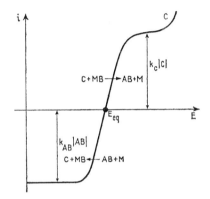

Fig. 62. Buffer solution of B; M and MB in excess; $|AB| = |C| = C_0$.
Reactions $AB + M + e \rightarrow C + MB$
$$C + MB - e \rightarrow AB + M$$
$$C - e \rightarrow A$$

This curve is represented by

$$E = E_0 + 0.058 \log K - 0.058 \log K' + 0.058 \log \frac{k_C k_{MB}}{k_{AB} k_M} + 0.058 \log \frac{(i - i_{AB})(i - i_M)}{(i_C - i)(i_{MB} - i)}$$

since i is negligible compared to i_M and i_{MB}, and $|M|_s = |MB|_s$,

$$E = E_0 + 0.058 \log K + 0.058 \log \frac{k_C}{k_{AB}} + 0.058 \log \frac{i - i_{AB}}{i_C - i} - 0.058 \log |B|_s$$

This is the equation for the system $AB + e \rightleftharpoons B + C$ when $|B|_s$ is large. $|B|_s$ is small in this case, but since the solution is buffered with respect to B, it does not limit the current.

III. THE GENERAL CASE

Arguments similar to those which we have used in the simplest case allow us to treat more complicated cases. In general, the substances form part of a redox system

$$aA + bB + \ldots + ne \rightleftharpoons mM + pP + \ldots$$

in which certain activities may be constant as a result of the formation of precipitates, while others may be held constant by buffer solutions. It should be remembered that all the substances forming part of the redox system help to determine the current–potential curve for the electrochemical oxidation (or reduction) reaction, even if they are not electroactive apart from the other components. The system may be used as an indicator for one of these substances during a chemical reaction in which it takes part.

IV. EXAMPLES

Formation of the complex Hg²⁺–EDTA

Ethylene diamine tetracetic acid (EDTA) will be represented by H_4Y. Mercuric ions form a very stable complex with this substance which may be represented by HgY^{2-}. Depending on the pH, one of the following reactions may occur

$$Hg^{2+} + Y^{4-} \rightleftharpoons HgY^{2-} \qquad \text{with} \quad \frac{|Hg^{2+}||Y^{4-}|}{|HgY^{2-}|} = K \qquad (9)$$

$$Hg^{2+} + HY^{3-} \rightleftharpoons HgY^{2-} + H^+ \quad \text{with} \quad \frac{|Hg^{2+}||HY^{3-}|}{|HgY^{2-}||H^+|} = K'$$

and similar reactions with H_2Y^{2-}, H_3Y^- and H_4Y. At a given pH, *i.e.* a constant value of $|H^+|$, all the equations have the same form, only differing in the value of the constant. In this and other examples, the chemical reaction will be denoted by: Eq. (9). The following redox systems may exist

$$Hg^{2+} + 2e \rightleftharpoons Hg \downarrow \qquad E_{eq} = E_0 + 0.029 \log |Hg^{2+}|$$

$$HgY^{2-} + 2e \rightleftharpoons Hg \downarrow + Y^{4-} \qquad E_{eq} = E_0 + 0.058 \log K + 0.029 \log \frac{|HgY^{2-}|}{|Y^{4-}|}$$

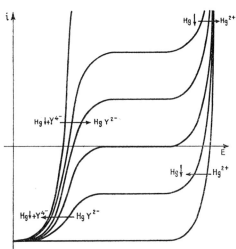

Fig. 63. The reaction $Hg^{2+} + Y^{4-} \rightarrow HgY^{2-}$.
Mercury electrode (idealized curves).

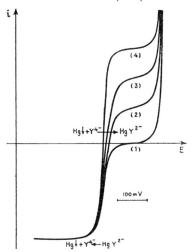

Fig. 64.
Oxidation of mercury and reduction of Hg(II) in the presence of EDTA
$|Hg(II)| = 10^{-3}$ M.
Curve 1: $|Y^{4-}| = 10^{-3}$ M.
Curve 2: $|Y^{4-}| = 1.4 \times 10^{-3}$ M.
Curve 3: $|Y^{4-}| = 1.7 \times 10^{-3}$ M.
Curve 4: $|Y^{4-}| = 2 \times 10^{-3}$ M.
(after MATYSKA and KOSSLER [1]).

This case is rather like that of the example treated above of $A + B \rightarrow AB$ and $A + e \rightleftharpoons C$; but in this case the activity of C ($Hg\downarrow$) is constant. The current–potential curves are shown in Fig.63 and 64. We may remark that the system HgY^{2-}/Hg may be used as an indicator for Y^{4-} in a number of reactions.

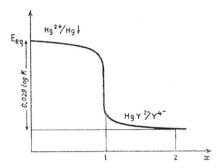

Fig.65. The variation of the equilibrium potential during the reaction
$$Hg^{2+} + Y^{4-} \rightarrow HgY^{2-}.$$
Initial concentration of Hg^{2+}: $1\ M$.

The reduction of water and hydrogen ions

Let us consider the neutralization of a strong acid with a strong base. The chemical reaction is

$$H^+ + OH^- \rightleftharpoons H_2O \quad \text{with} \quad |H^+|\,|OH^-| = K_{H_2O} = 10^{-14.2} \quad \text{at } 18^\circ\,C.$$

The only reducible substances present are H^+ and H_2O

$$2\ H^+ + 2e \rightleftharpoons H_2 \tag{10}$$

with

$$E_{eq} = E_1 + 0.029 \log \frac{|H^+|^2}{|H_2|}, \qquad E_1 = -0.09\ V$$

The concentration of dissolved hydrogen is proportional to its pressure above the solution. Under unit pressure of hydrogen, the concentration in the solution is $10^{-3}\ M$; with this concentration of hydrogen and $|H^+| = 1$, the equilibrium potential is then equal to 0.00 V.

$$2\ H_2O + 2e \rightleftharpoons H_2 + 2\ OH^- \tag{11}$$

with

$$E_{eq} = E_2 - 0.029 \log |H_2|\,|OH^-|^2$$

$$E_2 = E_1 + 0.058 \log K_{H_2O} = -0.09\ V - 0.82\ V = -0.91\ V$$

When $|OH^-| = 1$ and the pressure of hydrogen above the solution is unity, $E_{eq} = -0.82\ V$.

When the solution is saturated with hydrogen under atmospheric pressure, system (10) has $E_{eq} = -0.058$ pH.

The same correspondence also holds for system (11) under the same conditions.

This is another example of the system $A + B \rightleftharpoons AB$, i.e. $H^+ + OH^- \rightleftharpoons H_2O$, but the activity of the complex, H_2O, is constant; C is hydrogen.

Reduction at a platinized platinum electrode[2]

Experiment has shown that these electrochemical systems are fast at a platinized platinum electrode. We will investigate how the current–potential curves change during the neutralization under these conditions, especially as a function of pH. The equations of the curves corresponding to systems (10) and (11) are

$$E = E_1 + 0.029 \log \frac{k_{H_2}}{k_{H^+}^2} + 0.029 \frac{(i - i_{H^+})^2}{i_{H_2} - i} \tag{13}$$

$$E = E_2 + 0.029 \log k_{OH^-}^2 \cdot k_{H_2} - 0.029 \log (i_{OH^-} - i)^2 (i_{H_2} - i) \tag{14}$$

Since these redox systems are fast, the curves are different in the absence and presence of dissolved hydrogen.

Reduction in the absence of hydrogen. $i_{H_2} = 0$. Eq. (13), for the reduction of H[+], becomes

$$E = E_1 + 0.029 \log \frac{k_{H_2}}{k_{H_2}^2} + 0.029 \log \frac{(i - i_{H^+})^2}{-i}$$

The current is limited by the diffusion of H[+] ions. The halfwave potential is

$$E_{\frac{1}{2}} = E_1 + 0.029 \log \frac{k_{H_2}}{k_{H^+}} - 0.009 - 0.029 \, pH \approx E_1 - 0.029 \, pH$$

In very acid solution (pH $\leq$ 2) $i_{H^+} \gg i$ and the equation becomes

$$E = E_1 + 0.029 \log k_{H_2} - 0.058 \, pH - 0.029 \log (-i)$$

Similarly, when $i_{H_2} = 0$, Eq. (14) for the reduction of H_2O becomes

$$E = E_2 + 0.029 \log k_{OH^-}^2 \cdot k_{H_2} - 0.029 \log (-i) (i_{OH^-} - i)^2$$

No limitation of the current is observed. In acid, neutral and slightly alkaline solutions, where i_{OH^-} is negligible compared to i, this curve is independent ot the pH

$$E \approx E_2 - 0.087 \log (-i)$$

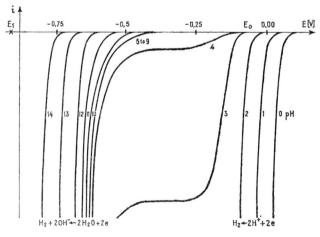

Fig. 66. The reaction H[+] + OH[−] → H_2O.
Platinized platinum electrode (after COUPEZ[3]).

If OH⁻ is in excess (excess of complexing ion), then

$$E = E_2 + 0.029 \log k_{H_2} - 0.029 \log (-i) - 0.029 \log |OH^-|^2$$
$$= E_1 + 0.029 \log k_{H_2} - 0.058 \text{ pH} - 0.029 \log (-i)$$

The curve for the reduction of water in alkaline solution moves towards more negative potentials as the pH increases.

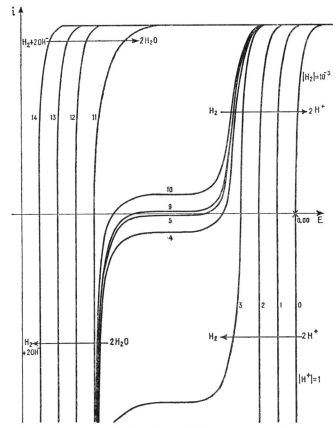

Fig. 67. The reaction $H^+ + OH^- \rightarrow H_2O$ in the presence of hydrogen. Platinized platinum electrode (after COUPEZ[4]).

These curves are given in Fig. 66, with the corresponding value of the pH beside each curve. At pH 0, 1 and 2, only H^+ is reduced, and its reduction constitutes a limit, in one direction, to the voltages at which the electrode can be used. At pH 3 to 4, a step appears, as the limiting rate of diffusion of H^+ is reached at small currents. In this region H^+ is reduced first, followed by H_2O. Above pH 5 the reduction of H^+ is negligible ($i_{H^+} \approx 0$), and only H_2O is reduced.

Reduction in the presence of hydrogen and oxidation of dissolved hydrogen. Let us suppose that the solution is saturated with hydrogen under a pressure of one atmosphere. The equations of the curves are given by (13) and (14) and the actual curves are shown in Fig. 67. $E_{eq} = -0.058$ pH.

On the cathodic side, the situation is nearly the same as in the absence of hydrogen: in acid media (pH < 3) only H^+ is reduced (curves o to 2); in slightly acid media the reduction of H^+ is limited by the diffusion of H^+ and followed by the reduction of H_2O (curves 3 and 4); in neutral or alkaline media only H_2O is reduced (curves 5 to 14).

On the anodic side hydrogen is oxidized according to

$$H_2 - 2e \rightarrow 2\,H^+ \qquad \text{in acid or neutral media,}$$

$$H_2 + 2\,OH^- - 2e \rightarrow 2\,H_2O \qquad \text{in sufficiently alkaline media.}$$

The current is thus limited by the diffusion of dissolved hydrogen ($\sim 10^{-3}\,M$) in acid media, by the diffusion of OH^- ions in slightly alkaline media, and again by the diffusion of dissolved hydrogen in very alkaline media (pH > 11), where the concentration of OH^- is greater than that of H_2.

Reduction at other electrodes. Experiment has shown that the systems

$$2\,H^+ + 2e \rightleftharpoons H_2 \quad \text{and} \quad 2\,H_2O + 2e \rightleftharpoons H_2 + 2\,OH^-$$

are slow at a bright platinum electrode. A theoretical treatment of slow electrochemical systems is given in the next chapter, but we shall give here (Fig. 68) the curves for the reduction of H^+ and H_2O at a smooth platinum electrode, in order to show

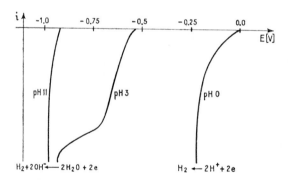

Fig. 68. Reduction curves for H^+ at a smooth platinum electrode (after COUPEZ).

the effect of the state of the platinum. It may be seen that the curves resemble those for the fast systems, with certain changes. These systems are even slower at a mercury electrode[5], and the reduction of water becomes so difficult that the 'indifferent' electrolyte (Na^+, K^+, etc.) is generally reduced before the H_2O. Results obtained with platinum and gold electrodes are given by KOLTHOFF and JORDAN[6]. The system H^+/H_2 is slow; the reduction curve of H^+ is therefore independent of the hydrogen concentration (see Chapter II, page 32). Similarly the reduction curve of H_2O is independent of the concentration of H_2, and under certain conditions is also independent of the concentration of OH^- (see Chapter IV). Calculation shows that $E_{\frac{1}{2}}$ varies as $\dfrac{-0.029}{\alpha}$ pH.

The reduction of weak acids

We will now consider the neutralization of a solution of a weak acid HB by a solution of a strong base OH⁻.

The reduction of this system is similar to that of water and hydrogen ion. We will suppose that the base B⁻ is neither oxidized nor reduced. The chemical reaction, which we will assume to be fast, is

$$HB + OH^- \rightleftharpoons B^- + H_2O$$

corresponding to the acid-base equilibrium

$$HB \rightleftharpoons B^- + H^+ \quad \text{with} \quad \frac{|B^-||H^+|}{|HB|} = K_A$$

The only substances which can be reduced are H⁺, the acid HB and water, the last two being complexes of H⁺, OH⁻ having a greater affinity than B⁻ for H⁺. The redox systems are similar to those which have been discussed already

$$\underset{(A)}{2\,H^+} + 2e \underset{(C)}{\rightleftharpoons H_2}, \qquad E_{eq} = E_1 + 0.029 \log \frac{|H^+|^2}{|H_2|} \tag{15}$$

$$2\,H_2O + 2e \rightleftharpoons 2\,OH^- + H_2, \qquad E_{eq} = E_2 - 0.029 \log |H_2| \cdot |OH^-|^2 \tag{16}$$

and also

$$\underset{(AB)}{2\,HB} + 2e \rightleftharpoons \underset{(B)}{2\,B^-} + \underset{(C)}{H_2}, \qquad E_{eq} = E_3 + 0.029 \log \frac{|HB|^2}{|B^-|^2|H_2|} \tag{17}$$

The standard potentials of these systems are related by

$$E_2 = E_1 + 0.058 \log K_{H_2O}, \qquad E_3 = E_1 + 0.058 \log K_A$$

The equilibrium potentials of all three systems are given by the simple relation $E_{eq} = -0.058\,pH$ when the solution is saturated with hydrogen under atmospheric pressure.

Reduction at a platinized platinum electrode

Systems (15) and (16) are fast, and (17) is generally fast too. The equations of the current–potential curves for these systems are

$$E = E_1 + 0.029 \log \frac{k_{H_2}}{k_{H_2}^2} + 0.029 \log \frac{(i - i_{H^+})^2}{(i_{H_2} - i)} \tag{18}$$

This reduction only occurs when the hydrogen ion concentration is at least 10^{-5} $(K_A \cdot |HB| \leq 10^{-10})$.

$$E = E_2 + 0.029 \log k_{H_2} \cdot k_{OH^-}^2 - 0.029 \log (i_{H_2} - i)(i_{OH^-} - i) \tag{19}$$

$$E = E_3 + 0.029 \log \frac{k_{B^-}^2 \cdot k_{H_2}}{k_{HB}^2} + 0.029 \log \frac{(i - i_{HB})^2}{(i_{B^-} - i)^2 (i_{H_2} - i)} \tag{20}$$

Fig. 69 shows how the reduction curves change during the neutralization of HB by OH⁻ in the absence of hydrogen (pK_A = 8, |HB| = 10⁻²). The pH is indicated at the side of each curve. The current is limited by the diffusion of HB when its concen-

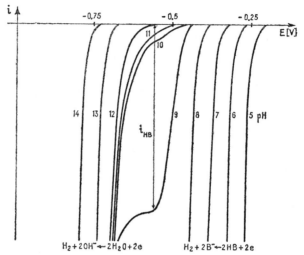

Fig. 69. The reaction HB + OH⁻ → B⁻ + H₂O. Platinized platinum electrode (after COUPEZ).

tration falls to a sufficiently low value during the neutralization. Hydrogen, when present, may be oxidized as follows

$$H_2 - 2e \rightleftarrows 2 H^+, \qquad \text{in very acid media (no free } B^- \text{ or } OH^-) \qquad (21)$$

$$H_2 + 2 OH^- - 2e \rightleftarrows 2 H_2O, \qquad \text{in alkaline media (excess of } OH^-) \qquad (22)$$

$$H_2 + 2 B^- - 2e \rightleftarrows 2 HB, \qquad \text{in media of pH near } pK_A \qquad (23)$$

We then obtain the curves of Fig. 70. When B⁻ is present the oxidation current is

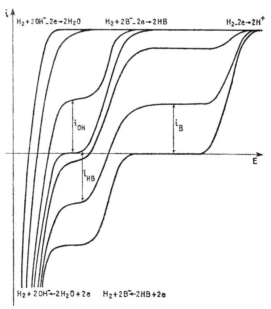

Fig. 70. The reaction HB + OH⁻ → B⁻ + H₂O in the presence of hydrogen.
Platinized platinum electrode (after COUPEZ).

initially limited by the diffusion of B⁻, but later by that of H_2. In the presence of a slight excess of OH⁻ ions, the current is initially limited by the diffusion of OH⁻.

The neutralization of a strong acid H⁺ by a weak base B⁻ (which is not reducible) may be treated similarly. The fast chemical reaction is

$$H^+ + B^- \rightleftharpoons HB, \qquad K_A = \frac{|H^+| \, |B^-|}{|HB|}$$
$$\text{(A)} \quad \text{(B)} \quad \text{(AB)}$$

The only substances which can be reduced are H⁺ and its complexes, the acid HB and water. Fig. 71 shows how the reduction curves change during the neutralization of millinormal H⁺ by B⁻, for $pK_A = 7$. When $x = 0$, only H⁺ is reduced and a single wave is observed whose equation is given by (18), the current being limited by the

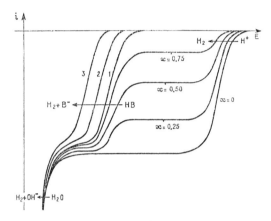

Fig. 71. The reaction $H^+ + B^- \rightarrow HB$.
Platinized platinum electrode (after COUPEZ).

diffusion of H⁺. For $0 < x < 1$, two waves are observed due to the reduction of free H⁺ followed by that of the acid HB formed. For $x > 1$, B⁻ is in excess and only HB is reduced. $E_{\frac{1}{2}}$ varies as $-0.058 \log |B^-|$, where $|B^-|$ is the concentration of the excess base. In addition to the substances mentioned above, water is always reduced whatever the value of x. This curve depends on the pH for values of the pH above 9.

Remark on reduction in a buffered medium. In non-buffered solutions between pH 5 and 9 the only possible reduction is that of water. This takes place only at very negative potentials. If, however, a buffer is added not only the pH is fixed but also the acid of the buffer may be reduced at a rate which depends only on the concentration of that acid.

If the concentration of buffer is large Eq. (20) is simplified, i becoming negligible compared to i_{HB} and i_{B^-}

$$E = E_3 + 0.029 \log k_{H_2} + 0.058 \log \frac{|HB|}{|B^-|} - 0.029 \log (-i)$$

$$= E_1 + 0.029 \log k_{H_2} - 0.058 \, pH - 0.029 \log (-i)$$

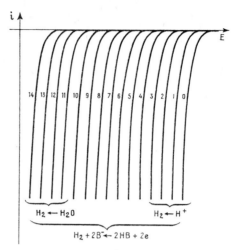

Fig. 72. Buffer solutions.

The equation is now the same as that for the reduction of H+ in very acid media or of water in very alkaline media (page 64). The reduction curves for H+, HB and H_2O under these conditions are given in Fig. 72. Some experimental curves are given in Fig. 73 and 74.

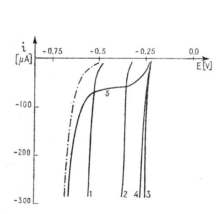

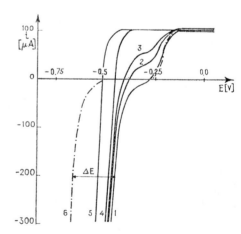

Fig. 73. Reduction curves.
The dotted and dashed curve: 1 M NaCl.

Curve 1: 0.1 M borate buffer, 1 M NaCl; pH 9
Curve 2: 0.1 M phosphate buffer, 1 M NaCl; pH 6.2
Curve 3: 0.1 M acetate buffer, 1 M NaCl; pH 4.5
Curve 4: 0.01 M acetate buffer, 1 M NaCl; pH 4.5
Curve 5: 0.001 M acetate buffer, 1 M NaCl; pH 4.5

Atmosphere of nitrogen, platinized platinum electrode (after Coupez[7]).

Fig. 74. Anode and cathode curves.

Curve 1: 0.1 M boric acid, 1 M NaCl.
Curve 2: 0.099 M boric acid, 0.001 M sodium borate, 1 M NaCl.
Curve 3: 0.098 M boric acid, 0.002 M sodium borate, 1 M NaCl.
Curve 4: 0.09 M boric acid, 0.01 M sodium borate, 1 M NaCl.
Curve 5: 0.1 M borate buffer, 1 M NaCl.
Curve 6: 1 M NaCl.

Atmosphere of hydrogen, platinized platinum electrode (after Coupez[7]).

Reduction at a mercury electrode. Like the reduction of H^+ and H_2O, the reduction of a weak acid (HB) is a slow reaction at a mercury electrode [3, 5, 7]. The reduction curves are independent of the presence of hydrogen (see Chapter IV).

The oxidation of water and hydroxyl ions

Let us consider the neutralization of a strong base by a strong acid. The only substances which can be oxidized are OH^- and H_2O. The chemical reaction is

$$\underset{(A)}{OH^-} + \underset{(B)}{H^+} \rightleftharpoons \underset{(AB)}{H_2O}$$

H^+ reacts with OH^- to give H_2O, whose activity is constant. Many redox systems are possible in principle, since OH^- and H_2O can be oxidized to hydrogen peroxide, which is further oxidized to oxygen. But in fact the second reaction is always faster than the first, so only the overall oxidation reaction is observed. The two possible reactions are then

1. When the concentration of OH^- is appreciable (pH > 9)

$$4\,OH^- - 4e \rightleftharpoons O_2 + 2\,H_2O$$

with

$$E_{eq} = E_1 + 0.015 \log \frac{|O_2|}{|OH^-|^4}, \qquad E_1 = 0.45\ V$$

When the solution is saturated with oxygen under atmospheric pressure,

$$|O_2| \sim 10^{-3}, \qquad E_{eq} = 1.23\ V - 0.058\ pH$$

2. At any pH

$$2\,H_2O - 4e \rightleftharpoons O_2 + 4\,H^+$$

with

$$E_{eq} = E_2 + 0.015 \log |O_2| \cdot |H^+|^4 \quad \text{and} \quad E_2 = E_1 - 0.058 \log K_{H_2O} = 1.27\ V$$

If both systems are rapid, the equilibrium potentials are given by

$$E_{eq} = 1.23\ V - 0.058\ pH$$

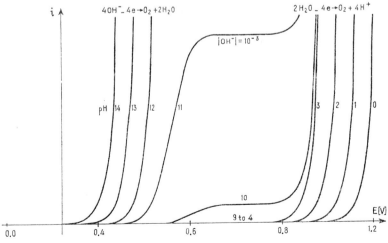

Fig. 75. Theoretical curves for the oxidation of water at different pH's.

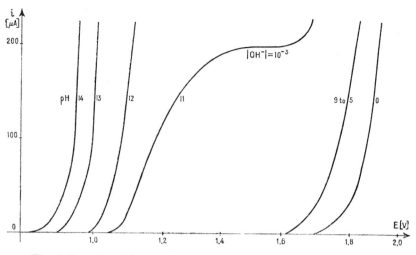

Fig. 76. Experimental curves for the oxidation of water at different pH's.
Smooth platinum electrode, surface area 0.15 cm² (after CONVERS [8]).

when the solution is saturated with oxygen under atmospheric pressure. In the absence of oxygen, and still supposing that systems (18) and (19) are rapid, the current–potential curves have the equations

$$E = E_1 + 0.015 \log \frac{k^4_{OH^-}}{k_{O_2}} - 0.015 \log \frac{(i_{OH^-} - i)^4}{i} \tag{24}$$

$$E = E_2 - 0.015 \log k_{O_2}. \, k^4_{H^+} + 0.015 \log (i - i_{H^+})^4 . \, i \tag{25}$$

These curves are shown in Fig. 75, the numbers of the curves correspond to the pH of the unbuffered solution. From pH 10 to 14, OH⁻ is oxidized first, and a limiting diffusion current is observed at low OH⁻ concentrations.

In fact, these electrochemical reactions are slow, or at any rate not very fast, even at a platinized platinum electrode. When the reaction is slow enough the curves no longer depend on the dissolved oxygen. Fig. 76 shows the oxidation as a function

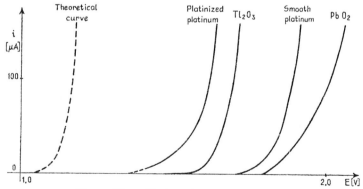

Fig. 77. The oxidation of water in N HClO₄.
Influence of the nature of the electrode, surface area 0.15 cm² (after CONVERS [8]).

of pH at a smooth platinum electrode, while in Fig. 77 are given curves for the oxidation in an acid medium at electrodes of platinized platinum, bright platinum, PbO_2 and Tl_2O_3. The theoretical curve as derived in Chapter IV is also given.

Oxidation in buffer solutions. In the presence of bases, a further reaction is possible (cf. page 67)

$$2 H_2O + 4 B^- - 4e \rightleftharpoons O_2 + 4 HB$$

Limitation of the current by the diffusion of B^- is found in such a system. If one works in a HB/B^- buffer solution with a sufficiently high concentration of B^-, the oxidation can be carried out at various pH's without the current being limited by diffusion.

Reduction of dissolved oxygen. Oxygen may be reduced, first to hydrogen peroxide (or its ions). The hydrogen peroxide may then be further reduced to water (or its ions). The redox systems involving O_2, H_2O_2 and H_2O (or OH^-) are slow, and the reduction of oxygen and of hydrogen peroxide and the oxidation of water can be treated separately. The reduction of O_2 and H_2O_2 is dealt with in Chapter IV.

The oxidation and reduction of water and its ions

Fig. 78 shows the oxidation and reduction curves for water and its ions in the absence of hydrogen or oxygen, on the assumption that the systems involved are fast.

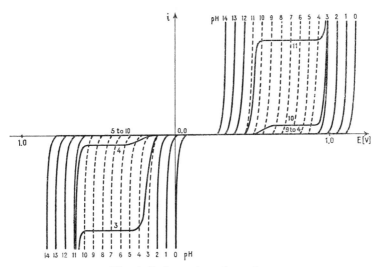

Fig. 78. Redox systems for water.
Idealized curves as a function of pH (the curves for buffer solutions are given by broken lines).

Remark. We have not given the curves corresponding to a mercury electrode. The overvoltage of hydrogen over mercury is very large, and the reduction curve of H^+ is situated at very negative potentials. Reduction curves for water are not generally found, since alkaline cations are usually reduced first to give amalgams. The oxidation curve of water cannot be obtained, as mercury is oxidized at considerably lower potentials.

The influence of the pH in the general case

1. Consider the redox system

$$aA + hH^+ + \ldots + ne \rightleftharpoons mM + \ldots \tag{26}$$

in which H^+ is one of the reactants. The equilibrium potential of this system is

$$E_{eq} = E_0 + \frac{0.058}{n} \log \frac{|A|^a |H^+|^h \ldots}{|M|^m \ldots}$$

If the system is fast, the equation of the current–potential curve is

$$E = E_0 + \frac{0.058}{n} \log \frac{k_M m \ldots}{k_A{}^a k_{H^+}{}^h \ldots} + \frac{0.058}{n} \log \frac{(i - i_A)^a (i - i_{H^+})^h \ldots}{(i_M - i)^m \ldots}$$

The reduction current is limited by the diffusion of A, H^+, or one of the other reactants on the left-hand side of Eq. (16). When H^+ is present in large concentrations, i is negligible compared to i_{H^+} and the above equation becomes

$$E = E_0 - \frac{0.058h}{n} \text{pH} + \frac{0.058}{n} \log \frac{k_M m \ldots}{k_A{}^a \ldots} + \frac{0.058}{n} \log \frac{(i - i_A)^a \ldots}{(i_M - i)^m \ldots}$$

When $|H^+|$ is very small (dilute acid) the reduction current corresponding to Eq. (26) is limited by the diffusion of H^+; and when $|H^+| < 10^{-5}$ or thereabouts (pH > 5) the reduction reaction of (26) is no longer possible.

2. Another possibility is the similar system

$$aA + hH_2O + \ldots + ne \rightleftharpoons mM + hOH^- + \ldots \tag{27}$$

with

$$E_{eq} = E_1 + \frac{0.058}{n} \log \frac{|A|^a \ldots}{|M|^m |OH^-|^h \ldots}$$

since $|H^+| \cdot |OH^-| = K_{H_2O}$ we see that

$$E_1 = E_0 + \frac{0.058h}{n} \log K_{H_2O}$$

The current–potential curve has the equation

$$E = E_1 + \frac{0.058}{n} \log \frac{k_M m k_{OH^-}{}^{-h} \ldots}{k_A{}^a} + \frac{0.058}{n} \log \frac{(i - i_A)^a \ldots}{(i_M - i)^m (i_{OH^-} - i)^h \ldots}$$

if the system is fast. The reduction current is limited by the diffusion of A and the other reactants on the left-hand side of Eq. (27), but H_2O, whose concentration remains practically constant, has no limiting effect. The oxidation current is limited by the diffusion of OH^- and the other reactants on the right-hand side of Eq. (27).

When $|OH^-|$ is large, i is negligible compared to i_{OH^-}, and as in the case of H^+ the above equation becomes

$$E = E_1 + \frac{0.058}{n} \log \frac{k_M m \ldots}{k_A{}^a \ldots} - \frac{0.058h}{n} \log |OH^-| + \frac{0.058}{n} \log \frac{(i - i_A)^a \ldots}{(i_M - i)^m \ldots}$$

$$= E_0 - \frac{0.058h}{n} \text{pH} + \frac{0.058}{n} \log \frac{k_M m \ldots}{k_A{}^a \ldots} + \frac{0.058}{n} \log \frac{(i - i_A)^a \ldots}{(i_M - i)^m \ldots}$$

When $|OH^-|$ is very small (very dilute base) the oxidation current for reaction (27) is limited by the diffusion of OH^-, and when $|OH^-| < 10^{-5}$ (pH < 9) or thereabouts, the oxidation reaction (27) cannot occur.

3. In the presence of a weak acid and a weak base, in particular in a solution buffered with respect to pH (HB + B⁻), the following system may be found

$$aA + hHB + \ldots + ne \rightleftharpoons mM + hB^- + \ldots \tag{28}$$

The equilibrium potential is given by

$$E_{eq} = E_2 + \frac{0.058}{n} \log \frac{|A|^a |HB|^h}{|M|^m |B^-|^h}$$

since $\dfrac{|B^-||H^+|}{|HB|} = K_A$ we have

$$E_2 = E_0 + \frac{0.058h}{n} \log K_A$$

If the system is fast, the equation of its current–potential curve is

$$E = E_2 + \frac{0.058}{n} \log \frac{k_M{}^m k_B{}^{-h} \ldots}{k_A{}^a k_{HB}{}^h \ldots} + \frac{0.058}{n} \log \frac{(i - i_A)^a (i - i_{HB})^h \ldots}{(i_M - i)^m (i_{B^-} - i)^h \ldots}$$

The oxidation current may be limited by the diffusion of B⁻, just as in reaction (27) it was limited by OH⁻, and the reduction current can be limited by HB, as by H⁺ in reaction (26). If HB and B⁻ are present in sufficiently large concentrations, however, they will not limit the current. If they are present in large concentrations, the equation of the curve becomes

$$E = E_2 + \frac{0.058}{n} \log \frac{k_M{}^m \ldots}{k_A{}^a \ldots} + \frac{0.058}{n} \log \frac{(i - i_A)^a \ldots |HB|^h}{(i_M - i)^m \ldots |B^-|^h}$$

$$= E_2 + \frac{0.058}{n} \log \frac{k_M{}^m \ldots}{k_A{}^a \ldots} - \frac{0.058h}{n} pH - \frac{0.058h}{n} \log K_A + \frac{0.058}{n} \log \frac{(i - i_A)^a \ldots}{(i_M - i)^m \ldots}$$

$$= E_0 - \frac{0.058h}{n} pH + \frac{0.058}{n} \log \frac{k_M{}^m \ldots}{k_A{}^a \ldots} + \frac{0.058}{n} \log \frac{(i - i_A)^a \ldots}{(i_M - i)^m \ldots}$$

This is the same as the equation for the system (26) when $|H^+|$ is large, and that for system (27) when $|OH^-|$ is large.

To sum up, for the three systems

$$aA + hH^+ + ne \rightleftharpoons mM \tag{29}$$

$$aA + hH_2O + ne \rightleftharpoons mM + hOH^- \tag{30}$$

$$aA + hHB + ne \rightleftharpoons mM + hB^- \tag{31}$$

the equilibrium potential is given by

$$E_{eq} = E_0 - \frac{0.058h}{n} pH + \frac{0.058}{n} \log \frac{|A|^a}{|M|^m}$$

The current–potential curve also has the same equation in all three cases, when H⁺, OH⁻, HB and B⁻ are present in high concentrations:

$$E = E_0 + \frac{0.058}{n} \log \frac{k_M{}^m}{k_A{}^a} - \frac{0.058h}{n} pH + \frac{0.058}{n} \log \frac{(i - i_A)^a}{(i_M - i)^m}$$

If the reactants A, etc. and M, etc. remain the same, their current–potential curves may be determined at any pH, without any limitation of the current by the pH. The electrochemical reaction is represented by the system (29) in very acid media, by the system (30) in very basic media and by the system (31) in buffer solutions. We give here the current–potential curves for the very simple system

$$A + H^+ + e \rightarrow M \quad \text{for} \quad |A| = |M| = 10^{-3}$$

and for various values of $|H^+|$ and $|OH^-|$ (Fig. 79, 80, 81).

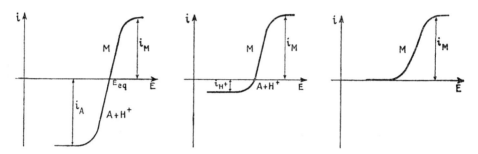

Fig. 79. The reaction $A + H^+ + e \rightleftharpoons M$.

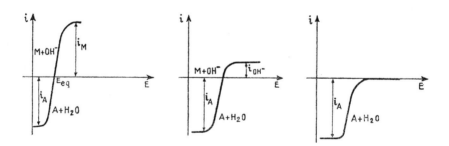

Fig. 80. The reaction $A + H_2O + e \rightleftharpoons M + OH^-$.

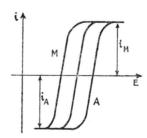

Fig. 81. The reaction $A + HB + e \rightleftharpoons M + B^-$.

The quinone–hydroquinone system [9]

We will represent benzoquinone by Q, and benzohydroquinone by H_2Q. We will now investigate the current–potential curves for a mixture of Q and H_2Q as a function of pH. Hydroquinone is a weak acid, so we have the following acid–base systems

$$H_2Q \rightleftharpoons HQ^- + H^+, \quad \text{with} \quad \frac{|HQ^-|\,|H^+|}{|H_2Q|} = K_2 = 10^{-10.0}$$

$$HQ^- \rightleftharpoons Q^{2-} + H^+, \quad \text{with} \quad \frac{|Q^{2-}|\,|H^+|}{|HQ^-|} = K_1 = 10^{-11.5}$$

The different redox systems possible are

$$Q + 2e \rightleftharpoons Q^{2-} \qquad\qquad E_0 = 0.08 \text{ V} \quad (C + 2e \rightleftharpoons A) \qquad (32)$$

$$Q + H_2O + 2e \rightleftharpoons HQ^- + OH^- \qquad E_1 \qquad\qquad\qquad (33)$$

$$Q + 2\,H^+ + 2e \rightleftharpoons H_2Q \qquad E_2 \quad (C + B + 2e \rightleftharpoons AB) \qquad (34)$$

$$Q + 2\,H_2O + 2e \rightleftharpoons H_2Q + 2\,OH^- \qquad E_3 \qquad\qquad\qquad (35)$$

The equilibrium potentials of the various systems are given by

$$E_{eq} = 0.08 \text{ V} + 0.029 \log \frac{|Q|}{|Q^{2-}|} \qquad\qquad \text{in very basic media}$$

$$E_{eq} = 0.08 \text{ V} - 0.029 \log K_1 + 0.029 \log \frac{|Q|}{|HQ^-|} - 0.029 \text{ pH} \qquad \text{about pH 10–11}$$

$$E_{eq} = 0.08 \text{ V} - 0.029 \log K_1 K_2 + 0.029 \log \frac{|Q|}{|H_2Q|} - 0.058 \text{ pH} \qquad \text{below pH 10}$$

Experiment has shown that these redox systems are fast at a number of kinds of electrodes.

We will consider a solution of 10^{-3} M quinone and 10^{-3} M hydroquinone (*i.e.* 10^{-3} M quinhydrone) in a strongly acid medium, and will discuss the effect of varying the pH gradually.

In a very acid medium, pH < 3, we find reaction (34)

$$E = E_2 + 0.029 \log \frac{k_{H_2Q}}{k_Q} - 0.058 \text{ pH} + 0.029 \log \frac{i - i_Q}{i_{H_2Q} - i}$$

The cathodic current is limited by the diffusion of H_2Q, and the anodic current by that of Q.

From pH 3 to 5, the same reaction occurs, but the limiting current is now dependent on $|H^+|$, and therefore decreases with $|H^+|$. When the limiting current for this reaction is reached, $|H^+|$ is very low, and the reaction (35) is produced as the potential is decreased (see Fig. 82). The total current is still limited by Q, which is reduced by both the above reactions. The second part of the curve, like the first, depends on the pH. The oxidation reaction remains that of (34).

From pH 5 to 9 reduction occurs according to reaction (35), and oxidation according to reaction (34).

About pH 10–11 the oxidation and reduction take place according to reaction (33). The anodic current is limited by the diffusion of HQ^-, and the cathodic current by the diffusion of Q.

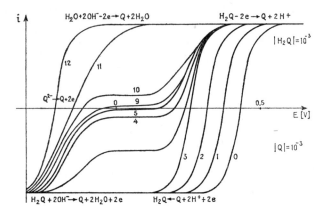

Fig. 82. The quinone–hydroquinone system in a non-buffered medium
(theoretical curves).

At pH $\geq$ 12 reaction (32) occurs, limited by the diffusion of Q^{2-} (oxidation) and
Q (reduction). The curves obtained are shown in Fig. 82. The number against each
curve is the pH.

In an unbuffered medium the pH at the electrode may be very different from
the pH in the body of the solution, and the conclusions given above will no longer
hold.

In a buffer solution, two further redox systems are possible

$$Q + HB + 2e \rightleftharpoons HQ^- + B^- \tag{36}$$

$$Q + 2 HB + 2e \rightleftharpoons H_2Q + 2 B^- \tag{37}$$

If the concentrations of HB and B^- are so high that their diffusion no longer limits
the current, we obtain the curves of Fig. 83. These have been verified in experiments
using a mercury electrode.

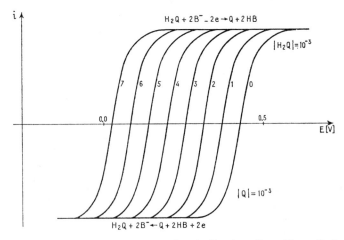

Fig. 83. The quinone–hydroquinone system in a buffered medium (theoretical curves).

As we have mentioned above, any one of the complex systems (33), (34) or (35) can be used as an indicator for H⁺ (or OH⁻). For example, an acid–base reaction may be followed by the addition of quinone and hydroquinone to the solution. Eq. (36) and (37) indicate that the quinone–hydroquinone system is also an indicator for weak acids and bases.

The precipitation of silver bromide [10]

A solution of a bromide is added gradually to a solution of silver nitrate. The chemical reaction is

$$\underset{(A)}{Ag^+} + \underset{(B)}{Br^-} \rightleftharpoons \underset{(AB\downarrow)}{AgBr\downarrow}$$

The solubility product $s = |Ag^+| \cdot |Br^-| = 10^{-12.3}$.

Let us determine the current–potential curves at a silver electrode during the course of this reaction. The redox systems are

$$Ag^+ + e \rightleftharpoons Ag\downarrow \qquad\qquad (A + e \rightleftharpoons C\downarrow) \tag{38}$$

$$AgBr\downarrow + e \rightleftharpoons Ag\downarrow + Br^- \qquad (AB\downarrow + e \rightleftharpoons C\downarrow + B) \tag{39}$$

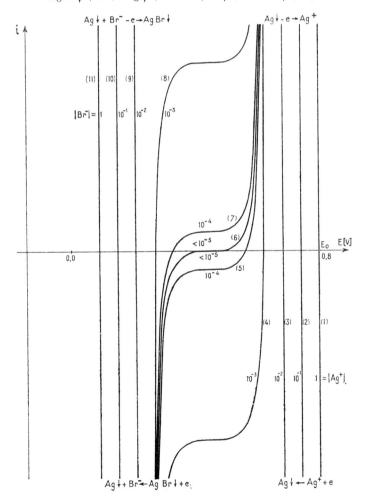

Fig. 84. The reaction $Ag^+ + Br^- \rightarrow AgBr\downarrow$. Silver electrode (theoretical curves).

The equilibrium potentials are

$$E_{eq} = E_0 + 0.058 \log |Ag^+| \qquad\qquad E_0 = 0.80 \text{ V} \qquad (40)$$

and

$$E_{eq} = E_1 - 0.058 \log |Br^-| \quad \text{with} \quad E_1 = E_0 + 0.058 \log s = 0.09 \text{ V} \qquad (41)$$

The equations of the curves are then

$$E = 0.80 \text{ V} - 0.058 \log k_{Ag^+} + 0.058 \log (i - i_{Ag^+}) \qquad (42)$$

$$E = 0.09 \text{ V} + 0.058 \log k_{Br^-} - 0.058 \log (i_{Br^-} - i) \qquad (43)$$

These curves are shown in Fig. 84. The concentration of the substance in excess (Ag^+ at the start of the reaction and Br^- after the equivalence point) is shown by each curve. When the concentration of Ag^+ is very large, $i \ll i_{Ag^+}$, Eq. (42) becomes

$$E = 0.80 \text{ V} + 0.058 \log |Ag^+|_s$$

This means that the electrode potential remains constant, whatever the current. Similarly, when the excess of Br^- is sufficiently large

$$E = 0.09 \text{ V} - 0.058 \log |Br^-|_s$$

Other similar examples [11], [12]

Fig. 85 shows the curves corresponding to the oxidation of silver in the presence of halides and Fig. 86 shows that for the oxidation of mercury (dropping electrode)

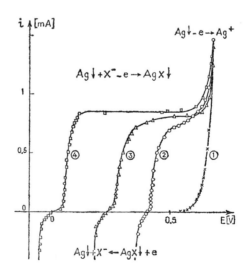

Fig. 85. Current–potential curves at a silver electrode in the presence of halides.

Curve 1: N $HClO_4$.   Curve 3: N $HClO_4$ + 10^{-3} M Br^-.
Curve 2: N $HClO_4$ + 10^{-3} M Cl^-.   Curve 4: N $HClO_4$ + 10^{-3} M I^-.

Surface area of electrode 1 cm² (after BADOZ–LAMBLING [10]).

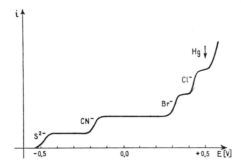

Fig. 86. The oxidation of mercury in the presence of various anions
(after REVENDA[11], KOLTHOFF and MILLER[12]).

in the presence of sulphide, cyanide, bromide and chloride ions. The successive electrochemical reactions in the latter case are

$$2 \text{ Hg} \downarrow + \text{HS}^- + \text{OH}^- - 2e \rightleftharpoons \text{Hg}_2\text{S} \downarrow + \text{H}_2\text{O}$$
$$2 \text{ Hg} \downarrow + 2 \text{ CN}^- - 2e \rightleftharpoons \text{Hg}_2(\text{CN})_2 \downarrow$$
$$2 \text{ Hg} \downarrow + 2 \text{ Br}^- - 2e \rightleftharpoons \text{Hg}_2\text{Br}_2 \downarrow$$
$$2 \text{ Hg} \downarrow + 2 \text{ Cl} - 2e \rightleftharpoons \text{Hg}_2\text{Cl}_2 \downarrow$$
$$2 \text{ Hg} \downarrow - 2e \rightleftharpoons \text{Hg}_2^{2+}$$

The precipitation of hydroxides

(a) Consider the chemical reaction of the precipitation of a hydroxide

$$\text{M}^+ + \text{OH}^- \rightleftharpoons \text{MOH} \downarrow \quad \text{with} \quad |\text{M}^+| \cdot |\text{OH}^-| = s$$

We will follow the current–potential curves as a function of the pH. In principle, three
redox systems are possible

$$\text{M}^+ + e \rightleftharpoons \text{M} \downarrow, \qquad E_{eq} = E_0 + 0.058 \log |\text{M}^+| \tag{44}$$
$$\text{MOH} \downarrow + e \rightleftharpoons \text{M} \downarrow + \text{OH}^-, \qquad E_{eq} = E_1 - 0.058 \log |\text{OH}^-| \tag{45}$$

with $\qquad E_1 = E_0 + 0.058 \log s$

$$\text{MOH} \downarrow + \text{H}^+ + e \rightleftharpoons \text{M} \downarrow, \qquad E_{eq} = E_2 + 0.058 \log |\text{H}^+| \tag{46}$$

with $\qquad E_2 = E_0 + 0.058 \log \dfrac{s}{10^{-14.2}}$

At a given pH, one or more of these systems may not exist, depending on the nature
of M.

(b) The hydroxide may also be precipitated by a weak base

$$\text{M}^+ + \text{H}_2\text{O} + \text{B}^- \rightleftharpoons \text{MOH} \downarrow + \text{HB}$$

We may now have the redox system

$$\text{MOH} \downarrow + \text{HB} + e \rightleftharpoons \text{M} \downarrow + \text{B}^- + \text{H}_2\text{O}, \tag{47}$$

$$E_{eq} = E_3 + 0.058 \log \frac{|\text{HB}|}{|\text{B}^-|} \quad \text{with} \quad \frac{|\text{B}^-| |\text{H}^+|}{|\text{HB}|} = K_A$$

This is the case when the pH is fixed by means of a buffer solution. The equilibrium potential of the reactions (44), (45) and (46) is given by the general equation

$$E_{eq} = E_2 - 0.058 \text{ pH} \quad \text{with} \quad E_1 = E_0 + 0.82 \text{ V} + 0.058 \log s$$

(c) The hydroxide MOH $\downarrow$ may be soluble in an excess of OH⁻ ions

$$\text{MOH} \downarrow + \text{OH}^- \rightleftharpoons \text{MO}^- + \text{H}_2\text{O}, \quad K = \frac{|\text{MO}^-|}{|\text{OH}^-|}$$

The additional redox systems are now

$$\text{MO}^- + \text{H}_2\text{O} + e \rightleftharpoons \text{M} \downarrow + 2 \text{ OH}^-, \qquad E_{eq} = E_3 + 0.058 \log \frac{|\text{MO}^-|}{|\text{OH}^-|^2} \tag{48}$$

$$\text{with} \qquad E_3 = E_1 + 0.058 \log K$$

$$\text{MO}^- + 2 \text{ H}^+ + e \rightleftharpoons \text{M} \downarrow + \text{H}_2\text{O}, \qquad E_{eq} = E_4 + 0.058 \log |\text{MO}^-| \cdot |\text{H}^+|^2 \tag{49}$$

$$\text{with} \qquad E_4 = E_3 - 0.116 \log K_{\text{H}_2\text{O}}$$

and also

$$\text{MO}^- + 2 \text{ HB} + e \rightleftharpoons \text{M} \downarrow + \text{H}_2\text{O} + 2 \text{ B}^- \tag{50}$$

In this case too, one or other of the species may not exist in the pH range under consideration.

(d) The reductant may be an ion and not a metal. The redox systems found in such a case are similar to those mentioned above.

Example: The precipitation of silver hydroxide

We will follow the behaviour of the current–potential curves during the chemical reaction

$$2 \text{ Ag}^+ + 2 \text{ OH}^- \rightleftharpoons \text{Ag}_2\text{O} \downarrow + \text{H}_2\text{O} \quad \text{with} \quad |\text{Ag}^+| \cdot |\text{OH}^-| = s = 10^{-7.8}$$

as a function of the pH. It will be seen from the value of s that Ag_2O will only start to be precipitated in an alkaline medium. The redox systems are then as follows:
In an acid medium

$$\text{Ag}^+ + e \rightleftharpoons \text{Ag} \downarrow, \qquad E_{eq} = 0.80 \text{ V} + 0.058 \log |\text{Ag}^+| \tag{51}$$

The equation of the current–potential curve is

$$E = 0.80 \text{ V} - 0.058 \log k_{\text{Ag}^+} + 0.058 \log (i - i_{\text{Ag}^+})$$

In an alkaline medium

$$\text{Ag}_2\text{O} \downarrow + \text{H}_2\text{O} + 2e \rightleftharpoons 2 \text{ Ag} \downarrow + 2 \text{ OH}^- \tag{52}$$

$$E_{eq} = E_1 - 0.058 \log |\text{OH}|^-$$

$$E = E_1 + 0.058 \log k_{\text{OH}^-} - 0.058 \log (i_{\text{OH}^-} - i)$$

$$\text{with} \quad E_1 = E_0 + 0.058 \log s = 0.35 \text{ V}$$

If the pH is fixed by a buffer solution, then

$$\text{Ag}_2\text{O} \downarrow + 2 \text{ HB} + 2e \rightleftharpoons 2 \text{ Ag} \downarrow + \text{H}_2\text{O} + 2 \text{ B}^- \tag{53}$$

$$\text{and} \qquad E_{eq} = 0.35 \text{ V} - 0.058 \log |\text{OH}^-|$$

for reactions (52) and (53). The curves are completely similar to those obtained for the precipitation of silver bromide.

The reduction of cupric ions during the addition of an excess of glycine [13]

An increasing excess of glycine G^- is added to a buffered solution of Cu^{2+} ($10^{-3}M$). The complex CuG_2 is first formed, then the complex CuG_3^-. Let us follow the reduction curves at a mercury electrode. The redox systems are

$$CuG_2 + Hg\downarrow + 2e \rightleftharpoons Cu(Hg) + 2 G^- \tag{54}$$

$$E_{eq} = E_1 + 0.029 \log \frac{|CuG_2|}{|G^-|^2 |Cu(Hg)|}$$

followed by

$$CuG_3^- + Hg\downarrow + 2e \rightleftharpoons Cu(Hg) + 3 G^- \tag{55}$$

$$E_{eq} = E_2 + 0.029 \log \frac{|CuG_3^-|}{|G^-|^3 |Cu(Hg)|}$$

The concentration $|G^-|$ is constant and equal to $|G^-|_s$ near the electrode (excess of glycine). The equations of the curves are

$$E = E_1 - 0.029 \log k_{CuG_2} - 0.058 \log |G^-|_s + 0.029 \log \frac{i - i_{CuG_2}}{i} \tag{56}$$

and

$$E = E_2 - 0.029 \log k_{CuG_3^-} - 0.097 \log |G^-|_s + 0.029 \log \frac{i - i_{CuG_3^-}}{i} \tag{57}$$

The shape of the curve is thus constant, and its height is more or less constant and equal to $k_{Cu^{2+}} |Cu^{2+}|_{total}$ (if $k_{Cu^{2+}} = k_{CuG_2} = k_{CuG_3^-}$), and the half-wave potential varies first as $-0.058 \log |G^-|_s$ and then as $-0.097 \log |G^-|_s$ (see Fig. 87).

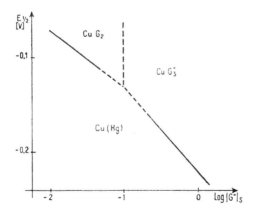

Fig. 87. The variation of the half-wave potential of the reduction curve of the copper (II)–glycine complexes with the concentration of free glycine (after KEEFER [13]).

The reduction of ferric ions during the addition of an excess of oxalate [14]

An increasing excess of oxalate ($C_2O_4^{2-}$) is added to a $10^{-3} M$ buffered solution of Fe^{3+}. Fe^{3+} forms the complex $Fe(C_2O_4)_3^{3-}$, while its reduction product (Fe^{2+}) forms two complexes: $Fe(C_2O_4)_2^{2-}$ and then $Fe(C_2O_4)_3^{4-}$. We will follow the reduction curves at a mercury electrode. The redox systems are

$$Fe(C_2O_4)_3^{3-} + e \rightleftharpoons Fe(C_2O_4)_2^{2-} + C_2O_4^{2-} \qquad (58)$$

$$E_{eq} = E_1 + 0.058 \log \frac{|Fe(C_2O_4)_3^{3-}|}{|Fe(C_2O_4)_2^{2-}| |C_2O_4^{2-}|}$$

$$Fe(C_2O_4)_3^{3-} + e \rightleftharpoons Fe(C_2O_4)_3^{4-} \qquad (59)$$

$$E_{eq} = E_2 + 0.058 \log \frac{|Fe(C_2O_4)_3^{3-}|}{|Fe(C_2O_4)_3^{4-}|}$$

The current–potential curves have the equation

$$E = E_{\frac{1}{2}} + 0.058 \log \frac{i - i_{Fe(III)}}{i}$$

and their half-wave potential varies first as $-0.058 \log |C_2O_4^{2-}|_s$, and then remains independent of the variation in the oxalate concentration.

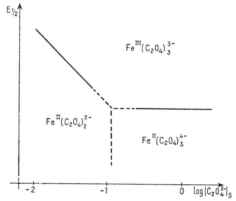

Fig. 88. The variation of the half-wave potential of the reduction curve of the ferri-oxalate complex, with the concentration of free oxalate (after LINGANE [14]).

The influence of the pH on the oxidation curves of mercury in the presence of sulphide

DUYCKAERTS [15] has studied the anode curves for this reaction at a dropping mercury electrode. Since the mercury surface is continually renewed, (see Chapter V, the dropping mercury electrode), the reduction of Hg_2S need not be taken into account. As H_2S is a weak dibasic acid ($pK_2 = 7.1$, $pK_1 = 13$), the following chemical reactions are possible

$$Hg_2^{2+} + S^{2-} \rightleftharpoons Hg_2S \downarrow$$
$$Hg_2^{2+} + HS^- \rightleftharpoons Hg_2S \downarrow + H^+$$
$$Hg_2^{2+} + H_2S \rightleftharpoons Hg_2S \downarrow + 2 H^+$$

The solubility product $s = |Hg_2^{2+}| |S^{2-}|$

(a) *In an acid medium,* we have the redox systems

$$2 Hg \downarrow + H_2S - 2e \rightleftharpoons Hg_2S \downarrow + 2 H^+ \qquad (60)$$

$$E_{eq} = E_1 + 0.029 \log \frac{|H^+|^2}{|H_2S|}, \qquad E_1 = -0.31 \text{ V}$$

and in the presence of the buffer system HB/B^-

$$2 \text{ Hg} \downarrow + \text{H}_2\text{S} + 2 \text{ B}^- - 2\text{e} \rightleftharpoons \text{Hg}_2\text{S} \downarrow + 2 \text{ HB} \tag{61}$$

$$E_{eq} = E_2 + 0.029 \log \frac{|\text{HB}|^2}{|\text{H}_2\text{S}|\,|\text{B}^-|^2} = E_1 + 0.029 \log \frac{|\text{H}^+|^2}{|\text{H}_2\text{S}|}$$

if $\qquad \dfrac{|\text{B}^-|\,|\text{H}^+|}{|\text{HB}|} = K_A, \qquad E_2 = E_1 - 0.058 \log K_A$

If the concentration of H$^+$ is large compared to that of H$_2$S in system (60), or if the buffer solution is strong in system (61), the equation of the anodic curve is

$$E = E_1 + 0.029 \log k_{\text{H}_2\text{S}} - 0.058 \text{ pH} - 0.029 \log (i_{\text{H}_2\text{S}} - i)$$

The current is limited by the diffusion of H$_2$S and the half-wave potential varies as -0.058 pH.

(b) *In a slightly alkaline medium* the redox system is

$$2 \text{ Hg} \downarrow + \text{HS}^- - 2\text{e} \rightleftharpoons \text{Hg}_2\text{S} \downarrow + \text{H}^+$$

$$E_{eq} = E_3 + 0.029 \log \frac{|\text{H}^+|}{|\text{HS}^-|} \quad \text{with} \quad E_3 = E_1 - 0.029 \text{ pK}_2$$

or, in a buffer solution

$$2 \text{ Hg} \downarrow + \text{HS}^- + \text{B}^- - 2\text{e} \rightleftharpoons \text{Hg}_2\text{S} \downarrow + \text{HB}$$

When the pH is buffered, the anodic curve has the equation

$$E = E_3 + 0.029 \log k_{\text{HS}^-} - 0.029 \text{ pH} - 0.029 \log (i_{\text{HS}^-} - i)$$

The current is still limited by the diffusion of HS$^-$, but the half-wave potential varies as -0.029 pH.

(c) *In a very alkaline medium* the redox system is

$$2 \text{ Hg} \downarrow + \text{S}^{2-} - 2\text{e} \rightleftharpoons \text{Hg}_2\text{S} \downarrow$$

and the half-wave potential is independent of the pH (Fig. 89).

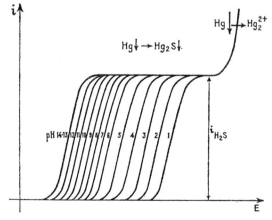

Fig. 89. Oxidation curves for mercury in the presence of sulphide, as a function of pH. Buffered medium (theoretical curves).

Fig. 90 shows the variation of $E_{\frac{1}{2}}$ as a function of the pH.

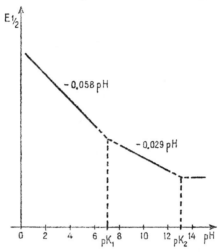

Fig. 90. The half-wave potential of the oxidation curves for mercury in the presence of sulphide, as a function of the pH (after DUYCKAERTS [15]).

The influence of the pH on the reduction curves of mercuric cyanide

(a) TOMES [5, 16] has determined the reduction curves of a solution of mercuric cyanide, $Hg(CN)_2$, at a dropping mercury electrode, without an excess of cyanide and in the presence of various buffers. Since HCN is a weak acid ($pK_A = 9.4$), we may have the two redox systems:

In acid and slightly alkaline media ($pH < 8$)

Very acid media

$$Hg(CN)_2 + 2\,H^+ + 2e \rightleftharpoons Hg\downarrow + 2\,HCN \qquad (62)$$

with $\qquad E_{eq} = E_1 + 0.029 \log \dfrac{|Hg(CN)_2|\,|H^+|^2}{|HCN|^2}$

and in a buffer solution

$$Hg(CN)_2 + 2\,HB + 2e \rightleftharpoons Hg\downarrow + 2\,HCN + 2\,B^-$$

with the same equilibrium potential.

In alkaline medium ($pH > 11$)

$$Hg(CN)_2 + 2e \rightleftharpoons Hg\downarrow + 2\,CN^- \qquad (63)$$

$$E_{eq} = E_2 + 0.029 \log \dfrac{|Hg(CN)_2|}{|CN^-|^2} \quad \text{with} \quad E_2 = E_1 - 0.058\,pK_A$$

The half-wave potential of the reduction curve in alkaline solution is independent of the pH, while in acid solution $E_{\frac{1}{2}}$ varies as -0.058 pH. This behaviour is shown in Fig. 91. The equation of the reduction curve in acid media may be written

$$E = E_1 - 0.058\,pH + 0.029 \log \dfrac{k_{HCN}^2}{k_{Hg(CN)_2}} + 0.029 \log \dfrac{i - i_{Hg(CN)_2}}{i^2} \qquad (64)$$

and the half-wave potential then depends on the concentration $|Hg(CN)_2|_s$.

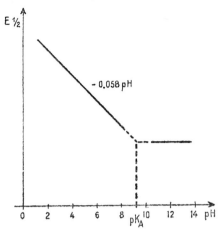

Fig. 91. $E_{\frac{1}{2}}$ as a function of the pH for the oxidation curves of mercury in the presence of cyanide (after TOMES [5, 16]).

(b) The pH of the solution is not buffered.

Let us consider a 10^{-3} M solution of $Hg(CN)_2$ in a high concentration of H^+, and let us follow the current–potential curves as the acid is gradually neutralized.

In a very acid medium (pH < 3), the redox system is the system (62) and the concentration of H^+ at the surface of the electrode remains practically constant. The equation of the reduction curve is therefore given by Eq. (64) and $E_{\frac{1}{2}}$ varies as -0.058 pH.

In a slightly acid medium (pH 3 to 5), the system (62) is initially present, so the equation of the curve is

$$ E = E_1 + 0.029 \log \frac{k^2_{HCN}}{k_{Hg(CN)_2} \, k^2_{H^+}} + 0.029 \log \frac{(i - i_{Hg(CN)_2}) \, (i_{H^+} - i)^2}{i^2} $$

and the current is limited first by $|Hg(CN)_2|_s$ and then by $|H^+|$, when this is small

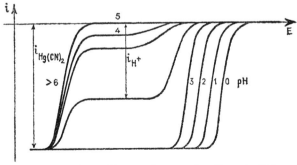

Fig. 92. Reduction of the mercuri-cyanide complex as a function of pH (non-buffered medium) (theoretical curves).

$$ Hg(CN)_2 + 2\,H^+ + 2e \rightarrow Hg\downarrow + 2\,HCN $$
$$ Hg(CN)_2 + 2e \rightarrow Hg\downarrow + 2\,CN^- $$

enough. When the limit of diffusion is reached, $|H^+|_e = 0$, so we have the redox system (63), and the equation of the curve is given by

$$E = E_2 + 0.029 \log \frac{k^2_{CN^-}}{k_{Hg(CN)_2}} + 0.029 \log \frac{i - i_{Hg(CN)_2}}{i^2}$$

In alkaline media (pH > 7) only this last curve is observed. The curves are shown in Fig. 92. The influence of the pH on the reduction of the Hg(II)–EDTA complex is shown by GOFFART, MICHEL and DUYCKAERTS [17].

V. REDOX REACTIONS

We will now consider the case where a reactant B is added to the electroactive substance A, and the chemical reaction is an oxidation–reduction reaction. Let us suppose for example that we have an oxidant A, which is reduced according to

$$A + e \rightleftharpoons C, \qquad \text{standard potential } E_1 \tag{65}$$

The substance B, which is a reducing agent

$$B - e \rightleftharpoons D, \qquad \text{standard potential } E_2 \tag{66}$$

reacts with A

$$A + B \rightleftharpoons C + D \tag{67}$$

We will suppose that the electrochemical reactions (65) and (66) are fast, and that the chemical reaction (67) in which A is reduced by B is quantitative, *i.e.* $E_2 \ll E_1$. The current–potential curves are shown in Fig. 93. Initially, when $x = 0$, A is reduced

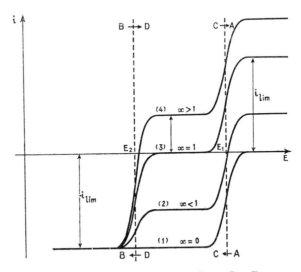

Fig. 93. The redox reaction $A + B \rightarrow C + D$.

at the cathode ($E_{\frac{1}{2}} \approx E_1$). When B is added, the concentration of A decreases and the height of the corresponding curve also decreases. D, which appears as a result of the reaction $A + B \rightarrow C + D$, is reduced at a lower potential ($E_{\frac{1}{2}} \approx E_2$). When $x \geq 1$, only the reduction curve of D remains.

The anodic reactions also play their part as the chemical reaction proceeds: the addition of B causes C to be formed, and this is oxidized at the electrode, ($E_{\frac{1}{2}} \approx E_1$). After the equivalence point, $x > 1$, the oxidation of the excess B is also observed.

The reaction of ferrous iron with ceric salts

The behaviour of the current–potential curves during the reaction is shown in Fig. 94. In practice the limit corresponding to the oxidation of Ce^{3+} cannot be obtained by oxidation at a platinum electrode, since the oxidation curve of water is partly superimposed on that of Ce^{3+}.

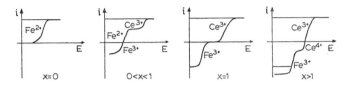

Fig. 94. The reaction $Fe^{2+} + Ce^{4+} \rightarrow Fe^{3+} + Ce^{3+}$ (ideal curves).

REFERENCES

[1] B. MATYSKA and I. KOSSLER, *Collection Czechoslov. Chem. Communs.*, 16 (1951) 221.
[2] J. COUPEZ, *Anal. Chim. Acta*, 16 (1957) 582.
[3] J. COUPEZ, *Actas do Congresso, Lisboa 1956*, p. 566.
[4] J. COUPEZ, *Actas do Congresso, Lisboa 1956*, p. 580.
[5] I. TOMES, *Collection Czechoslov. Chem. Communs.*, 9 (1937) 150.
[6] I. M. KOLTHOFF and J. JORDAN, *J. Am. Chem. Soc.*, 74 (1952) 4801.
[7] J. COUPEZ, *Anal. Chim. Acta*, 17 (1957) 300.
[8] M. CONVERS, *Bull. soc. chim. France*, (1959) 792.
[9] O. H. MÜLLER and J. P. BAUMBERGER, *Trans. Electrochem. Soc.*, 71 (1937) 169, 181.
[10] J. BADOZ–LAMBLING, *Bull. soc. chim. France*, (1954) 370.
[11] J. REVENDA, *Collection Czechoslov. Chem. Communs.*, 6 (1934) 453.
[12] I. M. KOLTHOFF and C. S. MILLER, *J. Am. Chem. Soc.*, 63 (1941) 1405.
[13] R. M. KEEFER, *J. Am. Chem. Soc.*, 61 (1939) 2329.
[14] J. J. LINGANE, *Chem. Revs.*, 29 (1941) 1.
[15] G. DUYCKAERTS, *Bull. soc. roy. sci. Liège*, 17 (1948) 313.
[16] J. TOMES, *Collection Czechoslov. Chem. Communs.*, 9 (1937) 12, 81.
[17] J. GOFFART, G. MICHEL and G. DUYCKAERTS, *Anal. Chim. Acta*, 9 (1953) 184.

Chapter IV

CURRENT–POTENTIAL CURVES DURING CHEMICAL REACTIONS

SLOW ELECTROCHEMICAL REACTIONS

I. CHEMICAL REACTION A + B $\rightleftharpoons$ AB

Consider the slow electrochemical reaction

$$A + e \rightarrow C, \qquad E_0 \tag{1}$$

Let us suppose that the reactant B is slowly added to a solution containing A and/or C, and the reaction

$$A + B \rightarrow AB, \qquad \frac{|A| \, |B|}{|AB|} = K \tag{2}$$

takes place. We will further suppose that this reaction is quantitative ($K \leq 10^{-8}$).

This reaction may be fast or slow, $i.e.$ the chemical equilibrium may be obtained quickly or slowly. Let us suppose that we wait sufficiently long after each addition of B for chemical equilibrium to be reached in the body of the solution. (This does not necessarily mean that it will also be attained in the diffusion layer around the electrode during the determination of the current–potential curve.)

Let us suppose to begin with that B is not electroactive; redox reactions will be treated separately. In the presence of B, another electrochemical reaction is possible

$$AB + e \rightarrow C + B, \qquad E_1 \tag{3}$$

This reaction may be slower or faster than reaction (1). Whatever the rates of the different reactions may be, the relation between the standard potentials of the systems (1) and (3) is the same as in the case of the fast reactions already discussed

$$E_1 = E_0 + 0.058 \log K$$

Cathodic curves

Initially, the solution contains only A ($i.e.$ $x = 0$). The equation of the reduction curve of A is then (see Chapter II)

$$E = E_{\frac{1}{2} \, \text{cat}} + \frac{0.058}{\alpha} \log \frac{i_A - i}{i}$$

where

$$E_{\frac{1}{2} \, \text{cat}} = E_0 - \frac{0.058}{\alpha} \log \frac{k_A}{i_0} < E_0$$

B is now added. For $x < 1$, we have a mixture of A and AB: $|A| = (1 - x)C_0$, $|AB| = xC_0$.

We will consider two limiting cases: 1. The electrochemical reaction (3) is slower than reaction (1). 2. Reaction (3) is so much faster than reaction (1) that AB is reduced at a more positive potential than A even though $E_1 < E_0$ (AB reduced before A).

First case: *A is reduced before AB.*

The first cathodic wave is that due to the reduction of A. Its equation has been given above, but now $i_A = k_A (1 - x)C_0$. Then, when the potential becomes sufficiently reducing, AB is reduced. The reduction of AB might occur in two ways: either directly, according to equation (3), or by reaction (1) after an initial dissociation into A and B. In general reactions (1) and (3) do not have the same velocity, and the two processes are not identical, as was the case with the fast electrochemical reactions.

Since we have supposed that reaction (1) is faster than reaction (3), the reduction of AB will proceed mainly by the dissociation of AB and the reduction of A, if the rate of dissociation of AB is fast enough. We thus have three cases:

a) *The dissociation of AB is instantaneous.* The reduction of the complex proceeds via this dissociation

$$AB \rightarrow A + B \quad \text{followed by} \quad A + e \rightarrow C$$

There is therefore a second reduction wave, with the equation (see page 00)

$$E = E_0 + \frac{0.058}{\alpha} \log i_0 + \frac{0.058}{\alpha} \log \frac{|A|_e}{i}$$

where

$$|A|_e = K \frac{|AB|_e}{|B|_e}$$

whence

$$E = E_1' + \frac{0.058}{\alpha} \log \frac{i - i_{AB}}{i^2}$$

$$E_1' = E_0 + \frac{0.058}{\alpha} \log i_0 + \frac{0.058}{\alpha} \log K + \frac{0.058}{\alpha} \log \frac{k_B}{k_{AB}}$$

The curves have the same general form as for fast systems (see page 42), apart from the coefficient α (curve 1, Fig. 95).

b) *The dissociation of AB is infinitely slow.* The reduction of the complex can now only occur by reaction (3). There is still a second reduction wave, but its equation is now (curve 2, Fig. 95)

$$E = E''_{\frac{1}{2} \text{ cat}} + \frac{0.058}{\alpha'} \log \frac{i_{AB} - i}{i}$$

$$E''_{\frac{1}{2} \text{ cat}} = E_1 - \frac{0.058}{\alpha'} \log \frac{k_{AB}}{i_0'} \quad (i_0' < i_0, \ \alpha' \neq \alpha)$$

c) *The rate of dissociation of AB is of the same order of magnitude as the rates of diffusion of A and AB; kinetic waves.* The reduction of AB can now occur in two ways, and a double reduction wave is observed for the complex. At first the reduction occurs by the dissociation $AB \rightarrow A + B$, followed by $A + e \rightarrow C$. As the potential is lowered, a point is reached where the A formed by the dissociation of the complex is immediately and completely reduced; the dissociation of AB thus limits the velocity of the electrochemical reaction. A limiting current is therefore observed; this current is called the kinetic current. When the potential is lowered further, a point is reached at which AB can be reduced directly. We then have curve 3 of Fig. 95.

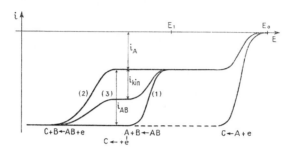

Fig. 95. The reduction of a mixture of A and AB. The reaction $AB + e \rightarrow C + B$ is slower than the reaction $A + e \rightarrow C$.

Curve 1: the dissociation of AB is instantaneous.
Curve 2: the dissociation of AB is infinitely slow.
Curve 3: the kinetic wave.

When $x > 1$, the cathodic wave due to free A disappears. There is only one wave in the cases a) and b), and two waves (one of them kinetic) in case c) (Fig. 96). As the excess of B increases, the dissociation of AB becomes more and more difficult and the height of the curve corresponding to the reduction of AB via the dissociation reaction decreases. The curve also moves towards lower potentials, the half-wave potential varying as $\dfrac{-0.058}{\alpha} \log |B|$, unlike the curve for the direct reduction of AB. When the excess of B is large enough the kinetic wave may disappear entirely.

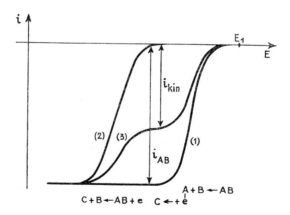

Fig. 96. The reduction of AB in the presence of an excess of B. The reaction $AB + e \rightarrow C + B$ is slower than the reaction $A + e \rightarrow C$.

Curve 1: the dissociation of AB is instantaneous.
Curve 2: the dissociation of AB is infinitely slow.
Curve 3: the kinetic wave.

Calculation of the kinetic current

Let us call the rate constant for the dissociation of AB, k_1, and that of the reverse reaction k_2

$$AB \underset{k_2}{\overset{k_1}{\rightleftharpoons}} A + B$$

The electrolysis of A leads to a dissociation of AB near to the electrode. We may suppose that this reaction only occurs in a layer of thicknes μ, called the reaction layer. The kinetic current i is due to the reduction of the molecules of A formed by the chemical reaction in this layer

$$i = - FS\mu \frac{d|A|}{dt} = - FS\mu(k_1|AB|_e - k_2|A|_e|B|_e)$$

where F is the faraday, S is the surface area of the electrode, $S\mu$ the reaction volume and $S\mu d|A|/dt$ is the number of molecules of A formed in unit time, it being assumed that they all react at the electrode. The limiting kinetic current i_{kin} is reached when $|A|_e = 0$

$$i_{kin} = - FS\mu k_1|AB|_e$$

or

$$|AB|_e = - \frac{i_{kin}}{FS\mu k_1}$$

On the other hand, in the stationary state the current is proportional to the concentration gradient of AB in the diffusion layer (of thickness δ_0)

$$i_{kin} = - k_{AB}(|AB|_s - |AB|_e)$$

so that:

$$i_{kin} = - \frac{FS\mu k_1 k_{AB}}{FS\mu k_1 + k_{AB}}|AB|_s$$

If we call the limiting diffusion current of AB, i_{AB}, where $i_{AB} = - k_{AB}|AB|_s$, the above equation may be rewritten

$$i_{kin} = \frac{i_{AB}}{1 + k_{AB}/FS\mu k_1}$$

This equation correctly implies that i_{kin} tends to zero when $k_1 \ll k_{AB}$ (very slow chemical reaction), and that i_{kin} tends to i_{AB} when $k_1 \gg k_{AB}$ (fast chemical reaction). The equation of the kinetic wave may be derived in the usual way, using the expressions for $|A|_e$, $|AB|_e$, $|B|_e$ and $|C|_e$.

When the direct reduction of AB is faster than the reduction via the dissociation (free A still being reduced at higher potentials than AB), the kinetic wave disappears. The rate of the chemical reaction no longer has any effect.

We have supposed here that both the reactions (1) and (3) are slow. The situation is similar when one of the reactions is fast.

Second case: AB is reduced before A. Catalysis.

As soon as AB is formed, the electrochemical reaction $AB + e \rightarrow C + B$ occurs, since we suppose that this reaction takes place at higher potentials than the reaction $A + e \rightarrow C$. In the presence of A ($x < 1$), the reduction of AB with formation of B may be followed by the regeneration of AB, $B + A \rightarrow AB$. This enables A to be reduced at higher potentials than is possible in the absence of AB. The electrochemical reaction is thus catalyzed, to an extent depending on the rate of regeneration of AB. We therefore have three cases again:

a) *AB is formed instantaneously.* Whatever the value of x, only one wave is observed, corresponding to the reduction of AB, either directly or after regeneration. The AB formed (xC_0) and the free A in excess $[(1 - x)C_0]$ diffuse simultaneously. The limiting diffusion current is reached when $|A|_e = |AB|_e = 0$, and has the constant value $i_{(AB + A)} = - k_A C_0$ (if $k_{AB} \approx k_A$). The equation of this curve is

$$E = E''_{\frac{1}{2}\text{ cat}} + \frac{0.058}{\alpha'} \log \frac{i_{(AB + A)} - i}{i}$$

$$E''_{\frac{1}{2}\text{ cat}} = E_1 - \frac{0.058}{\alpha'} \log \frac{k_A}{i_0'}$$

The curve is not affected by an excess of B (curve 1, Fig. 97).

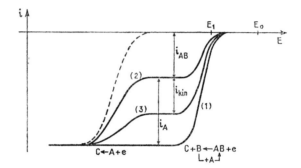

Fig. 97. The reduction of a mixture of A and AB. The reaction $AB + e \rightarrow C + B$ occurs before the reaction $A + e \rightarrow C$ (*i.e.* catalysis).

Curve 1: the formation of AB is instantaneous.
Curve 2: the formation of AB is infinitely slow.
Curve 3: the kinetic wave.

b) *The formation of AB is infinitely slow.* The reduction of AB (before A) is not followed by the regeneration of AB by $B + A \rightarrow AB$. There are therefore two waves for $x < 1$, the first corresponding to the reduction of AB

$$E = E''_{\frac{1}{2}\text{ cat}} + \frac{0.058}{\alpha'} \log \frac{i_{AB} - i}{i}, \qquad i_{AB} = - k_{AB} x C_0$$

and the second to the reduction of A (curve 2, Fig. 97)

$$E = E_{\frac{1}{2}\text{ cat}} + \frac{0.058}{\alpha} \log \frac{i_A - i}{i}, \qquad i_A = - k_A (1 - x) \cdot C_0, \quad E_{\frac{1}{2}\text{ cat}} < E''_{\frac{1}{2}\text{ cat}}$$

When $x > 1$, only the reduction wave of AB is observed, with $i_{AB} = - k_{AB} C_0$. This curve is independent of an excess of B.

c) *The rate of formation of AB is of the same order of magnitude as the rate of diffusion of A and AB; kinetic waves.* The regeneration of AB is only partial in this case: some A is reduced via AB, and some directly, by reduction of AB. Two waves are still observed: one corresponding to the reduction of AB either directly or after regeneration; the other to the reduction of A which has not had time to react with B (curve 3, Fig. 97). The first curve levels off when $|AB|_e = 0$. Since a part of AB is formed by the reaction of B liberated at the electrode with A, it is the rate of this reaction which finally limits the first wave. When $x < 1$, the first limiting current is the sum of the limiting diffusion current of AB, $i_{AB} = -k_{AB}xC_0$, and a kinetic current i_{kin}. When $x \geq 1$, the limiting current is entirely due to the diffusion of AB ($|A|_s = 0$).

Calculation of the kinetic current

The kinetic current is due to the reduction of the molecules of AB formed by the chemical reaction in the reaction layer

$$i = - FS\mu \frac{d|AB|}{dt} = - FS\mu(k_2|A|_e|B|_e - k_1|AB|_e)$$

The limiting kinetic current i_{kin} is reached when $|AB|_e = 0$, so

$$i_{kin} = - FS\mu k_2|A|_e|B|_e$$

On the other hand, in the stationary state the current is proportional to the concentration gradient of A in the diffusion layer

$$i_{kin} = - k_A(|A|_s - |A|_e) = i_A + k_A|A|_e$$

and finally, since B is formed entirely by the direct reduction of AB

$$|B|_e = - \frac{i_{AB}}{k_B}$$

it follows that

$$i_{kin} = FS\mu k_2 \frac{i_{AB}}{k_B k_A} (i_{kin} - i_A)$$

where i_{AB} and i_A are the limiting diffusion currents of AB and A

$$i_{AB} = - k_{AB}|AB|_s, \qquad i_A = - k_A|A|_s$$

$$\frac{i_{kin}}{i_A} = \frac{FS\mu k_2 i_{AB}}{FS\mu k_2 i_{AB} - k_B k_A}$$

This equation shows that i_{kin} tends to zero when $k_2 \ll k_B k_A$ (very slow chemical reaction) and i_{kin} tends to i_A when $k_2 \gg k_B k_A$ (fast chemical reaction). The system (3) may be fast. In that case, $E''_{\frac{1}{2}} \approx E_1$.

Anodic curves

The initial solution contains only C. The initial oxidation curve of C for the reaction

$$C - e \rightarrow A \qquad (1)$$

has the equation (see Chapter II)

$$E = E_{\frac{1}{2}\text{ an}} + \frac{0.058}{\beta} \log \frac{i}{i_C - i}$$

where

$$E_{\frac{1}{2}\text{ an}} = E_0 + \frac{0.058}{\beta} \log \frac{k_C}{i_0} > E_0$$

B is now added. A new electrochemical reaction is now possible

$$C + B - e \rightarrow AB \qquad (3)$$

We will again consider two cases, according to the relative rates of the electrochemical reactions (1) and (3): Either reaction (3) is considerably slower than reaction (1) so that the oxidation of C in the presence of B does not occur at lower potentials than in the absence of B (C is not oxidized more quickly in the presence of B) or the reaction (3) does occur at lower potentials than reaction (1) (C is oxidized more quickly in the presence of B).

First case: *C is not oxidized more quickly in the presence of B.*

Even in the presence of B, C is oxidized according to Eq. (1) though this may be followed by the reaction $A + B \rightarrow AB$. Since reaction (1) is slow, the presence of B has no influence on the oxidation curve, and its equation remains as given above (curve 1, Fig. 98).

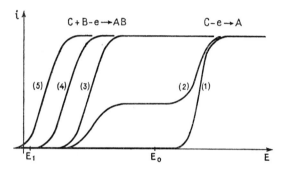

Fig. 98. The oxidation of C in the presence of B. If C is not oxidized more quickly in the presence of B, the oxidation curve is given by curve 1, whatever the concentration of B; if C is oxidized more quickly in the presence of B, curve 1 follows for no B present, curve 2 for $|B| < |C|$, curves 3, 4 and 5 for excess of B.

Second case: *C is oxidized more quickly in the presence of B.*

The first anodic wave due to reaction (3) is observed. The equation of this curve (see Chapter II) is

$$E = E_1 + \frac{0.058}{\beta'} \log \frac{k_C k_B}{i_0'} + \frac{0.058}{\beta'} \log \frac{i}{(i_C - i)(i_B - i)}$$

$$i_C = k_C |C|_s, \qquad i_B = k_B |B|_s$$

The step height is limited by $|B|_s$ or $|C|_s$, whichever is lower. When $|B|_s < |C|_s$, a second wave corresponding to reaction (1) is observed. The height of this wave is $i_C - i_B$. When $|B|_s > |C|_s$, there is only one wave of height i_C, and half-wave potential

$$E''_{\frac{1}{2} \text{ an}} = E_1 + \frac{0.058}{\beta'} \log \frac{k_C k_B}{i_0'} - \frac{0.058}{\beta'} \log (i_B - \tfrac{1}{2} i_C)$$

If B is present in considerable excess, so that $|B|_e \approx |B|_s$, $E'_{\frac{1}{2} \text{ an}}$ varies as $\frac{-0.058}{\beta'} \log |B|$ (Fig. 98).

Cathodic and anodic curves

The solution contains both A and C, and B is added to it. We have seen in Chapter II that when an electrochemical reaction is slow, the anodic curve is independent of the cathodic phenomena and vice versa. This is not true in the present case, however. In particular, the presence of AB may have an effect on the anodic curves, as we will show. We will still consider two main cases:

First case: *The system $AB + e \rightleftharpoons B + C$ is slower than the system $A + e \rightleftharpoons C$.*

The curve representing the net effect of the anodic and cathodic reactions is obtained simply by the superposition of the curves described above for the appropriate cases. In particular, if C is not oxidized more quickly in the presence of B, the anode curve is not affected by the addition of B (see p. 96).

If the rate of the chemical reaction of the formation of AB is of the same order of magnitude as the rate of diffusion of the substances, a cathodic kinetic wave appears (see p. 91).

Second case: *The system $AB + e \rightleftharpoons B + C$ is faster than the system $A + e \rightleftharpoons C$. Catalysis.*

We have already seen (p. 94) under what conditions the reduction of A is catalyzed by AB, sometimes accompanied by a kinetic wave. Briefly, the reduction of AB must be so much faster than that of A that AB is reduced before A, and the chemical reaction must also be fairly fast.

It may also happen that the oxidation of C is catalyzed by AB, if the system (3) is faster than (1), since in the reaction $C + B - e \rightarrow AB$, B can be regenerated by the dissociation of AB, $AB \rightarrow A + B$. The overall reaction is $C - e \rightarrow A$, but the kinetics are those of reaction (3). Here also, the dissociation of AB must be sufficiently rapid, so we have the same three cases as before:

a. *The dissociation of AB is instantaneous.* When AB is present (no B in excess, $|B|_e$ being due entirely to the dissociation of AB), the oxidation wave of C has the equation (curve 1, Fig. 99).

$$E = E_1 - \frac{0.058}{\beta'} \log i_0' - \frac{0.058}{\beta'} \log \frac{|C|_e \, |B|_e}{i}$$

where

$$\frac{|B|_e \, |A|_e}{|AB|_e} = K$$

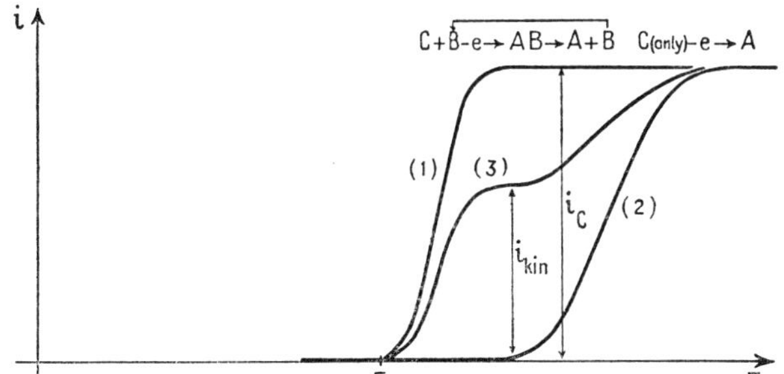

Fig. 99. The oxidation of C in the presence of AB. The reaction $C + B - e \rightarrow AB$ is faster than $C - e \rightarrow A$, whence catalysis.

Curve 1: the dissociation of AB is instantaneous.
Curve 2: the dissociation of AB is infinitely slow.
Curve 3: kinetic wave.

b. *The dissociation of AB is infinitely slow.* There is no catalysis, and the oxidation wave of C is given by (curve 2, Fig. 99)

$$E = E_0 - \frac{0.058}{\beta} \log i_0 - \frac{0.058}{\beta} \log \frac{|C|_e}{i}$$

c. *The rate of dissociation of AB is of the same order of magnitude as the rate of diffusion of the reactants; kinetic waves.* Some C is oxidized by reaction (3), and some directly by reaction (1). A double wave is observed, the first being limited by the rate of dissociation of AB (curve 3, Fig. 99).

The catalytic system may be very fast. Fig. 100 shows the curves obtained when the electrochemical reaction (3) and the chemical reaction (1) are both fast.

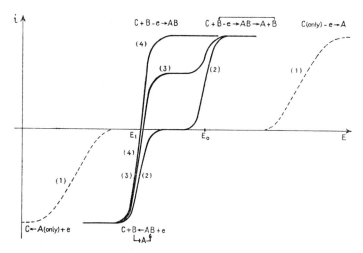

Fig. 100. Chemical catalysis of electrochemical reactions, where the reactions $AB + e \rightarrow B + C$ and $AB \rightarrow A + B$ are both fast.

Curve 1: A and C only.
Curve 2: A and C, B is added, not in excess $(x < 1)$.
Curve 3: A and C, B is added in excess $(x > 1)$ $|B|_s < |C|_s$.
Curve 4: A and C, B is added in excess $(x > 1)$ $|B|_s > |C|_s$.

II. EXAMPLES

The reduction of H^+, water and weak acids

It has already been mentioned (Chapter III, p. 63–70) that the systems

$$2 H^+ + 2e \rightleftharpoons H_2 \tag{4}$$

$$2 H_2O + 2e \rightleftharpoons H_2 + 2 OH^- \tag{5}$$

$$2 HB + 2e \rightleftharpoons H_2 + 2 B^- \tag{6}$$

are fast at an electrode of platinized platinum, but slow at most other electrodes (*e.g.* bright platinum, mercury).

The chemical reactions, *i.e.* acid–base equilibria, are generally fast. Moreover, the systems involving the reduction of weak acids are generally as slow or slower than the system $2H^+ + 2e \rightleftharpoons H_2$. The reduction curves are therefore similar to those obtained at a platinized platinum electrode (Fig. 67, p. 65), but shifted towards more negative potentials because reaction (1) is slow, and with a more noticeable slope because of the coefficient α (see Fig. 68, p. 66). In particular, in the presence of a sufficient excess of the base B^-, the half-wave potential varies as $-\dfrac{0.058}{\alpha} \log |B^-|$. The presence of hydrogen has no influence on the reduction curves.

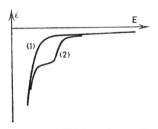

Fig. 101. Catalysis of the reduction of H^+ by a trace of protein; mercury electrode.
Curve 1: the reduction of 0.1 M NH$_4$Cl.
Curve 2: the reduction of 0.1 M NH$_4$Cl + a trace of protein
(after KOLTHOFF and LINGANE [48]).

It is known that the reduction of H^+ is catalyzed by certain bases, *i.e.* that there are certain weak acids which are reduced before H^+, such as cysteine and other thioacids, proteins and alkaloids. The reduction of a thio-acid

$$2\ R\text{–}SH + 2e \rightarrow 2\ R\text{–}S^- + H_2$$

occurs before that of H^+ at the same pH. $R\text{–}S^-$ then reacts further with the acid of the buffer to regenerate $R\text{–}SH$

$$R\text{–}S^- + HB \rightarrow R\text{–}SH + B^-$$

A kinetic wave will therefore be produced, whose height depends on the rate of regeneration of $R\text{–}SH$ (Fig. 101; *cf.* p. 94 and Fig. 97, p. 94). But it is difficult to give a theoretical treatment of this system, because the adsorption of the thio-acid on the electrode is involved (see Chapter V).

The reduction of dissolved oxygen and of hydrogen peroxide

Since the redox systems of O_2, H_2O_2 and H_2O (or OH^-) are slow, the reduction of oxygen is treated here independently of the oxidation of water (see Chapter III, p. 74).

The reduction of oxygen

In principle, oxygen is first reduced to hydrogen peroxide (or its ions); the hydrogen peroxide can then be reduced further to water (or its ions). The conditions under which the various reactants can exist are given below:

H_2O at any pH, constant activity; O_2 at any pH, 2×10^{-3} M in a solution saturated under unit pressure of oxygen; H^+, negligible concentration for pH > 5; OH^-, negligible concentration for pH < 9; H_2O_2 and HO_2^-, H_2O_2 predominates at pH < 11.7, and HO_2^- at pH > 11.7.

The theoretically possible reduction reactions in the absence of hydrogen peroxide are therefore

pH < 5:

$$O_2 + 2 H^+ + 2e \rightarrow H_2O_2 \tag{7}$$

$$O_2 + 4 H^+ + 4e \rightarrow 2 H_2O \tag{8}$$

pH > 12:

$$O_2 + H_2O + 2e \rightarrow HO_2^- + OH^- \tag{9}$$

$$O_2 + 2 H_2O + 4e \rightarrow 4 OH^- \tag{10}$$

5 < pH < 12:

$$O_2 + 2 H_2O + 2e \rightarrow H_2O_2 + 2 OH^- \tag{11}$$

$$O_2 + 2 H_2O + 4e \rightarrow 4 OH^- \tag{12}$$

In the presence of a weak acid HB, especially in a buffer solution, the following are also possible

$$O_2 + 2 HB + 2e \rightarrow H_2O_2 + 2 B^- \tag{13}$$

$$O_2 + 2 HB + 4e \rightarrow 2 OH^- + 2 B^- \tag{14}$$

The equilibrium potential for the system O_2/H_2O_2, saturated with oxygen under a pressure of one atmosphere, is

$$E_{eq} = 0.69 \text{ V} - 0.058 \text{ pH} - 0.029 \log |H_2O_2|$$

In general, oxygen will be reduced before hydrogen peroxide; sometimes two waves are observed before the reduction of water (mercury cathode), sometimes only one (platinum, silver). Fig. 102 shows some experimental curves determined in neutral media.

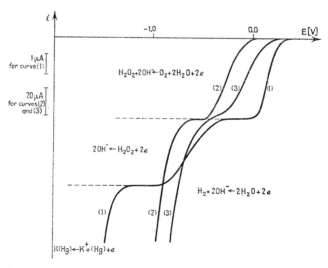

Fig. 102. Reduction curves of dissolved oxygen in neutral media.

Curve 1: Dropping mercury electrode; 0.1 N KCl (+ 0.01 % of thymol) saturated with air (after KOLTHOFF and MILLER [51]).

Curve 2: Rotating bright platinum electrode; 0.1 N KCl saturated with air (after LAITINEN and KOLTHOFF [49]).

Curve 3: Rotating silver electrode; 0.1 N KNO$_3$ saturated with air (after LAITINEN and KOLTHOFF [49]).

In acid media, the reactions should depend on the pH (reactions 7 and 8) as in buffer solutions (reactions 13 and 14). Reactions 9 to 12 do not depend on the pH, however, since the systems are slow. Experiment has shown that in acid media and in buffer solutions the current–potential curve is independent of the pH from pH 1 to pH 9 (at electrodes of mercury or bright platinum).

The reduction of hydrogen peroxide

The reactions which are possible in theory are

pH < 5:

$$H_2O_2 + 2\,H^+ + 2e \rightarrow 2\,H_2O \tag{15}$$

pH > 12:

$$HO_2^- + H_2O + 2e \rightarrow 3\,OH^- \tag{16}$$

5 < pH < 12:

$$H_2O_2 + 2e \qquad \rightarrow 2\,OH^- \tag{17}$$

and in a buffer solution (weak acid HB)

$$H_2O_2 + 2\,HB + 2e \rightarrow 2\,H_2O + 2\,B^- \tag{18}$$

The equilibrium potential of the system H_2O_2/H_2O is

$$E_{eq} = 1.77\ V - 0.058\ pH + 0.029\ \log |H_2O_2|$$

In fact, the reduction of H_2O_2 is a slow reaction, much slower than the reduction of O_2, for according to the values of the standard potentials hydrogen peroxide should dissociate to give water and oxygen. In acid or neutral media, it is only at a mercury electrode that the reduction of H_2O_2 can be observed (Fig. 102), since at this electrode the reduction of water and H^+ only takes place at very negative potentials. At pH 2 to 10 the curve is independent of the pH, with $E_{\frac{1}{2}\ cat} = -0.7$ volts. In sufficiently alkaline media the system becomes faster, and H_2O_2 may be reduced at various electrodes.

Catalysis of the reduction of hydrogen peroxide by Mo(VI), W(VI) or V(V)

The complexes of hydrogen peroxide with ions containing Mo(VI), W(VI) or V(V) are reduced before hydrogen peroxide itself. The chemical reaction, *e.g.* with an ion containing Mo(VI), may be rewritten

$$MoO_4^{2-} + H_2O_2 \rightleftharpoons MoO_5^{2-} + H_2O$$

The following redox system is therefore possible in the presence of

$$MoO_5^{2-} + 2\,H^+ + 2e \rightarrow MoO_4^{2-} + H_2O$$

This reduction reaction occurs before

$$H_2O_2 + 2\,H^+ + 2e \rightarrow 2\,H_2O$$

The current–potential curves are shown in Fig. 103. The reduction of H_2O_2 occurs at less reducing potentials in the presence of molybdate. MoO_4^{2-} liberated by the reduction of MoO_5^{2-} recombines with H_2O_2, thus catalyzing the reduction of the latter. Since the chemical reaction is fairly fast, there is a limiting kinetic current which

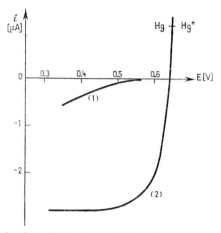

Fig. 103. Catalysis of the reduction of H_2O_2 by molybdate at a mercury electrode in 0.25 M H_2SO_4.
Curve 1: 0.0538 M H_2O_2 only.
Curve 2: 0.0538 M H_2O_2 + 1.09 × 10^{-6} M $MoO_4{}^{2-}$
(after KOLTHOFF and PARRY [60]).

depends on the rate of formation of peroxymolybdate. An increase in the concentration of H_2O_2 increases this rate, and thus also the value of the limiting current (Fig. 104).

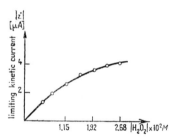

Fig. 104. Catalysis of the reduction of H_2O_2 by $MoO_4{}^{2-}$. The limiting kinetic current as a function of the concentration of H_2O_2; pH = 5.40, $|MoO_4{}^{2-}| = 8 . 10^{-7}$ M
(after KOLTHOFF and PARRY [60]).

Catalysis of the system Ti(III)/Ti(IV)

The system Ti(III)/Ti(IV)

$$TiOH^{3+} + H^+ + e \rightleftharpoons Ti^{3+} + H_2O,$$

E_0 is slow in hydrochloric acid or perchloric acid solution; the reduction of Ti(IV) is shown in curve (1) of Fig. 105, and the oxidation of Ti(III) in curve (2).

In the presence of SCN$^-$, the following rather unstable complexes are formed

$$Ti^{3+} + SCN^- \rightarrow TiSCN^{2+} \tag{19}$$

$$TiOH^{3+} + SCN^- \rightarrow TiOHSCN^{2+} \tag{20}$$

and the new redox system

$$TiOHSCN^{2+} + e \rightarrow TiSCN^{2+} + OH^- \tag{21}$$

becomes possible; this is a fast system ($E_{\frac{1}{2}\,an} \approx E_{\frac{1}{2}\,cat} \approx E_1$). Since the complexes are not very stable, E_1 is nearly equal to E_0. The chemical reactions (19) and (20) are fairly slow, and their velocity increases with the concentration of SCN⁻ ions. In the presence of a great excess of SCN⁻, the rate of formation of the complex ions is so great compared to the rate of diffusion of the reactants that the overall rate of their formation or dissociation is determined by the electrochemical reaction. Since the system (21) is fast, the system $Ti^{3+}/TiOH^{3+}$ is catalyzed by the formation of thiocyanate complexes, even at low concentrations (curve (3), Fig. 105).

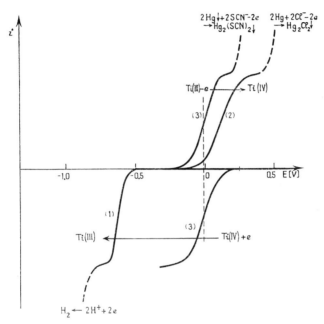

Fig. 105. Catalysis of the system Ti(III)/Ti(IV) at a mercury electrode in the presence of thiocyanate. Ti(III) and Ti(IV) 5×10^{-3} M.

Curve 1: reduction of Ti(IV) in N HCl.
Curve 2: oxidation of Ti(III) in N HCl.
Curve 3: oxidation of Ti(III) and reduction of Ti(IV) in N HCl + 0.1 M SCN⁻
(after TRIBALAT and DELAFOSSE [61]).

When the concentration of SCN⁻ is not very great, the rate of the chemical reactions (19) and (20) is rather low. In this case we will find first oxidation or reduction of the complexes, limited by the rate of their formation or dissociation (kinetic waves), and then oxidation or reduction of the uncomplexed Ti^{3+} or $TiOH^{3+}$.

Other examples of catalysis

Reduction of Co(II) and Ni(II) in concentrated solutions of hydrochloric acid [62-64]

In non-complexing media, the reduction of the ions $Co(H_2O)_m^{2+}$ and $Ni(H_2O)_n^{2+}$ is slow:

for $\quad Co^{2+} + Hg + 2e \rightarrow Co(Hg), \quad E_0 = -0.028$ V and $E_{\frac{1}{2}\,cat} = -1.15$ V;
for $\quad Ni^{2+} + Hg + 2e \rightarrow Ni(Hg), \quad E_0 = -0.24$ V and $E_{\frac{1}{2}\,cat} = -0.85$ V.

But in the presence of a large excess of chloride ion, the Co^{2+} and Ni^{2+} ions form complexes with Cl^-, and these complexes are reduced much more quickly; the reduction waves of Co(II) and Ni(II) in a concentrated chloride solution occur at higher potentials and have a larger coefficient α than in the absence of chloride.

Reduction of Ni(II) in the presence of thiocyanate or pyridine [65]

In molar thiocyanate solution the reduction wave of Ni(II) at a mercury electrode has an $E_{\frac{1}{2}\ cat}$ of -0.45 V, corresponding to the reaction

$$NiSCN^+ + Hg\downarrow + 2e \rightarrow Ni(Hg) + SCN^-$$

which is much faster than

$$Ni^{2+} + Hg\downarrow + 2e \rightarrow Ni(Hg)$$

although the complex is not very stable.

The reduction of formaldehyde

Formaldehyde exists in two forms in aqueous solution, as the aldehyde CH_2O and as the glycol form $CH_2(OH)_2$. These two forms are in equilibrium according to

$$CH_2O + H_2O \rightleftharpoons CH_2(OH)_2 \qquad K = \frac{|CH_2O|}{|CH_2(OH)_2|} \approx 10^{-4}$$

This is a fairly quantitative reaction of the form $A + B \rightarrow AB$, where the complexing agent (H_2O) is present in great excess. The glycol form is a weak acid ($pK_A \approx 12.8$), and in very alkaline medium the equilibrium is

$$CH_2O + OH^- \rightleftharpoons CH_2O_2H^-$$

Only the aldehyde form can be reduced, by a reaction which we may write as

$$CH_2O + 2 H_2O + 2e \rightarrow CH_3OH + 2 OH^- \qquad \text{in alkaline medium}$$

or

$$CH_2O + 2 H^+ + 2e \rightarrow CH_3OH \qquad \text{in acid medium}$$

Since the aldehyde form is present in very small concentrations in solution, the total reduction of formaldehyde can only occur if the dissociation of methylene glycol precedes the reduction reaction. The dissociation reaction is not very fast, so a kinetic wave is observed, the limiting current being a function of the rate of the dissociation reaction (see Fig. 96, p. 92). In alkaline media, the dissociation reaction is

$$CH_2O_2H^- \rightarrow CH_2O + OH^-$$

The rate of this reaction decreases as the concentration of OH^- increases, which agrees with the values of the kinetic current found by experiment (Fig. 106).

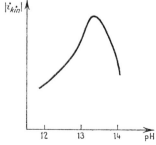

Fig. 106. The limiting kinetic current of the reduction of 3.75×10^{-3} M formaldehyde at a mercury electrode as a function of the pH (after VESSELÝ and BRDIČKA [66]).

Reduction of the base corresponding to certain organic acids

The bases B^- corresponding to a certain number of organic acids HB are reducible

$$B^- + ne \rightarrow C$$

The reduction of the acid, *i.e.* of the base complexed with H^+, is sometimes easier than the direct reduction of B^-

$$HB + ne \rightarrow C + H^+$$

This is specially true of certain keto-acids such as pyruvic and phenylglyoxylic acids, of dibasic acids like maleic and fumaric, and of cupferron (phenylnitrosohydroxyl-amine).

The reaction of formation of these acids, $B^- + H^+ \rightarrow HB$, is in general fairly slow so that two reduction waves are observed, the first corresponding to the reduction of HB, directly or after the combination of B^- with the H^+ liberated (kinetic current), and the second due to the reduction of the B^- which had no time to react with H^+ (see Fig. 97, p. 94).

The height of these two waves is dependent on the pH. In very acid media only HB exists, so there is only one wave, due to the reduction of HB. In very alkaline media, there is practically no HB, and the rate of the reaction $B^- + H^+ \rightarrow HB$ is very low since the concentration of H^+ is very low. Here also, therefore, there is only one wave, due this time to the reduction of B^-. At intermediate values of the pH and in buffer solutions two waves are observed; the height of the first decreases as the pH increases, partly because the ratio $|HB|/|B^-|$ becomes smaller and partly because the reaction $B^- + H^+ \rightarrow HB$ becomes slower.

Fig. 107 shows the variation of the limiting current of the first wave with the pH, for pyruvic acid. At about pH 5.5, pH being equal to pK_A, the limiting current is greater than $i_{HB} = i_{B^-} = \frac{1}{2} i_{B\ total}$.

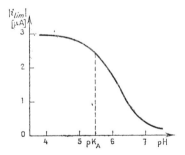

Fig. 107. The reduction of pyruvic acid at a mercury electrode. The limiting current as a function of the pH (after BRDIČKA[16]).

The half-wave potential $E_{\frac{1}{2}\ cat}$ varies from -1.15 V in very acid media to -1.50 V in alkaline media.

The reduction of the Cd (II)–EDTA complex in acid media

The reaction of Cd(II) with EDTA (Y^{4-}) may be written

$$Cd^{2+} + Y^{4-} \rightarrow CdY^{2-}$$

In fact, this is not quite accurate: EDTA is a weak acid, and different complexing reactions are found as the pH changes. It follows from the values of the various equilibrium constants that the main reactions are

pH < 2:

$$Cd^{2+} + H_4Y \rightarrow HCdY^- + 3\ H^+$$

2 < pH < 3:

$$Cd^{2+} + H_3Y^- \rightarrow HCdY^- + 2\ H^+$$

3 < pH < 6:

$$Cd^{2+} + H_2Y^{2-} \rightarrow CdY^{2-} + 2\ H^+$$

There are thus two reducible complexes, $HCdY^-$ and CdY^{2-}. At a mercury electrode the following electrochemical reactions are possible

$$Cd^{2+} + Hg\downarrow + 2e \rightarrow Cd(Hg) \tag{22}$$

pH < 2:

$$HCdY^- + 3\ H^+ + Hg\downarrow + 2e \rightarrow Cd(Hg) + H_4Y \tag{23}$$

2 < pH < 3:

$$HCdY^- + 2\ H^+ + Hg\downarrow + 2e \rightarrow Cd(Hg) + H_3Y^- \tag{24}$$

pH > 3:

$$CdY^{2-} + 2\ H^+ + Hg\downarrow + 2e \rightarrow Cd(Hg) + H_2Y^{2-} \tag{25}$$

The system (22) is fast. Both systems (23) and (24) are slow, but at very negative potentials $HCdY^-$ can be reduced directly. System (25) is very slow, and CdY^{2-} is not electroactive at a mercury electrode.

Fig. 108 shows the reduction curves obtained during the addition of EDTA in a solution buffered to pH 4.2; at such a pH the chemical reaction is

$$Cd^{2+} + H_2Y^{2-} \rightarrow CdY^{2-} + 2\ H^+$$

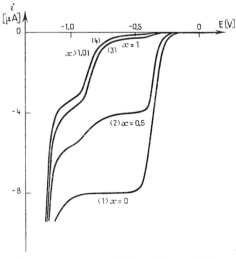

Fig. 108. Reduction curves during the reaction $Cd^{2+} + Y^{4-} \rightarrow CdY^{2-}$ in acetate buffer, pH 4.2; $|Cd^{2+}| = 0.97 \cdot 10^{-4}\ M$ (after TANAKA et al.[84]).

Initially, at $x = 0$, there is only the reduction curve of Cd^{2+} (curve 1). Then for $x < 1$, there is a reduction wave of the excess Cd^{2+}, followed by another wave whose height is less than would be expected for the reduction of the complex formed. Since CdY^{2-} is not reducible, this second wave corresponds to the reduction of $HCdY^-$ following its formation by the reaction

$$CdY^{2-} + H^+ \rightarrow HCdY^- \tag{26}$$

The reduction of CdY^{2-} is thus catalyzed by the formation of $HCdY^-$. Since reaction (26) is fairly slow, the corresponding wave is a kinetic one whose height is limited by the rate of formation of $HCdY^-$.

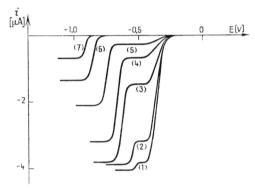

Fig. 109. Curves for the reduction of 10^{-3} M Cd(II) $+$ 10^{-3} M Y^{4-} ($x = 1$) at a mercury electrode at various pH's.

Curve 1: pH 1.7.   Curve 5: pH 4.0.
Curve 2: pH 2.2.   Curve 6: pH 4.3.
Curve 3: pH 2.8.   Curve 7: pH 4.6.
Curve 4: pH 3.4.   (after SCHMID and REILLEY [85]).

Fig. 109 shows the influence of the pH on the reduction curve for $x = 1$. In sufficiently acid media there is a double wave which can be explained as follows. The first wave is due to the reduction of Cd^{2+}, either directly (since the complex $HCdY^-$ is not very stable, some of the Cd^{2+} is not complexed) or following the dissociation of the complex $HCdY^-$. The reduction of $HCdY^-$ is thus catalyzed by means of Cd^{2+}. Since the rate of this dissociation is not very high, the wave is a kinetic wave, whose height is a function of the dissociation rate (see p. 91 and Fig. 96). The dissociation is accelerated by addition of hydrogen ions, by the reaction

$$HCdY^- + 2 H^+ \rightarrow Cd^{2+} + H_3Y^-$$

so the height of the wave increases with the acidity, and vanishes when the pH > 4.3 or thereabouts. (Since the complex $HCdY^-$ is not very stable, this wave does not differ much from the reduction wave for Cd^{2+} alone.) The second wave corresponds to the direct reduction of $HCdY^-$ and that of CdY^{2-} catalyzed by $HCdY^-$. This wave is thus also partly kinetic, and the kinetic part becomes more important as the ratio $|CdY^{2-}|/|HCdY^-|$ increases, i.e. as the acidity decreases. The kinetic current increases with the acidity, since the rate of reaction (26) is increased by the addition of H^+ ions.

III. OXIDATION–REDUCTION REACTIONS

If a reducing agent B is added to a reducible substance A, a redox reaction is produced

$$A + B \rightarrow C + D \tag{27}$$

We will suppose that this reaction is quantitative, *i.e.* that the standard potentials E_1 and E_2 of the systems

$$A + e \rightleftharpoons C, \qquad E_1 \tag{28}$$

$$B - e \rightleftharpoons D, \qquad E_2 \tag{29}$$

are very different, $E_2 \ll E_1$, *e.g.* by 500 mV.

The electrochemical reactions involved may be represented by reactions (28) and (29). The case where both these systems are fast has been treated in Chapter III, p. 88. We will now consider the case when the two systems (28) and (29) are slow. The broad picture of the shifting of the curves during the chemical reaction remains qualitatively the same, but when one of the electrochemical reactions (28) and (29) is much faster than the other, the slower electrochemical reaction is catalyzed by means of the chemical reaction, if the latter is fast enough.

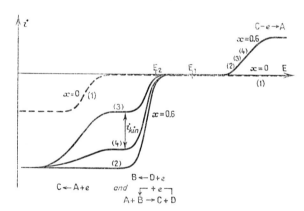

Fig. 110. Catalysis of the reduction of A via the chemical reaction $A + B \rightarrow C + D$, where D is reduced before A.
Curve 1: reduction of A alone ($x = 0$).
Curve 2: reduction of A + D ($x = 0.6$), the chemical reaction being fast.
Curve 3: reduction of A + D ($x = 0.6$), the chemical reaction being very slow.
Curve 4: reduction of A + D ($x = 0.6$), kinetic wave.

We will suppose that the electrochemical reaction (28), $A + e \rightarrow C$, is so slow that D is reduced before A. The current–potential curves corresponding to this situation are given in Fig. 110 for $x = 0$ (broken line) and $x = 0.6$ (full lines).

As the potential is lowered, D is reduced first

$$D + e \rightarrow B$$

but if B reacts chemically with A

$$B + A \rightarrow C + D$$

D is regenerated. The electrochemical reduction of D thus catalyzes that of A.

If the chemical reaction is very fast, a diffusion limit is not reached until $|A|_e = 0$ and $|D|_e = 0$. The reduction curve then consists of a single wave whose height corresponds to the sum of the concentrations of A and D, with an $E_{\frac{1}{2}}$ equal to that of the reaction $D + e \rightarrow B$ (curve 2).

If the chemical reaction is infinitely slow, D and A are reduced separately and two distinct reduction waves are observed, one for the reduction of D, with a height corresponding to $|D|_s$, and the other for the reduction of A with a height corresponding to $|A|_s$ (curve 3).

In the intermediate case when the rate of the chemical reaction is of the same order of magnitude as the rate of diffusion of the substances, there are still two waves with the same half-wave potentials, but the height of the first is greater than in the previous case; part of the limiting current is a kinetic current, depending on the rate of the reaction $A + B \rightarrow C + D$ (curve 4).

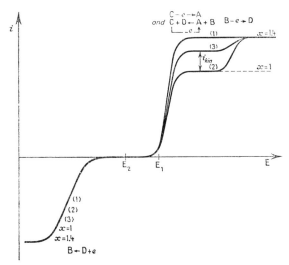

Fig. 111. Catalysis of the oxidation of B by the chemical reaction $B + A \rightarrow C + D$, where C is oxidized before B. Oxidation curves of $B + C$ ($x = 1.4$).

Curve 1: the chemical reaction is fast.
Curve 2: the chemical reaction is very slow.
Curve 3: the kinetic wave.

When, on the other hand, the electrochemical reaction (29), $B - e \rightarrow D$, is so slow that the oxidation of C, $C - e \rightarrow A$, takes place before that of B, the oxidation of B is catalyzed by means of the chemical reaction $B + A \rightarrow C + D$. The curves corresponding to this situation are shown in Fig. 111.

All other cases may be treated similarly. In particular, the faster electrochemical system may be a fast system. A substance may thus give a current–potential curve even though it is not electroactive. All that is needed is to generate by an electrochemical reaction a substance which undergoes a rapid chemical reaction with it.

Calculation of the kinetic current

We will derive the expression for the kinetic current in the case of catalysis, represented in Fig. 110. The limiting diffusion current for the reaction $D + e \rightarrow B$ in the

absence of A will be denoted by i_D. The limiting kinetic current i_{kin} is due to the reduction of the D regenerated by the chemical reaction. The kinetic current is

$$i_{kin} = - FS\mu(k_1|A|_e |B|_e - k_2|C|_e |D|_e)$$

and this reaches its limiting value i_{kin} when $|D|_e = 0$

$$i_{kin} = FS\mu k_1 |A|_e |B|_e$$

In the stationary state, the kinetic current is proportional to the concentration gradient of A in the diffusion layer

$$i_{kin} = - k_A(|A|_s - |A|_e) = i_A + k_A|A|_e$$

Now the B at the electrode is formed by the reduction of the D which arrives there,
and supposing that $k_B \approx k_D$

$$|B|_e \approx |D|_s = - i_D/k_D$$

whence

$$\frac{i_{kin}}{i_A} = \frac{FS\mu k_1 i_D}{k_A k_D + FS\mu k_1 i_D}$$

$i_{kin} = i_A$ if the chemical reaction is very fast (k_1 large), and $i_{kin} = 0$ if the chemical
reaction is very slow (k_1 small).

IV. EXAMPLES OF OXIDATION–REDUCTION REACTIONS

Catalysis of the reduction of hydrogen peroxide by iron (III)

The reduction of ferric ions, $Fe^{3+} + e \rightarrow Fe^{2+}$, is fairly rapid at a mercury electrode
as $E_0 \approx 0.75$ V, and $E_{\frac{1}{2} \, cat} = 0.63$ V. The reduction of H_2O_2 on the other hand,
$H_2O_2 + 2H^+ + 2e \rightarrow 2H_2O$, is slow: $E_0 = 1.77$ V and $E_{\frac{1}{2} \, cat} = -0.69$ V. Fe^{3+} ions are
therefore reduced electrochemically before hydrogen peroxide. The chemical reaction

$$H_2O_2 + 2\,Fe^{2+} + 2\,H^+ \rightarrow 2\,Fe^{3+} + 2\,H_2O \tag{30}$$

is quite fast, however. The reduction of Fe^{3+} in the presence of hydrogen peroxide is
therefore accompanied by a partial regeneration of the ferric ions by reaction (30);
i.e. the reduction of H_2O_2 is catalyzed. Since reaction (30) is not very fast, a kinetic
wave is produced (curve 3, Fig. 112).

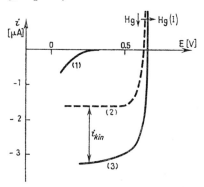

Fig. 112. Catalysis of the reduction of hydrogen peroxide by ferric ions, in 0.25 M H_2SO_4.
Curve 1: reduction of 0.147 M H_2O_2 alone.
Curve 2: reduction of 2 . 10^{-4} M Fe^{3+} alone.
Curve 3: reduction of 0.147 M H_2O_2 + 2 . 10^{-4} M Fe^{3+}
(after KOLTHOFF and PARRY [101]).

Many redox systems apart from $Fe^{3+} + e \rightleftharpoons Fe^{2+}$ catalyze the reduction of hydrogen peroxide.

Reduction of the uranyl ions in acid media

The redox systems involving uranium ions in aqueous solutions of strong acids are

$$UO_2^{2+} + e \rightleftharpoons UO_2^+, \qquad E_1 = + 0.06 \text{ V} \qquad (31)$$

$$UO_2^+ + 4 H^+ + e \rightleftharpoons U^{4+} + 2 H_2O, \qquad E_2 = + 0.55 \text{ V} \qquad (32)$$

$$U^{4+} + e \rightleftharpoons U^{3+}, \qquad E_3 = - 0.64 \text{ V} \qquad (33)$$

and

$$UO_2^{2+} + 4 H^+ + 2e \rightleftharpoons U^{4+} + 2 H_2O, \qquad E_4 = + 0.31 \text{ V}$$

Systems (31) and (33) are fairly fast at a mercury electrode. According to the standard potentials of these reactions, the reduction of a solution of a uranyl (VI) salt to a uranyl (III) salt in a strongly acid medium should proceed by the steps: U(VI) → U(IV) → U(III). In fact, the reduction of U(VI) to U(IV) is very slow, so the reduction U(VI) → U(V), which is fast, occurs first at fairly high potentials. The subsequent reduction U(V) → U(IV) is very slow, and occurs to an appreciable extent at the same potentials as U(IV) → U(III), so we may treat U(V) as being directly reduced to U(III). U(III) is a very strong reducing agent, and is unstable.

Since $E_2 > E_1$ and $E_2 > E_4$, U(V) is unstable in aqueous solution. It disproportionates into U(VI) and U(IV), and the reaction in acid media may be written as

$$2 UO_2^+ + 4 H^+ \rightarrow UO_2^{2+} + U^{4+} + 2 H_2O$$

The rate of this chemical reaction is low. It increases as the concentration of hydrogen increasis, *i.e.* as the pH decreases. Under these conditions, UO_2^{2+} is reduced as follows

$$2 UO_2^{2+} + 2e \rightarrow 2 UO_2^+$$

followed by

$$2 UO_2^+ + 4 H^+ \rightarrow UO_2^{2+} + U^{4+} + 2 H_2O$$

UO_2^{2+} is partially regenerated by dismutation, and the overall reaction is

$$UO_2^{2+} + 4 H^+ + 2e \rightarrow U^{4+} + 2 H_2O$$

U(VI) is thus directly reduced to U(IV), but at the potentials corresponding to the fast reaction U(VI) → U(V). In other words, the slow system U(VI) → U(IV) is catalyzed by the fast system U(VI) → U(V).

The dismutation reaction is fairly slow, so a kinetic current is observed in practice. The current–potential curves are shown in Fig. 113. In slightly acid media (10^{-2} N HCl) the dismutation is very slow, and there is a wave corresponding to U(VI)→U(V), followed by a second wave twice as high, corresponding to U(V)→U(III) or U(V) → U(VI) → U(III) (curve 1). As the acidity increases, the height of the U(VI) → U(V) wave increases owing to catalysis. The kinetic current increases with the acidity (curves 2, 3 and 4). If the acidity were such that the dismutation were instantaneous, curve 5 would be produced: a wave corresponding to U(VI) → U(IV), catalyzed by U(VI) → U(V), followed by a wave of half the height corresponding to U(IV) → U(III).

The sum of the heights of the two waves remains constant, and corresponds to the overall reduction U(VI) → U(III).

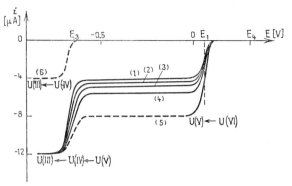

Fig. 113. Reduction of UO_2^{2+} (10^{-3} M) at a mercury electrode.

Curve 1: in 10^{-2} N HCl.   Curve 4: in 3.78 N HClO$_4$.
Curve 2: in 0.9 N HClO$_4$.   Curve 5: in 1.89 N HClO$_4$ + 0.4 M H$_2$C$_2$O$_4$.
Curve 3: in 1.89 N HClO$_4$.   Curve 6: reduction of 10^{-3} M U^{4+} under the same conditions
(after KOLTHOFF and HARRIS [107] and HARRIS and KOLTHOFF [108]).

Curve 5 can actually be observed in fairly acid media in the presence of a complexing agent like oxalic acid, probably because the rate of dismutation of the oxalate complexes of UO_2^{2+} is very great.

In slightly acid, neutral or slightly basic media the problem becomes very complicated because of the hydrolysis of the various uranium ions.

Reduction of nitrates and nitrites

The direct reduction of nitrates and nitrites at a mercury electrode is very slow, and does not occur until the potential nears that at which indifferent electrolytes are reduced; in the presence of Na^+ and K^+ they are not electroactive.

But they may be reduced chemically by a number of reducing agents, for in-

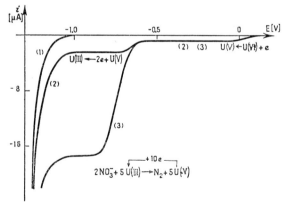

Fig. 114. Catalysis of the reduction of nitrates at a mercury electrode by uranyl ions, in a solution of 10^{-2} N HCl + 0.1 N KCl.

Curve 1: 3 . 10^{-4} M KNO$_3$.
Curve 2: 2 . 10^{-4} M UO$_2$Cl$_2$.
Curve 3: 4 . 10^{-4} M KNO$_3$ + 2 . 10^{-4} M UO$_2$Cl$_2$
(after KOLTHOFF et al. [115]).

stance U(III). We have seen above that in decinormal HCl the reduction curve of UO_2^{2+} consists of two waves corresponding to the consecutive reactions $U(VI) + e \rightarrow U(V)$ and $U(V) + 2e \rightarrow U(III)$ (curve 2, Fig. 114). If nitrate is added, the first wave remains unchanged, but the height of the second is very considerably increased (curve 3, Fig. 114). This is because U(V) is partially regenerated during the reaction $U(V) + 2e \rightarrow U(III)$, by a reaction which may be written

$$2 NO_3^- + 5 U^{3+} + 4 H_2O \rightarrow N_2 + 5 UO_2^+ + 8 H^+$$

There is thus catalysis of the reduction of NO_3^- by UO_2^{2+}. The effect is precisely the same with nitrite.

Catalysis of the reduction of iodates at a platinum electrode by the system I_3^-/I^-

Iodates are reduced slowly in acid solution ($HClO_4$) at a smooth platinum electrode (curve 1, Fig. 115). The system I_3^-/I^- is fast, on the other hand (curve 2, Fig. 115). The rate of reduction of iodate is increased by the addition of iodine, as is shown by curve 3. The chemical reaction

$$IO_3^- + 6 H^+ + 5 I^- \rightarrow 3 I_2 + 3 H_2O \tag{34}$$

brings about catalysis of the reduction of iodate by the system I_3^-/I^-: the electrochemical reaction is $I_3^- + 2e \rightarrow 3 I^-$ and the iodide ions formed are oxidized by iodate ions according to equation (34). According to this mechanism, the rate of reduction of iodate can be limited either by the rate of diffusion of the substances reacting at the electrodes, or by the rate of the chemical reaction (34) (kinetic wave). The rate of the chemical reaction depends on the pH and on the concentrations of I^- and IO_3^- ions at the electrode.

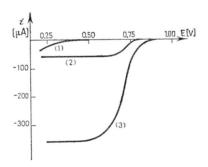

Fig. 115. The reduction of IO_3^- and I_2 in N $HClO_4$ at a smooth platinum electrode.
Curve 1: 10^{-3} M IO_3^-.
Curve 2: 10^{-3} N I_2.
Curve 3: 10^{-3} M IO_3^- + 10^{-3} N I_2.
(after BADOZ-LAMBLING and GUILLAUME [117]).

When iodate is present in a concentration of 10^{-3} M, and iodine in a concentration of 10^{-3} N, the concentrations of iodide formed and of iodate at the electrode are sufficient to make the rate of reaction (34) greater than that of the diffusion of the iodine and iodate; it is therefore the latter which determines the rate of electrolysis (Fig. 115). If, however, the concentration of iodine is reduced to 10^{-4} N, thus reducing the iodide concentration at the electrode, the rate of the chemical reaction decreases and becomes limiting (curve 3, Fig. 116). The limiting current is now much less than when the current is limited by diffusion (curve 4, Fig. 116). If the concentration of iodate is also reduced to 10^{-4} N, the rate of reaction (34) is so low that catalysis no longer occurs.

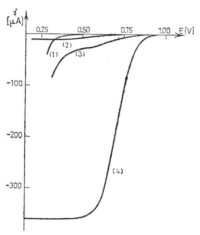

Fig. 116. The reduction of IO_3^- and I_2 in N HClO$_4$ at a rotating platinum electrode.
Curve 1: 10^{-3} M IO_3^-.   Curve 3: 10^{-3} M IO_3^- + 10^{-4} N I_2.
Curve 2: 10^{-4} N I_2.   Curve 4: 10^{-3} M IO_3^- + 10^{-3} N I_2
(after BADOZ-LAMBLING and GUILLAUME [117]).

REFERENCES

Reviews, theoretical discussions of kinetic waves and experimental details

[1] I. M. KOLTHOFF and J. J. LINGANE, *Polarography*, Interscience, New York, 2nd ed., 1952, Vol. I, p. 268.

[2] P. DELAHAY, *New Instrumental Methods in Electrochemistry*, Interscience, New York, 1954, p. 87, 100.

[3] P. DELAHAY, *Proceedings of the 6th meeting of the C.I.T.C.E.* Poitiers 1954, Butterworths, London, 1955, p. 518.

[4] R. BRDIČKA, *Collection Czechoslov. Chem. Communs.*, 19 (1954) Suppl. 41.

[5] R. BRDIČKA and J. KOUTECKÝ, *J. Am. Chem. Soc.*, 76 (1954) 907.

[6] K. WIESNER, *Anal. Chem.*, 27 (1955) 1712.

[7] W. HANS, *Z. Elektrochem.*, 59 (1955) 623.

[8] P. DELAHAY, *Ann. Rev. Phys. Chem.*, 8 (1957) 233.

[9] A. DELMARCO, *Ricerca sci.*, 27 (1959) 5135.

[10] R. BRDIČKA, *Proc. Polarog. Conf.*, Warsaw 1956, (1957) 53.

The kinetic current

[11] R. BRDIČKA and K. WIESNER, *Naturwiss.*, 31 (1943) 247, 391.

[12] R. BRDIČKA and K. WIESNER, *Chem. listy*, 40 (1946) 66.

[13] R. BRDIČKA and K. WIESNER, *Collection Czechoslov. Chem. Communs*, 12 (1947) 138.

[14] R. BRDIČKA, *Chem. listy*, 39 (1945) 35.

[15] R. BRDIČKA, *Chem. listy*, 40 (1946) 232.

[16] R. BRDIČKA, *Collection Czechoslov. Chem. Communs.*, 12 (1947) 212.

[17] J. KOUTECKÝ and R. BRDIČKA, *Collection Czechoslov. Chem. Communs.*, 12 (1947) 337.

[18] J. KOUTECKÝ and R. BRDIČKA, *Collection Czechoslov. Chem. Communs.*, 18 (1953) 11, 183, 597.

[19] J. KOUTECKÝ and R. BRDIČKA, *Collection Czechoslov. Chem. Communs.*, 19 (1954) 857, 1045, 1093.

[20] J. KOUTECKÝ and R. BRDIČKA, *Collection Czechoslov. Chem. Communs.*, 20 (1955) 116.

[21] J. KOUTECKÝ and R. BRDIČKA, *Collection Czechoslov. Chem. Communs.*, 21 (1956) 652, 1056.

[22] J. KOUTECKÝ, *Proc. 1st Intern. Polarog. Congr.*, Prague 1951, Vol. I, p. 826.

[23] J. KOUTECKÝ, *Chem. listy*, 45 (1951) 241, 245.
[24] J. KOUTECKÝ, *Chem. listy*, 46 (1952) 193.
[25] J. KOUTECKÝ, *Chem. listy*, 47 (1953) 323.
[26] J. KOUTECKÝ and J. KORYTA, *Z. Elektrochem.*, 57 (1953) 591, 595.
[27] J. KOUTECKÝ and J. KORYTA, *Collection Czechoslov. Chem. Communs.*, 19 (1954) 845.
[28] J. KOUTECKÝ and V. HANUS, *Collection Czechoslov. Chem. Communs.*, 20 (1955) 124.
[29] J. WEBER and J. KOUTECKÝ, *Collection Czechoclov. Chem. Communs.*, 20 (1955) 980.
[30] J. KOUTECKÝ and J. CIZEK, *Collection Czechoslov. Chem. Communs.*, 21 (1956) 836.
[31] J. KOUTECKÝ, *Collection Czechoslov. Chem. Communs.*, 22 (1957) 160.

Equation of the kinetic wave
[32] Z. VAVRIN, *Chem. listy*, 41 (1947) 77.
[33] Z. VAVRIN, *Collection Czechoslov. Chem. Communs.*, 14 (1949) 367.
[34] R. TAMAMUSHI and N. TANAKA, *Bull. Chem. Soc. Japan*, 23 (1950) 110.
[35] R. TAMAMUSHI and N. TANAKA, *Proc. 1st Intern. Polarog. Congr., Prague 1951*, Vol. I, p. 503.
[36] M. SMUTEK, *Collection Czechoslov. Chem. Communs.*, 18 (1953) 171.
[37] J. BADOZ-LAMBLING and R. GAUGUIN, *Anal. Chim. Acta*, 8 (1953) 471.
[38] P. KIVALO, *Acta Chem. Scand.*, 9 (1955) 221.
[39] Y. KOUTETSKÝ and V. G. LEVICH, *Doklady Akad. Nauk U.S.S.R.*, 117 (1957) 441.
[40] S. TRIBALAT and D. DELAFOSSE, *Anal. Chim. Acta*, 19 (1958) 74.

The reaction layer
[41] E. F. ORLEMAN and D. M. H. KERN, *J. Am. Chem. Soc.*, 75 (1953) 3058.
[42] M. SMUTEK, *Collection Czechoslov. Chem. Communs.*, 19 (1954) 24.

Influence of the drop time on the height of the kinetic waves
[43] K. WIESNER, *Z. Elektrochem.*, 49 (1943) 164.
[44] K. WIESNER, *Collection Czechoslov. Chem. Communs.*, 12 (1947) 64.
[45] O. H. MÜLLER and J. S. DAVIS JR., *J. Biol. Chem.*, 159 (1945) 667.

Catalysis of the reduction of H+
[46] J. HEYROVSKY and J. BABICKA, *Collection Czechoslov. Chem. Communs.*, 2 (1930) 270.
[47] R. BRDIČKA, *Collection Czechoslov. Chem. Communs.*, 8 (1936) 366.
[48] I. M. KOLTHOFF and J. J. LINGANE, *Polarography*, Interscience, New York, 2nd ed., 1952, Vol. II, p. 849–883.

Reduction of oxygen,
—, *platinum and silver electrodes*
[49] H. A. LAITINEN and I. M. KOLTHOFF, *J. Phys. Chem.*, 45 (1941) 1061, 1079.

—, *mercury electrode*
[50] J. HEYROVSKY, *Trans. Faraday Soc.*, 19 (1924) 785.
[51] I. M. KOLTHOFF and C. S. MILLER, *J. Am. Chem. Soc.*, 63 (1941) 1013.
[52] D. M. H. KERN, *J. Am. Chem. Soc.*, 76 (1954) 4208.

—, *gold electrode*
[53] P. SILVESTRONI, *Ann. chim. (Rome)*, 44 (1954) 464.
[54] I. M. KOLTHOFF and J. JORDAN, *J. Am. Chem. Soc.*, 74 (1952) 4801.

—, *graphite electrode*
[55] A. A. MOUSSA, H. K. EMBABY, and H. M. SAMMOUR, *J. Chem. Soc.*, (1958) 2481.

Reduction of hydrogen peroxide, mercury electrode
[56] H. PELLEQUER, *Compt. rend.*, 222 (1946) 1220.
[57] H. PELLEQUER, *Compt. rend.*, 225 (1947) 116.
[58] P. A. GIGUÈRE and J. B. JAILLET, *Can. J. Research*, B. 26 (1948) 767.

Catalysis of the reduction of hydrogen peroxide
[59] E. P. PARRY, *Ph. D. Thesis*, University of Minnesota, 1950.
[60] I. M. KOLTHOFF and E. P. PARRY, *J. Am. Chem. Soc.*, 73 (1951) 5315.

Catalysis of the system titanium (III)/titanium (IV)
[61] S. TRIBALAT and D. DELAFOSSE, *Actas do Congresso, Lisboa 1957*, p. 971.

Other examples of catalysis
[62] R. BRDIČKA, *Collection Czechoslov. Chem. Communs.*, 2 (1930) 489, 545.
[63] R. BRDIČKA, *Collection Czechoslov. Chem. Communs.*, 3 (1931) 396.
[64] M. PAVLICK, *Collection Czechoslov. Chem. Communs.*, 3 (1931) 223.
[65] J. J. LINGANE and H. KERLINGER, *Ind. Eng. Chem., Anal. Ed.*, 13 (1941) 77.

Reduction of formaldehyde
[66] K. VESELÝ and R. BRDIČKA, *Collection Czechoslov. Chem. Communs.*, 12 (1947) 313.
[67] R. BIEBER and G. TRÜMPLER, *Helv. Chim. Acta*, 30 (1947) 706.

Reduction of the base corresponding to certain organic acids

[68] D. ILKOVIČ, *Collection Czechoslov. Chem. Communs.*, 6 (1934) 498.
[69] D. ILKOVIČ, *J. chim. phys.*, 35 (1938) 129.
[70] I. M. KOLTHOFF and A. LIBERTI, *J. Am. Chem. Soc.*, 70 (1948) 1885.
[71] E. G. CLAIR and K. WIESNER, *Nature*, 165 (1950) 202.
[72] V. HANUS and R. BRDIČKA, *Chem. listy*, 44 (1950) 291.
[73] Z. VODRAZKA, *Chem. listy*, 45 (1951) 293.
[74] Z. VODRAZKA, *Chem. listy*, 46 (1952) 210.
[75] V. NIKOLAJENKO, *Dissertation*, Charles' University, Prague, 1952.
[76] A. KIRRMANN, R. SCHMITZ, P. FEDERLIN and M. L. DONDON, *Bull. soc. chim. France*, (1952) 612.
[77] P. RUETSCHI and G. TRÜMPLER, *Helv. Chim. Acta*, 35 (1953) 1947.
[78] P. RUETSCHI, *Z. phys. Chem.*, 5 (1955) 323.
[79] P. DELAHAY and W. VIELSTICH, *J. Am. Chem. Soc.*, 77 (1955) 4955.
[80] S. G. MAIRANOVSKY, *Doklady Akad. Nauk S.S.S.R.*, 114 (1957) 1272.

Reduction of the cadmium (II)-EDTA complex

[81] J. KORYTA and I. KOESSLER, *Collection Czechoslov. Chem. Communs.*, 15 (1950) 241.
[82] J. HEYROVSKY and M. MATYAS, *Collection Czechoslov. Chem. Communs.*, 16 (1951) 455.
[83] R. L. PECSOK, *J. Chem. Educ.*, 29 (1962) 597.
[84] N. TANAKA, I. T. OIWA and M. KODAMA, *Anal. Chem.*, 28 (1956) 1555.
[85] R. W. SCHMID and C. N. REILLEY, *J. Am. Chem. Soc.*, 80 (1958) 2101.

Oxidation-reduction reactions

[86] R. BRDIČKA and C. TROPP, *Biochem. Z.*, 289 (1937) 301.
[87] R. BRDIČKA and K. WIESNER, *Collection Czechoslov. Chem. Communs.*, 12 (1947) 39.
[88] D. M. H. KERN, *Ph. D. Thesis*, University of California, 1949.
[89] P. DELAHAY and G. L. STIEHL, *J. Am. Chem. Soc.*, 74 (1952) 3500.
[90] S. L. MILLER, *J. Am. Chem. Soc.*, 74 (1952) 4130.
[91] M. G. EVANS and N. S. HUSH, *J. chim. phys.*, 49 C (1952) 159.
[92] J. KOUTECKÝ, *Collection Czechoslov. Chem. Communs.*, 18 (1953) 311.
[93] Z. POSPISIL, *Collection Czechoslov. Chem. Communs.*, 18 (1953) 337.
[94] D. M. H. KERN, *J. Am. Chem. Soc.*, 75 (1953) 2473.
[95] K. H. HENKE and W. HANS, *Z. Elektrochem.*, 59 (1955) 676.
[96] J. KOUTECKÝ and J. CIZEK, *Collection Czechoslov. Chem. Communs.*, 21 (1956) 1063.
[97] I. M. KOLTHOFF and J. J. LINGANE, *Polarography*, Interscience, New York, 2nd ed., 1952, Vol. I, p. 281.
[98] P. DELAHAY, *New Instrumental Methods in Electrochemistry*, Interscience, New York, 1954, p. 106.

Catalysis of the reduction of hydrogen peroxide by iron (III)

[99] J. H. BAXENDALE, M. G. EVANS and G. S. PARK, *Trans. Faraday Soc.*, 42 (1946) 155.
[100] P. VAN RYSSELBERGHE, P. DELAHAY, A. H. GROPP, J. M. MCGEE and R. D. WILLIAMS, *J. Phys. & Colloid Chem.*, 54 (1950) 754.
[101] I. M. KOLTHOFF and E. P. PARRY, *J. Am. Chem. Soc.*, 73 (1951) 3178, 5315.
[102] J. DOSKOCIL, *Proc. 1st Intern. Polarog. Congr., Prague 1951*, Vol. II, p. 674.
[103] I. M. KOLTHOFF and E. P. PARRY, *Proc. 1st Intern. Polarog. Congr., Prague 1951*, Vol. I, p. 145.
[104] J. SVATEK, *Proc. 1st Intern. Polarog. Congr., Prague 1951*, Vol. I, p. 789.

Reduction of the uranyl ions

[105] P. HERASYMENKO, *Chem. listy*, 19 (1925) 172.
[106] P. HERASYMENKO, *Trans. Faraday Soc.*, 24 (1928) 272.
[107] I. M. KOLTHOFF and W. E. HARRIS, *J. Am. Chem. Soc.*, 68 (1946) 1175.
[108] W. E. HARRIS and I. M. KOLTHOFF, *J. Am. Chem. Soc.*, 67 (1945) 1484.
[109] D. M. H. KERN and E. F. ORLEMAN, *J. Am. Chem. Soc.*, 71 (1949) 2102.
[110] K. A. KRAUS, *J. Am. Chem. Soc.*, 71 (1949) 2510.
[111] H. G. HEAL and J. G. N. THOMAS, *Trans. Faraday Soc.*, 45 (1949) 11.
[112] H. IMAI, *Bull. Chem. Soc. Japan*, 30 (1957) 873.

Reduction of nitrates and nitrites

[113] M. TOKUOKA, *Collection Czechoslov. Chem. Communs.*, 4 (1932) 444.
[114] M. TOKUOKA and J. RUZICKA, *Collection Czechoslov. Chem. Communs.*, 6 (1934) 339.
[115] I. M. KOLTHOFF, W. E. HARRIS and G. MATSUYAMA, *J. Am. Chem. Soc.*, 66 (1944) 1782.
[116] B. KEILIN and J. W. OTVOS, *J. Am. Chem. Soc.*, 68 (1946) 2665.

Reduction of iodates

[117] J. BADOZ-LAMBLING and C. GUILLAUME, *Proc. 2nd Intern. Polarog. Congr., Cambridge 1959,*.

Chapter V

INFLUENCE OF PHYSICAL FACTORS
ON THE ELECTROCHEMICAL PHENOMENA

We have seen in the preceding chapters how chemical reactions (such as acid–base reactions, complex formation and redox reactions) can displace the current–potential curves in a way which often lends itself to a quantitative treatment.

We shall now see what physical factors can modify the current–potential curves, and precisely what influence they have. Some of these factors affect mainly the kinetics of the electrochemical reaction (surface area and nature of the electrode), others the transport phenomena in the solution (stirring, etc.) while some factors have an influence on both (temperature, adsorption). There are also some parasitic phenomena which sometimes distort the current–potential curves and prevent them being used for quantitative purposes.

I. INFLUENCE OF PHYSICAL FACTORS ON THE RATE
OF ELECTROCHEMICAL REACTIONS

Influence of the surface area of the electrode

In the previous chapters we have shown a large number of curves in which the electrolysis current is plotted against the electrode potential. Now all these currents are proportional to the surface area of the electrodes, although the current density, the current per unit surface area, is not. This makes it difficult to compare curves corresponding to electrodes of widely different surface areas, as in voltammetry and industrial electrolysis. It may, however, be an advantage in problems involving two electrodes in the same cell, when the current is the same for both of them though the two electrodes may have different surface areas. The current density is in general ill defined, since the exact surface area of the electrode is usually not known.

The apparent geometrical surface area of an electrode can be measured readily enough; but the surface on which the electron exchange actually takes place is often several times larger than this, because of the roughness shown on the microscopic scale by solids, even by polished metals.

The ratio of the real surface area for electron exchange and the apparent surface area is defined by a 'roughness factor', as shown in Table I.

TABLE I

ROUGHNESS FACTORS OF SOME METALS [1]

Metal	Roughness factor
Nickel wire (drawn)	1.3 to 3
Copper wire	1.3 to 2
Silver wire	~ 10
Platinum wire	1 to 2
Platinized platinum	up to several hundred

The surface area corresponding to the diffusion layer around the electrode is intermediate between the geometrical surface area and the electron-exchange surface area. The thicker this layer becomes, the closer its surface area approaches the geometrical area. In the case of a liquid electrode (mercury) all the surface areas are the same.

In the equations of the current–potential curves, the constant i_0 is proportional to the surface area of the electrode at which the electron exchange takes place, while the diffusion coefficients k_D are proportional to the diffusion surface area; the current i is thus more or less proportional to the surface area (Fig. 117).

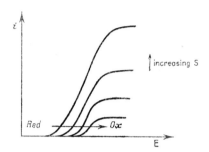

Fig. 117. The influence of the surface area of the electrode.

The influence of the physical state and the chemical nature of the electrode

A change in the nature of the electrode may have a great effect on the rate of the electrochemical reaction. The value of i_0 and that of the transfer coefficients α and β is particularly sensitive to the nature of the electrode, though the exact values depend on the redox system in question.

A system which is fast at one electrode may be slow at another, although it is often the case that a system which is fast at one electrode is fast at a large number of other electrodes, and thus gives the same current–potential curves at all of them. Moreover, changes in the value of i_0 do not have much effect on the curves as long as the value itself is large; in slow systems, on the other hand, they may have a considerable effect.

Finely divided metals

When the metal forming the electrode is very finely divided, the real surface area is much greater than the apparent geometrical surface area. Experiment shows that the diffusion current does not vary much on passing from a polished platinum electrode to one of the same area covered with finely divided platinum; but the electrochemical reactions become much faster, just as if the nature of the electrode had changed (Fig. 118).

The nature and the surface area of the electrode may change continuously during electrolysis. This is the case when the metal of the electrode is oxidized, for example $Al\downarrow - 3e \rightarrow Al^{3+}$; the surface varies as a result of the passage of metal into solution. This is also the case when a deposit is produced on the electrode, as in oxidation at a platinum electrode. At sufficiently high potentials the surface of the platinum is covered with a film of oxide, and the electrolysis no longer takes place over platinum, but over platinum oxide. Another example is the oxidation of Pb^{2+} at a platinum electrode: the oxide PbO_2 is deposited on the electrode, which thus effectively becomes a PbO_2 electrode. The same phenomenon occurs during the reduction of a metallic cation to the metal.

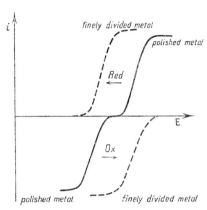

Fig. 118. Increase of the state of division of the metal.

The formation of hydrogen or oxygen or the deposition of very slight amounts of certain impurities may have a considerable effect on the nature of the surface of several metals. Platinum is very sensitive to such effects, even when it is polished (see the pretreatment of electrodes, Chapter VI).

Examples

We give here some examples of the displacement of the curves due to a change in the nature of the electrode.

The system $2H^+ + 2e \rightleftharpoons H_2$. This system is especially sensitive to variations in the nature of the electrode. Below are tabulated the values of the overvoltage of the cathode reaction

$$2 H^+ + 2e \rightarrow H_2$$

at various electrodes, in N HCl and with a current density of 10^{-3} A/cm².

TABLE II

Values for the overvoltage at various electrodes[2] during the cathode reaction $2 H^+ + 2e \rightarrow H_2$ in N HCl, with a current density of 10^{-3} A/cm²

Ag	− 0.59 V	In	− 0.80 V
Au	− 0.12 V	Ni	− 0.32 V
Be	− 0.63 V	Pb	− 0.85 V
Cd	− 0.99 V	Pd	− 0.09 V
Cr	− 0.42 V	Pt	− 0.29 V
Cu	− 0.50 V	Ta	− 0.20 V
Fe	− 0.40 V	Tl	− 0.80 V
Ga	− 0.68 V	W	− 0.11 V
Hg	− 1.03 V	Zn	− 0.80 V

TABLE III

FINELY DIVIDED METALS

Current density	10^{-4} A/cm^2	10^{-3} A/cm^2
Polished (smooth) platinum	-0.09 V	-0.68 V
Platinized platinum	-0.003 V	-0.05 V

A more exact measure of the effect is given by the values of log i_0 (a/b of Tafel's law) for the same redox system at various electrodes as shown in Table IV.

TABLE IV

Values of log i_0 for the system 2 H$^+$ + 2e → H$_2$ in N HCl at various electrodes

Au	5.0–6.0	Ag	6.3 (7.2–3.7)
Cd	5.3	Al	9.5
Co	6.1	Be	9.0
Cu	6.5–8.0	Bi	7.0
Fe	5.8	Hg	12.3 (12.6–11.2)
Ge	4.7	Nb	11.0
Mo	6.2	Pb	12.7
Ni	6.0 (6.3–5.4)	Sb	8.9
Pd	3.6	Sn	7.3
Pt	4.7–2.8	Ta	9.1
Pt, platinized	3.4–3.0	Tl	16.0
W	5.6–6.0	Zn	7.9

The values in the first column were collected by M. POURBAIX and N. DE ZOUBOV, Centre Belge d'étude de la corrosion, Bruxelles. The values in the second column are taken from G. KORTÜM and J. O'M. BOCKRIS, *Textbook of Electrochemistry*, Elsevier, Amsterdam, 1951.

The system Bi↓/Bi(III). The value of i_0 for the system Bi^{3+}/Bi↓ is much greater at a bismuth electrode than at electrodes of copper or platinum (Fig. 119). But the reduction curves of Bi^{3+} at a copper or platinum electrode can only be determined at the beginning of the reaction, since the deposition of bismuth changes the nature of the electrode. When a solution of Bi^{3+} is reduced at constant potential (-0.15 V) at a platinum electrode, an increase in the current is observed, as the platinum becomes covered with bismuth.

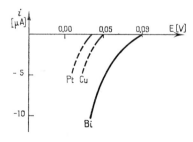

Fig. 119. Influence of the nature of the electrode on the reaction Bi(III) + 3e → Bi↓ in a tartrate medium at pH 5 (after BUC[3]).

Formation of a film on the electrode. When Cr(VI) is reduced at a platinum electrode in a slightly acid medium, *e.g.* 10^{-2} to 10^{-3} M HCl, a film is formed on the surface of the electrode, which prevents the reduction of Cr(VI), Fe(III) and Cu(II), but allows Ag^+, Tl^+ and H^+ to be reduced[4]. For other examples see Fig.120 and 121.

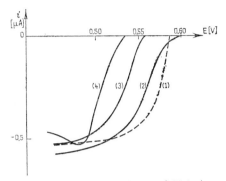

Fig. 120. The reduction of 2 . 10^{-4} M Ag^+ in 0.1 N H_2SO_4.
(1) Theoretical curve, (2) Gold, (3) Platinum, (4) Graphite.
After LORD and ROGERS[5].

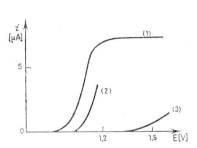

Fig. 121. The oxidation of 10^{-3} M hydroxylamine hydrochloride at pH 2, at electrodes of: (1) Platinum, (2) Gold, (3) Graphite.
After LORD and ROGERS[5].

Pretreatment of the electrode. The nature of the electrode surface depends markedly on the preliminary treatment which it receives. The form of the curves and the values of the half-wave potentials for slow systems therefore depend on the pretreatment given to the electrodes (washing, mechanical or chemical cleaning, preliminary oxidation or reduction; see Chapter VI).

Example. The reduction of 4 · 10^{-4} M Fe^{3+} at a graphite electrode. The limiting diffusion current depends on the pretreatment given to the electrode (Fig. 122).

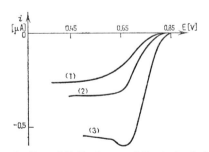

Fig. 122. The reduction of Fe^{3+} at a graphite electrode in 0.1 N HCl.
(1) After preliminary oxidation, (2) Freshly broken graphite, (3) After preliminary reduction.
After LORD and ROGERS[5].

Influence of the temperature [7]

An increase in the temperature increases the rates of the electrochemical reactions as well as those of diffusion. The diffusion coefficient increases by $1 - 4\%$ per degree. $E_{\frac{1}{2}}$ for fast systems varies more or less as E_0, *i.e.* as RT/nF, but the change in a slow system may be considerable. It may be remarked that at high temperatures, as in fused salt systems, the reactions are often very fast. As an example, Fig. 123 shows the reduction curves of Cu^{2+} and Ag^+ in cyanide solutions at various temperatures.

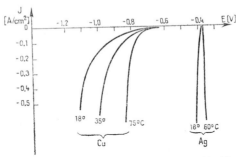

Fig. 123. The influence of the temperature on the rate of reduction of Ag(I) and Cu(II) (CN⁻ solution). After GAERTNER [6].

Adsorption phenomena

Dissolved substances may be adsorbed on the electrodes. Two main cases may be considered

1. *The electroactive substance is adsorbed on the electrode.* The electrolysis current is no longer limited by diffusion; this is similar to the case of the formation of oxide or salt films. These phenomena have been studied under non-stationary conditions.

For example, certain alkaloids can have two opposite effects on the reduction of H^+ ions at mercury surfaces. Since the alkaloid R is a base, it can form the acid cation HR^+, which has the effect of making the reduction of the complexed hydrogen ions more difficult. If, however, the HR^+ is adsorbed on the surface of the mercury, the reduction of the complexed hydrogen ions is faster than that of the H^+ alone. The constant i_0 may thus be decreased or increased, depending on which of these effects predominates. BOCKRIS et al. [8] have shown that the presence of quinine increases i_0 for the reduction of H^+ at a mercury electrode, while the presence of narcotine decreases it. The value of i_0 also depends on the concentration of the alkaloid (Fig. 124).

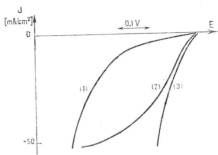

Fig. 124. The influence of quinine on the reduction of H^+ at a mercury electrode. (1) $2 \cdot 10^{-6}$ M quinine, (2) $2 \cdot 10^{-5}$ M quinine, (3) $2 \cdot 10^{-4}$ M quinine. After CONWAY et al. [8].

2. *A non-electroactive substance is adsorbed on the electrode.* This changes the state of the electrode surface, and therefore changes i_0, α or β for the electrochemical reaction, generally making them smaller. If the system is slow to begin with, it becomes even slower, and certain rapid reductions become slow ones.

The substances which may show this effect are inorganic anions (CN^-, I^-, Br^-, Cl^-, SO_4^{2-}, OH^-), organic or metallic cations (quaternary ammonium salts) or organic molecules (alkaloids, surface-active substances). Their effect depends on the degree to which they are absorbed.

Fig. 125 illustrates the action of dibenzyl sulphoxide on the reduction of Zn^{2+} ions. In the absence of dibenzyl sulphoxide, the value of i_0 is independent of the anion present (Cl^-, SO_4^{2-}, ClO_4^-), as shown in curves 1 and 2. In the presence of dibenzyl sulphoxide, i_0 is decreased to a degree which is greater the smaller the adsorption of the anion present ($ClO_4^- < SO_4^{2-} < Cl^-$): the more anion is adsorbed, the less room there is for the adsorption of the organic compound (curves 3, 4 and 5).

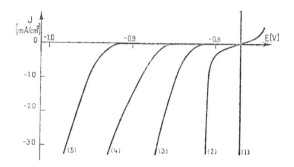

Fig. 125. The influence of adsorption on the rate of electrochemical reactions.
Curve 1: Salt of Zn^{2+}, pH 4, zinc amalgam electrode.
Curve 2: Zinc sulphate, chloride and perchlorate, pH 4, zinc electrode.
Curve 3: Zinc chloride + dibenzyl sulphoxide, pH 4, zinc electrode.
Curve 4: Zinc sulphate + dibenzyl sulphoxide, pH 4, zinc electrode.
Curve 5: Zinc perchlorate + dibenzyl sulphoxide, pH 4, zinc electrode.
After SCHWABE [9].

Fig. 126 shows the influence of the adsorption of I^- ions and of $(C_4H_9)_4N^+$ ions on the rate of oxidation of iron to Fe^{2+} and the rate of reduction of H^+ ions to hydrogen. The curves for these two reactions in the absence of adsorption are shown as broken lines. These two reactions can occur simultaneously; the total current as determined experimentally is shown in curve 1. When the total current is zero, a current i_1 is produced by the oxidation of iron and a current $-i_1$ by the reduction of H^+; the iron is attacked by the hydrogen ions, and hydrogen is evolved. If I^- ions are added they are adsorbed at the cathode and the rates of the electrochemical reactions (i_0 for the systems H^+/H_2 and Fe/Fe^{2+}) are decreased (curve 3). Under these conditions, it is no longer possible to oxidize iron and reduce hydrogen ions simultaneously to an appreciable extent; the metal is therefore no longer attacked by H^+. The presence of the cation $(C_4H_9)_4N^+$ by itself has relatively little effect (curve 2), but in the presence of adsorbed I^- ions the supplementary adsorption of the cations decreases the i_0 values still further (curve 4).

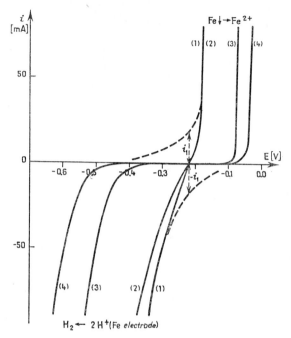

Fig. 126. The influence of adsorption on the rate of electrochemical reactions.
Curve 1: 6 N H_2SO_4,
Curve 2: 6 N H_2SO_4 + 10^{-3} M $[(C_4H_9)_4N]_2SO_4$,
Curve 3: 6 N H_2SO_4 + 2 . 10^{-3} M KI,
Curve 4: 6 N H_2SO_4 + 2 . 10^{-3} M KI + 10^{-3} M $[(C_4H_9)_4]_2SO_4$.
After FRUMKIN[10].

Adsorption also generally involves a change in the effective surface area of the electrode, and this is one of the causes of the change in the diffusion current.

The adsorption of certain substances can cause oxidation or reduction waves to disappear, often in a selective manner. Fig. 127 shows the action of gelatine on the

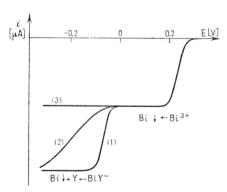

Fig. 127. The reduction of Bi(III) in the presence of gelatine. Dropping mercury electrode.
2 . 10^{-3} M Bi^{3+} and 2.3 . 10^{-3} M BiY^-.
Curve 1: 0.005 % gelatine,   Curve 3: 0.033 % gelatine
Curve 2: 0.012 % gelatine,   After REILLEY et al.[11].

reduction of Bi^{3+} and BiY^- (Bi^{3+}–EDTA) at a mercury electrode. The gelatine has no effect on the reduction curve for Bi^{3+}, but the reduction curve for BiY^- is displaced towards lower potentials, and disappears completely when the concentration of gelatine is increased sufficiently.

The effect of adsorption on the state of the electrode can clearly only be found in the potential range in which adsorption actually occurs. It is known that anions are only adsorbed in the potential range in which the surface of the metal is positively charged. Desorption will thus occur when the potential is reduced to a value which depends on the anion in question, giving rise to an abrupt change in i_0, α or β as a function of potential. Similarly, organic compounds are only adsorbed at potentials more or less close to that potential at which the charge on the surface of the metal is zero.

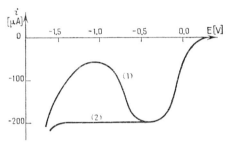

Fig. 128. The influence of adsorption on the limiting diffusion current. Mercury electrode.
Curve 1: 10^{-3} M $K_2S_2O_8$,
Curve 2: 10^{-3} M $K_2S_2O_8 + 5 . 10^{-5}$ M La^{3+}.
After FRUMKIN[10].

Fig. 128 shows an example of this: the reduction curve of 10^{-3} M $K_2S_2O_8$ at a mercury electrode. The decrease in the limiting current at about -0.6 V is due to the negative charge of the mercury surface, which repels the $S_2O_8^{2-}$ anions (curve 1). But in the presence of a highly charged cation (e.g. $5 \cdot 10^{-5}$ M La^{3+}) the minimum disappears (curve 2).

We have limited ourselves to giving a few examples illustrating the effect of adsorption on the current–potential curves. Further details are to be found in the references[14–48].

II. INFLUENCE OF PHYSICAL FACTORS ON MIGRATION, DIFFUSION AND CONVECTION

Conductance of the solution

Most of the usual solvents do not conduct electricity when they are pure; this is so for the most common of all solvents, water. It is therefore necessary to add an electrolyte, i.e. a compound which will be ionized in the solvent, to make it conduct and to allow the passage of the migration current.

Ohmic drop

The solution contained between the two electrodes is equivalent to a resistance R, which is inversely proportional to the equivalent conductivity of the electrolyte at that concentration. When the resistance R is appreciable, a potential difference $|i|R$ must be added to the potential difference between the electrodes, $E_A - E_C$, in order to obtain the value of the applied voltage $\Delta E = E_A - E_C + iR$. The term $|i|R$ is generally negligible, however, because of the large concentration of indifferent electrolyte used, which makes R small, and the low currents which are usually used.

If no indifferent electrolyte is used, however, the resistance R may be very large, especially if the concentration of the substance to be electrolyzed is low. The ohmic drop $|i|R$ also ceases to be negligible when the electrolysis current i is large.

If the potential difference between the electrodes is V, then i is given by

$$i = \frac{V - (E_A - E_C)}{R}$$

The current–potential curve for an infinitely fast system for which $R = 0$ is the straight line (1) of Fig. 129. If R increases, the straight line becomes sloping, with the equation $V = iR$.

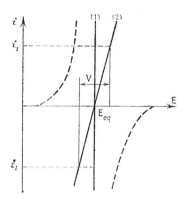

Fig. 129. Ohmic drop.

Curve 1: The current–potential curve for a fast system when the ohmic drop is negligible.
Curve 2: The variation of the current with the applied voltage V when the ohmic drop is appreciable.

We have supposed that the rate of the electrochemical reactions is not limited by transport phenomena, and that $E_A = E_C$, whatever the value of i. For deformation of current–potential curves by ohmic drop, see PEISKER [12].

Junction potential

In certain cases the two electrodes may dip into the same electrolysis cell; but it is often necessary to separate the anode and cathode compartments, which must then be joined by a junction which allows the passage of ions but does not permit the solutions to mix. This may be done by means of a porous diaphragm, *e.g.* sintered glass, a semi-permeable membrane, an agar bridge rendered conducting by an electrolyte, or more simply by a closed tap slightly wetted by the electrolyte solution.

Such a junction always has a fairly high resistance, involving an appreciable ohmic drop, and also a slight potential difference (usually less than 20 mV) called the junction potential, which must be taken into account.

This junction potential is due to the fact that the rate of diffusion of ions across the junction depends on their nature and their concentration. Let us suppose for example that we have two solutions of sodium chloride of different concentrations, separated by a liquid junction. The Cl^- and Na^+ ions will then diffuse from the more concentrated solution to the other one, but at different rates. A net positive charge will then arise at one side of the junction, and a net negative charge at the other, *i.e.* a potential difference will be set up between the two solutions, which will have the effect of slowing down the ion which is diffusing faster and speeding the other one up, until an equilibrium is established. There is then a potential difference E_j between the two solutions, and the ions diffuse at the same rate. The same effect is found at the junction between solutions of two different electrolytes, or solutions in which the solvents are different.

The junction potential is less when the ions of the electrolyte has nearly the same mobilities. For example, it is only about 1 mV between $10^{-2} M$ and $10^{-3} M$ solutions of potassium chloride at 25° C, while it is about 39 mV between $10^{-3} M$ and $10^{-2} M$ solutions of hydrochloric acid at the same temperature (equivalent conductivities: Cl^- 76.3, K^+ 73.5, H^+ 350). The junction electrolyte is therefore generally a salt whose ions have similar mobilities (KCl, NH_4NO_3, etc.).

The potential difference at the junction between different solvents may be considerable: it is about 140 mV between alcohol and water saturated with KCl.

References [49, 50] may be consulted for further particulars.

Rate of diffusion of the electrolyzed substances

Pure diffusion

If all convection could be prevented in the solution undergoing electrolysis, all the transport of material would occur by diffusion alone. There are three simple types of diffusion, depending on the shape of the electrode: planar, cylindrical and spherical. It may be shown that the diffusion layer gradually extends throughout the solution, thus causing the rate of diffusion to decrease so that the current theoretically tends to zero in the case of planar or cylindrical diffusion, or to a very low value in the case of spherical diffusion. It is thus theoretically impossible to achieve a steady state when all the transport occurs by pure diffusion.

In practice, it is impossible to abolish convection completely; for example, the decrease in concentration at the surface of the electrodes will give rise to a very slight change in the density of the solution, which in its turn will cause a slight convection. Any departure from isothermal conditions in the solution will have a similar effect. Finally, and most important, it is impossible to suppress all parasitic movement, caused *e.g.* by vibrations of the supports of the cell. This explains why it has been possible to determine current–potential curves with solid fixed electrodes without stirring the solution, albeit with poor accuracy and reproducibility, and very slowly.

Increasing convection artificially. The steady state

There are two reasons for increasing the degree of convection artificially during electrolysis:

1. The variation in the results caused by irregular convection can be eliminated if a much greater degree of convection, which is kept constant, is superposed on the original convection; it is now possible to attain a steady state.

2. The sensitivity of the measurements will be low when the rate of diffusion is low, and will increase if the transport of material is increased. The solution is very rapidly made homogeneous by stirring, so that differences of concentration due to electrolysis can be eliminated.

This may be done in two ways: by keeping the electrodes fixed and setting the solution in motion, or on the other hand by allowing the solution to remain at rest and moving the electrodes. We have seen that in both cases, when the electrode moves with respect to the solution a limiting layer may be supposed to exist between the electrode and the solution and to move with the electrode. Diffusion is limited to this layer of thickness δ_0. In general, transport by convection in the bulk of the solution is much faster than the transport by diffusion in the limiting layer, so that the electrolysis current is finally limited by the latter process. The greater the relative movement of the electrode and the solution, the thinner the diffusion layer will be, thus allowing more rapid diffusion and thus a greater electrolysis current.

Since the diffusion layer is caused by mechanical effects, it should have the same thickness for all the chemical species taking part in the electrochemical reaction.

The attainment of a steady state is dependent upon the constancy of the movement of the solution or the electrode.

Factors determining the rate of diffusion in the steady state

Nernst's hypothesis is only an approximation: in fact, the solution moves right up to the surface of the electrode, but the layers of liquid near the electrode are slowed down by viscosity. It may therefore be expected that the simple relation:

$$i_{\lim} = k_D C_s \tag{1}$$

where

$$k_D = \frac{nFSD_0}{\delta_0} \tag{2}$$

(see page 23) will be found not to fit the facts.

The quantitative interpretation of the transport of matter by convection is very difficult. We may, however, make a few general remarks on this subject here.

The limiting current is generally proportional to the concentration of the electrolyzed substance. The simple relation (1), $i_{lim} = k_D C_s$, still holds, therefore, but the constant of proportionality k_D only holds for the given experimental conditions (*i.e.* Eq. (2) is invalid).

The principal factors which have an effect on k_D are:

1. The surface area S of the electrode. For normal electrodes, the proportionality of $i_{\lim}$ to S may still be assumed to hold.

2. The diffusion constant D_0. The current $i_{\lim}$ always increases with D_0, the relation being of the form $i_{\lim} = kD_0^a$, where the value of a varies according to the type of electrode, usually being between 0.5 and 1.

3. The thickness δ_0 of the diffusion layer. Although as mentioned above no sharply defined diffusion layer exists, the value of δ_0, defined as

$$\delta_0 = \frac{nFSD_0^a}{k_D} = \frac{nFSD_0^a C_s}{i_{\lim}}$$

is a useful criterion for comparing the sensitivities.

TABLE V

THE DIFFUSION CONSTANTS FOR VARIOUS IONS[13]
AT INFINITE DILUTION AND AT 25° C

Ions	D_0 $[cm^2/s]$	Ions	D_0 $[cm^2/s]$
H^+	$9.34 \cdot 10^{-5}$	OH^-	$5.23 \cdot 10^{-5}$
Li^+	$1.04 \cdot 10^{-5}$	Cl^-	$2.03 \cdot 10^{-5}$
K^+	$1.98 \cdot 10^{-5}$	NO_3^-	$1.92 \cdot 10^{-5}$
Na^+	$1.35 \cdot 10^{-5}$	$CH_3CO_2^-$	$1.09 \cdot 10^{-5}$
Cs^+	$2.11 \cdot 10^{-5}$	IO_3^-	$1.09 \cdot 10^{-5}$
Tl^+	$2.00 \cdot 10^{-5}$	BrO_3^-	$1.44 \cdot 10^{-5}$
Pb^{2+}	$0.98 \cdot 10^{-5}$	SO_4^{2-}	$1.08 \cdot 10^{-5}$
Cd^{2+}	$0.72 \cdot 10^{-5}$	CrO_4^{2-}	$1.07 \cdot 10^{-5}$
Zn^{2+}	$0.72 \cdot 10^{-5}$	$Fe(CN)_6^{3-}$	$0.89 \cdot 10^{-5}$
Cu^{2+}	$0.72 \cdot 10^{-5}$	$Fe(CN)_6^{4-}$	$0.74 \cdot 10^{-5}$
Ni^{2-}	$0.69 \cdot 10^{-5}$		

of different electrodes, and may also be used as a measure of the efficiency of stirring (the better the stirring, the smaller δ_0). An increase in the viscosity increases δ_0 and decreases D_0, while an increase in the temperature increases D_0.

The rapidity with which the steady state is established

Instruments are now available which can record an experimental curve, in particular a current–potential curve, automatically. The problem now arises as to how closely the curve determined in this way corresponds to the current–potential curve in the stationary state.

In general, if the electrode potential is controlled the rate at which it is varied must be slow compared with the rate at which the steady state is approached. It is also possible to make a recording by fixing the electrolysis current (see Instrumentation, Chapter VI).

III. PARASITIC PHENOMENA AT THE ELECTRODES

Residual current

If a fairly low voltage is applied between two electrodes in a solution of an indifferent electrolyte, then theoretically no current should pass. In practice, however, a small current is always observed; this is known as the residual current. It is due to two causes:

a. Traces of electroactive impurities are always present, even in the purest reagents, and these are thus oxidized or reduced. It is also never possible to remove all traces of dissolved oxygen from the water, and this is easily reduced. This part of the residual current is known as the faradic residual current, since it obeys Faraday's law, and increases with the degree of stirring of the solution. It may sometimes be reduced by a preliminary electrolysis of the impurities. As the applied voltage increases, moreover, a moment arrives at which the solvent itself begins to be electrolyzed at a significant rate.

b. In general, a potential difference exists at the interface between two phases containing electrical charges (ions or electrons). The interface between a metallic electrode and the solution thus gives rise to an electrical double layer which acts as a capacitor, whose capacitance depends on the nature of the electrode and the composition of the solution, especially the presence of adsorbable substances, and of surface-active substances in the case of liquid electrodes (i.e. mercury).

If the electrode is now given a certain potential, the capacitor will be charged to a degree which depends on the potential (the positive charge may be on the electrode or in the solution, depending on the value of the potential). If the electrolysis circuit is now closed, the capacitor will discharge, giving rise to a current which is called the capacitive residual current ('condenser current'). This current is independent of the stirring of the solution.

When the electrode has a constant shape and size, and when a measurement is made of the stationary current at a constant potential, the condenser current falls off very quickly, since the capacitance of the double layer is very small (a few microfarads). The condenser current may therefore be neglected in this case. It will be shown below, however, that in certain cases the condenser current may be considerable, and allowance must then be made for this. The condenser current is important because it is this which limits the sensitivity of the measurement in practice: an electrode is only usable if the condenser current is negligible compared to the limiting diffusion current of an electroactive substance.

Abnormal movements of the solution: polarographic maxima

The current–potential curves obtained with certain electrodes often show undesirable peaks just before the limiting diffusion current is reached. These peaks are called 'polarographic maxima' (see Chapter VI, the dropping mercury electrode).

REFERENCES

[1] E. C. POTTER, Electrochemistry, Cleaver-Hume Press, London, 1956, p. 129.
[2] P. DELAHAY, Instrumental Analysis, Macmillan, London, 1957.
[3] H. BUC, unpublished.
[4] I. M. KOLTHOFF and A. M. SHAMS EL DIN, J. Phys. Chem., 60 (1956) 1564.
[5] S. S. LORD and L. B. ROGERS, Anal. Chem., 26 (1954) 284.
[6] V. GAERTNER, Electrochimie pratique, Gauthier-Villars, Paris, 1955.
[7] E. BODOR, Acta Chim. Hung., 15 (1958) 191.
[8] B. E. CONWAY, J. O'M. BOCKRIS and B. LOVRECEK, Electrochemical Thermodynamics and Kinetics, C.I.T.C.E. 6th Meeting, Liège 1954, Butterworths, London, 1955, p. 210.
[9] K. SCHWABE, Z. Elektrochem., 59 (1955) 663.
[10] A. N. FRUMKIN, Z. Elektrochem., 59 (1955) 807.
[11] C. N. REILLEY, W. G. SCRIBNER and C. TEMPLE, Anal. Chem., 28 (1956) 450.
[12] J. PEIZKER, Chem. listy, 52 (1958) 1699.
[13] I. M. KOLTHOFF and J. J. LINGANE, Polarography, Interscience, New York, 2nd ed., 1952.

Influence of adsorption on the electrochemical phenomena

[14] J. HEYROVSKY and R. BRDIČKA, Collection Czechoslov. Chem. Communs., 2 (1930) 370.
[15] R. BRDIČKA, Collection Czechoslov. Chem. Communs., 5 (1933) 112, 148.
[16] R. BRDIČKA, Collection Czechoslov. Chem. Communs., 8 (1936) 366.
[17] R. BRDIČKA, J. chim. phys., 35 (1938) 89.
[18] P. HERASYMENKO and I. SLENDYK, Collection Czechoslov. Chem. Communs., 6 (1934) 204.
[19] E. JURKA, Collection Czechoslov. Chem. Communs., 11 (1939) 243.
[20] R. BRDIČKA, Collection Czechoslov. Chem. Communs., 11 (1939) 614.

[21] H. Fischer, Z. Elektrochem., 49 (1943) 342, 376.
[22] A. N. Frumkin and V. I. Melik-Gaïkazyan, Doklady Akad. Nauk S.S.S.R., 77 (1951) 855.
[23] V. I. Melik-Gaïkazyan, Zhur. Fiz. Khim., 26 (1952) 560, 1184.
[24] A. N. Frumkin, Doklady Akad. Nauk S.S.S.R., 85 (1952) 373.
[25] R. Piontelli, G. Bianchi and R. Aletti, Z. Elektrochem., 56 (1952) 86.
[26] T. Berzins and P. Delahay, J. Phys. Chem., 59 (1955) 906.
[27] H. Fischer, Elektrolytische Abscheidung und Elektrokristallisation von Metallen, Springer, Berlin, 1954, p. 210.
[28] R. Tamamushi and T. Yamanaka, Bull. Chem. Soc. Japan, 28 (1955) 673.
[29] L. S. Zagaynova and A. G. Stromberg, Doklady Akad. Nauk S.S.S.R., 105 (1955) 747.
[30] E. P. Andreeva, Zhur. Fiz. Khim., 29 (1955) 699.
[31] K. Schwabe, Z. Elektrochem., 59 (1955) 663.
[32] W. Lorenz, Z. Elektrochem., 59 (1955) 730.
[33] W. Lorenz and H. Mühlberg, Z. Elektrochem., 59 (1955) 736.
[34] H. A. Laitinen and J. E. B. Randles, Trans. Faraday Soc., 51 (1955) 54.
[35] E. G. Neal and L. L. Schrier, Trans. Faraday Soc., 52 (1956) 703.
[36] W. Lorenz and F. Möckel, Z. Elektrochem., 60 (1956) 507.
[37] N. A. Balashova, V. A. Ivanov and V. E. Kazarinov, Doklady Akad. Nauk S.S.S.R., 115 (1957) 336.
[38] A. N. Frumkin and N. V. Nikolaeva-Fedorovich, Vestnik Moskov. Univ., 12 (1957) 169.
[39] P. Delahay, J. chim. phys., 54 (1957) 369.
[40] P. Delahay, Ann. Rev. Phys. Chem., 8 (1957) 229.
[41] P. Delahay and I. Trachtenberg, Intern. Congr. Pure and Appl. Chem., 9th Congr., Lisbon, 1956, Actas do Congresso, Lisboa, 1957, Vol. I, p. 605.
[42] P. Delahay and I. Trachtenberg, Anal. Chim. Acta, 18 (1958) 69.
[43] P. Delahay and I. Trachtenberg, J. Am. Chem. Soc., 79 (1957) 2355.
[44] P. Delahay and I. Trachtenberg, J. Am. Chem. Soc., 80 (1958) 2094.
[45] R. W. Schmid and C. N. Reilley, J. Am. Chem. Soc., 80 (1958) 2087.
[46] H. A. Laitinen and W. J. Subcasky, J. Am. Chem. Soc., 80 (1958) 2623.
[47] P. Delahay and C. T. Fike, J. Am. Chem. Soc., 80 (1958) 2628.
[48] H. Fischer and G. Thoresen, Z. Elektrochem., 62 (1958) 235.

Junction potential

[49] R. G. Bates, Electrometric pH Determinations, Wiley, New York, 1954.
[50] G. Maronny and G. Valensi, in Electrochemical Thermodynamics and Kinetics, C.I.T.C.E. 7th Meeting, Lindau 1955, Butterworths, London, 1957.

Fixed electrodes, platinum

[51] S. Glasstone, Trans. Am. Electrochem. Soc., 59 (1931) 277.
[52] S. Glasstone and G. D. Reynolds, Trans. Faraday Soc., 29 (1933) 399.
[53] H. A. Laitinen and I. M. Kolthoff, J. Phys. Chem., 45 (1941) 1061.
[54] I. M. Kolthoff and J. J. Lingane, Polarography, Interscience, New York, 1952, p. 399.

——, graphite

[55] R. E. Wilson and M. A. Youtz, Ind. Eng. Chem., 15 (1923) 603.

——, copper, mercury, silver

[56] E. Salomon, Z. phys. Chem., 24 (1897) 55.
[57] E. Salomon, Z. phys. Chem., 25 (1898) 365.
[58] D. L. Lydersen, Acta Chem. Scand., 3 (1949) 259.

——, platinum 'amalgam'

[59] T. L. Marple and L. B. Rogers, Anal. Chem., 25 (1953) 1351.

——, gold, graphite, platinum, PbO$_2$

[60] S. S. Lord Jr. and L. B. Rogers, Anal. Chem., 26 (1954) 284.

Theory of diffusion

[61] P. Delahay, New Instrumental Methods in Electrochemistry, Interscience, New York, 1954.

Thickness of the diffusion layer and stirring

[62] S. Glasstone and G. D. Reynolds, Trans. Faraday Soc., 28 (1932) 582.

Condenser current

[63] D. C. Grahame, Chem. Revs., 41 (1947) 44.
[64] D. C. Grahame, Z. Elektrochem., 59 (1955) 773.
[65] Centre national de la recherche scientifique, 73th Colloquium, Paris, 1957, p. 7–106.

Chapter VI

EXPERIMENTAL DETERMINATION OF THE CURRENT–POTENTIAL CURVES

The principles of the various methods used to determine the current–potential curves in the steady state are described in this chapter. This description is divided into two parts:

1. the determination, and possibly the recording, of the current and the potential of the indicator electrode, *i.e.* the study of the electrical circuit;

2. the various types of cells and electrodes which allow a steady state (or pseudo-steady state) to be reached.

I. ELECTRICAL CIRCUIT

Basic electrical circuit

The block diagram is shown in Fig. 130. The circuit consists of an electrolysis cell with two electrodes dipping into it, an adjustable source of electric current, an electronic voltmeter to measure the potential difference between the electrodes and a microammeter to measure the electrolysis current.

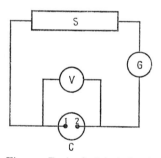

Fig. 130. Basic electrical circuit.
C = electrolysis cell, S = current source, G = microammeter, V = millivoltmeter.

The electrode at whose surface the electrochemical processes under investigation occur is called the *indicator electrode*. The other electrode has a known potential which is independent of the current passing through the electrode, and is called the *reference electrode* or comparison electrode.

The potential difference between the two electrodes, $E_A - E_C$, is thus equal to the potential of the indicator electrode plus a determined constant.

Ohmic drop

We have seen that in general the ohmic drop due to the resistance R of the cell have to be taken into account. If a current i flows through the cell, the potential difference V measured between the two electrodes is

$$V = (E_A - E_C) + |i|R$$

If R and i are both small, e.g. $R < 1000$ ohms and $i < 10$ μA, the ohmic drop is less than a millivolt and may therefore be neglected. This is often the case with the dropping mercury electrode (classical polarography).

But in general the current is more than 10 μA, and the resistance of the cell is several thousand ohms if the cell contains a junction (see page 126); so that it is necessary to correct for the ohmic drop. If R is known, the correction may be calculated for each measured value of i. Devices also exist for compensating for the ohmic drop by means of a potential difference equal to $R|i|$ and opposed to V. The measured voltage is then

$$V - |i|R = E_A - E_C$$

It is preferable, and simpler, to use a three-electrode assembly.

Three-electrode assembly

This is shown in Fig. 131. Instead of measuring the potential difference between the two electrodes used to produce the electrolysis, one measures the potential difference between the indicator electrode and a third electrode whose potential is constant and known (the reference or comparison electrode). No current passes through the auxiliary circuit, and in principle there should be no ohmic drop, the potential measured being the exact potential of the indicator electrode. In fact, however, the two circuits share part of the electrolysis cell between the electrodes, so there is also an ohmic drop in the measuring circuit. This may be made negligible, when it exists, by placing the reference electrode, or the junction joining it to the cell, as close as possible to the indicator electrode.

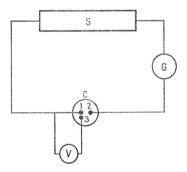

Fig. 131. Three-electrode assembly.
S = current generator, C = electrolysis cell, G = microammeter, V = millivoltmeter.

The remaining electrode, indicated by 2 in Fig. 131, may in principle be of any desired material and form.

Fixing the potential or the current

When the electrolysis is begun, there is a transition period before the steady state is reached, in which the system changes with time (see Chapter I). Measurements cannot be made in this period, and should only be made when the steady state has been reached. The experimental conditions must therefore favour the rapid attainment of the steady state.

We may distinguish two ways of carrying out the measurements:

1. Fix the electrode potential and measure the steady value of the current; or fix the electrolysis voltage V and measure the current and the potential when the steady state has been reached.

2. Alternatively, fix the current and measure the steady value of the electrode potential.

Theoretically, the current–potential curve for the steady state should be the same whatever the means used to obtain it; but in practice a given experimental method rarely allows the steady state to be reached over the whole range of the current–potential curve. This is why experimental curves vary slightly according to the method used to determine them.

Controlled potential

Simple method. The voltage difference between the two electrodes may be very simply fixed at the desire value by means of a battery or set of accumulators (4–6 V) and a rheostat, as shown in Fig. 132. The potential difference $E_A - E_C$ given by this arrangement is constant if the ohmic drop $iR = V - (E_A - E_C)$ is small. The voltage V applied between the two electrodes is independent of the electrolysis current i if i is negligible compared with the current I flowing through the rheostat. The resistance of the rheostat must therefore be fairly low (about 10–100 ohms).

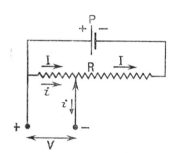

Fig. 132. Electrical circuit giving a
constant voltage.
P = battery or accumulator (4–6
V). R = rheostat.

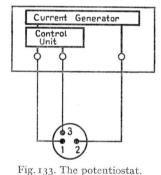

Fig. 133. The potentiostat.
1. Electrode with the stabilized potential.
2. Other electrolysis electrode.
3. Comparison electrode for the stabilization.

Potentiostat. A potentiostat is an apparatus which automatically maintains a constant potential difference between two electrodes. It consists of a d.c. current generator which feeds the electrolysis circuit, and a control system. The principle of operation of the control system is as follows: it measures the potential difference between one of the electrodes of the electrolysis circuit and a comparison electrode (three-electrode assembly), and it controls the current generator so that the measured potential difference is kept constant at a predetermined value. A block diagram of the potentiostat is shown in Fig. 133.

Either the simple method or the potentiostat may be used for the determination of the current–potential curves and for amperometric measurements (see Chapter

VIII), where the electrolysis current is usually in the range 0 to 1 mA; but the poten-tiostat is mainly used when the electrolysis current is considerably larger, sometimes up to 1 A (electrolytic separations and preparations, fixed-potential coulometry). The main types of potentiostats are described in the chapter on coulometry.

Controlled current

Simple method [12, 18]. The current may be kept practically constant by means of a generator of high constant voltage (*e.g.* 100 V), *i.e.* an H.T. battery or a stabilized power supply, and a large resistance (1–30 MΩ) in series with the electrolysis circuit (Fig. 134).

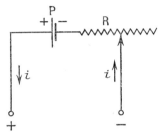

Fig. 134. Arrangement giving a constant current.
P = battery (about 100 V), R = resistance (1–30 MΩ).

Applying Ohm's law to the circuit as a whole

$$i = \frac{V + \Delta E}{R + R'}$$

where V is the voltage of the battery, ΔE is the potential difference between the electrodes, and $R + R'$ is the total resistance in the circuit. As long as V is much greater than ΔE, i will be independent of ΔE. Since the potential difference between the electrodes is usually not greater than 1 V, when $V = 100$ V the current i will be constant to within about 1 %.

Amperostat. An amperostat is a device which keeps the current constant no matter how much the potential difference between the electrodes varies. The constant value of the current chosen may be varied within certain limits.

A potentiostat may also be used as an amperostat [16].

Determination of the current–potential curves

Plotting the curves point by point

Either the applied voltage V or the potential difference $E_A - E_C$ or the current i is varied in suitable steps, and at each value of the variable the electrolysis current is measured with a microammeter, and the potential difference between the indicator electrode and the comparison electrode is measured with a millivoltmeter. By drawing a smooth curve through the experimental points we obtain the desired current–potential curve.

Some time must elapse each time the independent variable is changed before the steady state is reached. It has been found that the length of time needed varies according to which variable is chosen as the independent variable (V, E or i), and with the distance between the successive points on the curve (ΔV, ΔE, Δi). When the potential is fixed with a potentiostat, a variation of $\Delta E = 20$ to 25 mV needs an equilibrating period of 2 to 3 minutes with most solid electrodes. The steady state is often reached more quickly when the current is fixed than when the potential is fixed, but it is always reached most slowly when the voltage is fixed.

It may be stated as a general rule that it is best to control the potential if the magnitude of the limiting current is of particular interest, whilst if the form of the wave is important it is best to control the current.

The rate at which the steady state is reached also depends on the nature and form of the electrode. If the surface of the electrode changes during the determination, *e.g.* as a result of deposition or adsorption, it is difficult to obtain steady readings. The dropping mercury electrode gives the quickest results: in most cases the mean current becomes stable in a few seconds.

Finally, the length of the equilibration period also depends on the nature of the electrochemical reaction (fast or slow systems, reactions involving complexes); this period is very long for the electrolysis of water.

The determination of a potential difference

Null-point method. The potential difference ΔE to be measured is balanced by a known variable potential difference AD (Fig. 135). When the null point is reached, no current flows through the arms AE and FD of the circuit. The null point can be detected by means of the device G. This method thus requires a calibrated voltage source and a null-point detector.

Calibrated voltage source. A d.c. generator of current (battery, accumulator, stabilized power supply) is connected in series with a variable resistance R_1 across a potentiometer AC of resistance R_2. For a given current i through this circuit, the potential difference between the points A and C is $R_2 i$. The potentiometer can only be graduated in volts for a single value of the current i, so the current must always be set to this value before the apparatus is used, *i.e.* the apparatus must be calibrated.

A standard cell is used for the calibration, which gives a known voltage as long as the current flowing through it is zero. A Weston cell is generally used for this purpose; it has an emf of 1.018 V. The standard cell is placed in opposition to the potential difference $R_2 i \times$ AB/AC provided by the potentiometer, the point B being chosen to correspond to 1.018 V. The current i is now varied by means of the resistance R_1 until the null-point indicator placed between A and H shows that the two voltages are balanced. The graduations of the potentiometer now indicate the correct voltage, and the variable voltage across AD may be used to balance the potential difference ΔE to be measured. The same null-point indicator may be used for calibrating and for the measurements.

Null-point indicator. A sensitive galvanometer may be used in a laboratory apparatus. Many commercial pH-meters replace this by a 'magic eye'. The sensitivity of the null-point indicator limits the sensitivity of the apparatus. Commercial instruments have an accuracy of $\pm$ 1 mV. They generally have the basic circuit shown in Fig. 135.

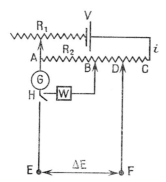

Fig. 135. Determination of the potential difference ΔE by a null-point method.
G = null-point indicator, W = Weston standard cell.

Measuring the potential by means of a high-impedance amplifier. The potential differ-ence to be measured is fed to an amplifier with a high input resistance so that a negligible current is taken from the cell, and the output of the amplifier is connected to a voltmeter, which must of course be calibrated. The potential range is of the order of 750 mV, and the origin may also be displaced so that the voltage range covers the range of potentials to be measured. Such an apparatus gives quicker readings, but less accuracy than the null-point method ($\pm$ 5 mV as against $\pm$ 1 mV). Some of these direct-reading instruments can be set to one of a series of sensitivities, but such instruments are rather cumbersome in use.

In the direct-reading instruments the Weston cell is often replaced by a glow-discharge reference tube, which gives a discharge at a well-defined voltage.

Polarographs

This is the name given to complete instruments which are used for the determina-tion of current–potential curves with a dropping mercury electrode. One simple type of manually operated polarograph works as follows.

A carriage which carries the transparent graph paper on a sheet of glass moves on two rails; the carriage is attached to the sliding contact of the rheostat which controls the voltage across the polarographic cell. The voltage is thus the abscissa. The galvanometer spot moves at right angles to the direction of motion of the car-riage (ordinate). The centre of the galvanometer spot is marked with a pencil for each value of the voltage, thus giving the current–voltage curve, or polarogram.

Recording apparatus

There are two distinct problems which must be solved:
1. How to fix the voltage, the potential difference or the current, and how to vary the chosen variable automatically.
2. How to record the current and the potential of the indicator electrode.

We will consider first the automatic variation of the electrolysis voltage. We have seen that this voltage is applied across the two electrodes by means of a source of constant voltage (4–6 V battery, accumulators, etc.) and a rheostat. The voltage across the electrodes is varied by moving the sliding contact of the rheostat. This may be done automatically by means of a synchronous motor. The variation of the voltage is then linear with respect to time. If the ohmic drop is negligible, the potential difference $E_A - E_C$ also varies linearly with time, and so does the potential of the indicator electrode if the other electrode has a constant potential. If the ohmic drop is not negligible, the potential may be made to vary linearly with respect to time by means of a potentiostat [16].

The rate of change of the voltage may be varied. The choice of the speed to be used must take into account the rate at which the steady state is reached. If the curve is to be of any significance, the steady state must have time to establish itself continuously as the voltage is varied. This means that, except in the case of the dropping mercury electrode, the voltage must be varied very slowly (0.02–0.4 V/min). The rate of change of the voltage which is used with the dropping mercury electrode would give rise to errors with most solid electrodes.

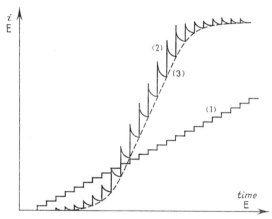

Fig. 136. Recording the current–potential curves with discontinuous automatic variation of the potential.
Curve 1: variation of the potential with respect to time.
Curve 2: variation of the current with respect to time.
Curve 3: resulting current–potential curve.

For most solid electrodes, therefore, it is best to vary the potential discontinuously. The potential is kept constant for a certain time, and is then changed rapidly by a small amount. The time between steps is chosen so that the current can reach a steady value: two or three minutes is usually enough if the variation of the potential does not exceed 25–50 mV per step. The discontinuous variation is controlled by a time-switch, which regulates the voltage source (rheostat and motor) or the potentiostat.

The current may also be varied automatically, continuously or discontinuously, in a similar way [16, 17].

Recording the measurements

This may be done in various ways, depending on the way in which the independent variable varies. When the potential varies linearly with respect to time, it is enough to record the current as a function of time with a pen recorder, with the paper moving at a constant rate. The instrument can then be calibrated to change the time scale into a potential scale.

A similar method may be used when the current varies linearly with respect to time.

If is often desirable to check that the potential in fact varies as it should, by recording both the potential and the current. Several multi-channel recorders exist which can give a simultaneous plot of the current and the potential as functions of time on a paper which moves at a constant speed. In this case there is no need to calibrate the paper speed: the current–potential curve is constructed point by point, plotting values of i against the values of E recorded at the same time. These instruments can also be used with a discontinuous variation of the potential as discussed above, if a time-switch is added. The variation of the current with time at each value of the potential may be used to check that the equilibrium value of the current is in fact obtained (Fig. 136). Such an instrument is the best to use with solid electrodes.

There is also a third type of recorder, called the XY-type, in which the displacement of the pen is proportional to the current and the distance moved by the paper is proportional to the potential difference between the electrodes. This therefore gives a direct record of the current–potential curve, however the potential or the current varies.

Recording polarographs

Recording polarographs, like manually operated polarographs, use the two-electrode system, and the applied voltage is equated with the potential difference between the reference electrode and the dropping mercury electrode. This is justified, since the current is rarely larger than 50 μA and the internal resistance of the cell is a few hundred ohms. The potential generally varies linearly with respect to time, since the dropping mercury electrode very rapidly reaches a pseudo-steady state. The current is then recorded on a paper strip moving at a constant rate. In order to prevent large oscillations due to the periodic growth of the mercury drop either a galvanometer with a long period (about 20 seconds) or a system of filter circuits is used. These have the disadvantage that the real value of the current is only indicated after rather a long time and, since the potential changes rather rapidly, the current–potential curves produced are distorted. Some instruments only measure the current during a brief period just before the fall of each drop, in order to correct this defect [22].

A large number of instruments for the automatic recording of current–potential curves are available.

II. THE ELECTROLYSIS CELLS

These consists of a vessel containing either a single solution in which all the electrodes dip or several solutions for the various electrodes joined by junctions.

The junctions

A sintered glass disc or a bridge consisting of a glass tube filled with a conducting jelly is often used as the junction (Fig. 137). The jelly may be made by pouring hot

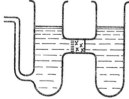

Fig. 137. Junction formed by a sintered glass disc and an agar plug.

agar into a solution of KCl or KNO_3 and allowing the mixture to cool, or by the action of an acid on a silicate, forming silica gel.

Agar bridge

This junction can only be used at room temperature: in particular heating caused by the dissipation of energy in the bridge can cause it to become fluid. The jelly is made by heating 3 g of agar powder with 100 ml of water and 30 g of a potassium salt (KCl or KNO_3) gently until a homogeneous viscous fluid is obtained; fill a bent tube (internal diameter 0.3 to 0.5 mm) with the liquid jelly by sucking and allow to cool. Make sure that there are no bubbles of air at the ends by breaking a short piece off each end after the jelly has set.

Other salts may also be used for making the agar bridge. Perchlorates prevent the jelly from setting very easily. When solvents other than water are used, different conditions must be used to obtain gelling.

It may be mentioned again that junctions cause a potential difference of a few millivolts and a resistance which is often quite large (some thousands of ohms) (see page 126).

Elimination of dissolved oxygen

Dissolved oxygen may be reduced, and its presence generally makes it difficult to study cathode phenomena. The solution is usually freed from oxygen by bubbling an inert gas (nitrogen) through it at a rate of about 50 ml/min for a sufficient length of time (10 to 30 minutes). Nitrogen pure enough for this purpose is available commercially.

III. THE ELECTRODES

The reproducibility and the significance of an experimental current–potential curve depends on the attainment of a steady diffusion state at the indicator electrode. We will describe several means of realizing this condition.

On the other hand, the form and position of the curves depends on the nature of the electrodes and the treatment which they receive. We will also give some information on this subject.

Finally, we will discuss the problem of reference electrodes.

Means used to obtain a steady state

Fixed electrodes, stirring of the solution

Solid microelectrodes (Fig. 138) have been used, together with mechanical stirring of the solution.

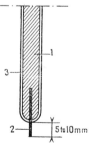

Fig. 138. Solid microelectrode.
1) Mercury. 2) Conducting wire (platinum, graphite, silver, etc.) of diameter about 1 mm. 3) Insulating tube (glass, etc.).

A stirrer driven by a synchronous motor ($>$ 600 revs/min) may be used, or some-times more simply a magnetic stirrer. Parasitic movements such as vibrations of the stirrer must be avoided as much as possible. It is often necessary to maintain the solution at a constant temperature in order to avoid thermal convection.

Fixed mercury electrodes (hanging drop, and mercury pool of area from 0.05 to 3 cm²)
     These electrodes have also been used in a stirred solution (Fig. 139 to 142).

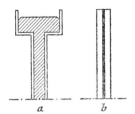

Fig. 139. Stationary mercury electrodes.
a) Mercury pool (about 3 cm²).
b) Microelectrode (about 1 mm²).

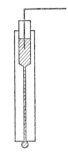

Fig. 141. Hanging mercury drop electrode
(after KEMULA and KUBLIK).

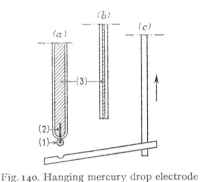

Fig. 140. Hanging mercury drop electrode
(after BERZINS and DELAHAY).
1) Mercury drop, 2) platinum wire, 3) mercury, a) hanging mercury drop electrode,
b) mercury dropper, c) teflon arm.
The mercury drops are formed by b), and
one is collected in the little cup at the end
of c), and transferred from there to the end
of the platinum wire of a).

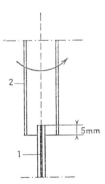

Fig. 142. Fixed mercury electrode
(after ARTHUR et al.,[47]).
1) Fixed mercury microelectrode (diameter 1.72 mm).
2) Coaxial glass tube, 7 mm in diameter
and rotating at 600 revs/min.

A very stable and efficient method of stirring is to rotate a tube coaxial with the electrode (Fig. 142).
     These fixed mercury electrodes have the advantage of giving very low residual currents and rarely giving maxima.

Various other electrodes
     MÜLLER has designed a by-passed electrode, in which the solution under inves-tigation flows through a tube containing a platinum wire. This electrode is used for biological studies (blood) and for measuring the concentration of flowing liquids.

LYALIKOV and KARMAZIN have designed a bubble electrode in which the solution near the electrode is renewed by bubbling gas. NIKELLY and COOKE also used bubbling nitrogen to stir the solution near a mercury electrode.

Moving electrodes

Better results have been obtained when the electrodes rather than the solution move.

The rotating solid electrode (Fig. 143) is rotated at a constant rate. The reproducibility and sensitivity are best when the rate of rotation is about 600 revs/min, and are then slightly better than those obtained by stirring the solution. The limiting current depends on a fractional power of the rate of rotation, and tends to a limit at high values of the rotation rate. It also depends on the diffusion constant D_0 of the electrolyzed substance: $i_1 = kD_0{}^a$, where a varies from 1 to $\frac{2}{3}$ as the rate of rotation of the electrode increases.

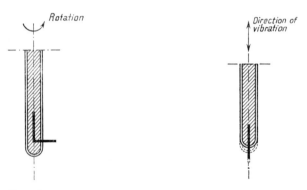

Fig. 143. Rotating solid electrode.   Fig. 144. Vibrating solid electrode.

The vibrating solid electrode (Fig. 144) consists of a conducting wire (*e.g.* platinum) vibrating in the longitudinal direction at a frequency of 50 to 100 c/s and with an amplitude of about 0.5 to 1 mm. Under these conditions the limiting current is practically independent of the actual values of the amplitude and the frequency.

This electrode is very simple, and is suitable for use with small volumes of solution and electrodes with a small surface. If the surface area of the electrode is large, it is easier to stir the solution or to rotate the electrode.

Various other electrodes. A mercury electrode can also be rotated. LEE's rotating mercury electrode (Fig. 145) consists of an annular vessel containing 0.1 ml of mercury, which is rotated at 200–1800 revs/min. The mercury is kept in place by the centrifugal force, and the rapid movement causes the solution to be continuously renewed at the surface of the electrode.

Steady currents are observed if the substances produced in the electrochemical reaction are soluble; but if the electrolysis produces an amalgam on the surface of the mercury, the electrolytic current at constant potential decreases with time.

This can only be prevented by renewing the mercury surface, and various ways of doing this (whilst still maintaining a steady state) have been suggested. The best known of these is the streaming mercury electrode proposed by HEYROVSKY (Fig. 146).

This gives a column of mercury with a constant surface area, and a surface which is continually renewed; but it has the disadvantage that it uses a lot of mercury.

The use of a rotating hanging mercury drop electrode has recently been suggested. A hanging mercury drop electrode is set in rapid rotation (Fig. 147). The drop remains on the platinum wire up to speeds of 750 revs/min.

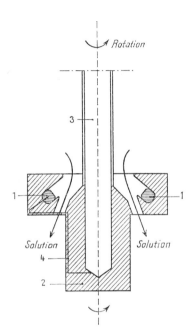

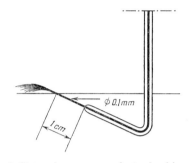

Fig. 146. Streaming mercury electrode, (simplified).

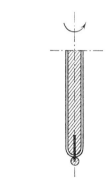

Fig. 145. Rotating mercury electrode
(after LEE).

1) Ring of mercury,
2) insulating material,
3) metal rod (steel),
4) platinum contact wire.

Fig. 147. Rotating hanging mercury drop electrode
(after BARENDRECHT).

This electrode has the advantage of great sensitivity (large diffusion currents and small residual currents); according to BARENDRECHT, it can be used to determine concentrations down to 10^{-7} M.

'*Convection*' *electrode*. Transport by convection is generally much faster than the transport by diffusion in the diffusion layer, so the current is finally limited by diffusion. If however the diffusion layer can be made very thin, transport by diffusion becomes so rapid that the reacting substances are carried to the electrode surface as soon as they reach the diffusion layer by convection. The current is then limited by the convection. If τ microlitres of solution per square centimeter area of the electrode and per second are carried by convection, the limiting current is of the form

$$i_{conv} = n\mathrm{F}A\tau c_s = k_c c_s$$

These conditions have been realized with the aid of a rotating platinum microelectrode (600–900 revs/min) in a solution stirred by a concentric four-blade stirrer rotating at the same speed, or by means of a mercury microelectrode in a solution stirred at 900–1200 revs/min. The limiting currents are independent of the diffusion coefficients. In both cases, τ is of the order of 18–19 cm/sec.

Dropping mercury electrode. Pseudo-steady state

This electrode is the one most frequently used in unstirred solutions. It has several large advantages over other types of electrodes:

The mercury surface is continuously renewed, so that there is no risk of its being contaminated, especially by substances which might be precipitated thereon.

The electrode area is very well defined and can be determined with precision.

It has one advantage in common with all mercury electrodes: the overvoltage for the reduction of H^+ and H_2O is very high. On the other hand they are all severely limited on the anodic side by the easy oxidation of mercury.

It gives the most reproducible results.

The dropping mercury electrode consists of a capillary tube of 0.03–0.05 mm internal diameter through which mercury flows into the solution as small spherical droplets which are detached from the capillary at regular intervals. The flow is assured by a column of mercury whose height is adjusted so that the formation time of a single drop ('drop time') is between 2 and 6 seconds.

The actual electrode is the drop which is in the process of formation. Its surface area varies continuously during the electrolysis. If all stirring were absent, the electrolyzed substances would be brought to the surface of the electrode by diffusion

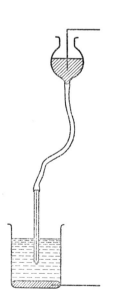

Fig. 148. Dropping mercury electrode.

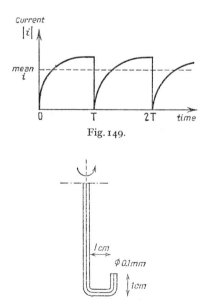

Fig. 149.

Fig. 150. Rotating dropping mercury electrode (after STRICKS and KOLTHOFF).

only; but the periodic growth of the drops has two effects which compensate for the gradual decrease of the current due to the decrease of the rate of pure diffusion:

i) the surface area of the electrode increases steadily during the period of formation of the drop, so with a constant current density the current increases in proportion to the area;

ii) the electrode surface moves through the solution as the drop grows, thus causing stirring around the diffusion layer. As the electrolysis proceeds the electrode comes into contact with new liquid layers which have not yet been much effected by the electrolysis.

At a constant potential, therefore, the absolute value of the current increases during the formation period of the drop. The 'mean' current is found to be constant and very stable, and is given to a first approximation by the Ilkovic equation

$$i = 607 \, nm^{2/3} \, T^{1/6} \, D_0^{1/2} \, c_s \qquad [\mu A]$$

where n = number of electrons exchanged, m = flow rate of mercury [mg/sec], T = drop time [sec], D_0 = diffusion constant [cm²/sec] and c_s = concentration of electrolyzed substance [millimoles/litre].

All parasitic movements capable of disturbing the diffusion must be eliminated; means of doing this have been devised.

Other electrodes

The vibrating dropping mercury electrode. This is a dropping mercury electrode in which the capillary vibrates with an amplitude of 0.5 mm and a frequency of 50–100 c/s, so that the drops are very small and are formed very quickly. This eliminates the variation of the current with time, and also has the advantage of stirring the solution slightly without affecting the mean current.

The rotating dropping mercury electrode (Fig. 150). This electrode was developed for the same purpose, and also to increase the sensitivity of the dropping mercury electrode. It consists of a bent capillary tube rotating at 200–300 revs/min. The bore of the capillary is larger than in the normal dropping mercury electrode, in order to keep the drop time of the same order of magnitude. The drops are therefore 3 to 4 times larger. The optimum rate of rotation corresponds to the maximum number of revolutions during the period of formation of a single drop (about 17). The increase in the mean area of the drops and the rotation increase the sensitivity appreciably.

Condenser residual current at the dropping mercury electrode

We have seen above that the electrode-solution interface acts as a condenser, giving rise to a discharge current when the electrical circuit is closed. This condenser current falls off very quickly when the electrode surface remains constant during electrolysis.

With a dropping mercury electrode, on the other hand, the electrode surface is renewed every 3 to 6 seconds. Each new drop takes up a new charge and one amount of electricity flows at the moment when short circuit is made. Consequently, a continuous current flows. The 'mean' condenser residual current is then no longer negligible, and in polarography this makes up a large part of the total residual current.

This current varies more or less linearly with the potential, since the capacitance of the double layer is approximately constant.

The large condenser residual current and the small mean surface area of the drops are the reasons why the dropping mercury electrode is not very sensitive.

With the *rotating dropping mercury electrode*, however, $k_D = i_e/c$ is 12 to 15 times larger than for the dropping mercury electrode, while the residual current is not made much larger (the capacitive residual current remains practically constant). The sensitivity is thus increased about 10 times. The surface area of the *rotating mercury electrode* is about 50 times bigger than that of the dropping mercury electrode, and here again the residual current is not increased appreciably. The sensitivity is therefore about 200 times that of the dropping mercury electrode.

Polarographic maxima

The current–potential curves obtained with the dropping mercury electrode often show anomalies called 'polarographic maxima' (see Fig. 151). Much work has been done in an attempt to find the reason for these; it may be that while the diffusion current is due to transport of the electroactive substances at right angles to the mercury–solution interface (spherical diffusion), the maxima are caused by movements tangential to the surface of the drop.

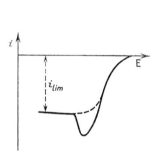

Fig. 151.
Polarographic 'maximum'.

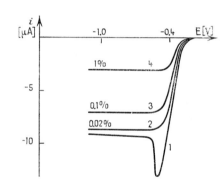

Fig. 152. Reduction curves at a dropping mercury electrode. 10^{-3} M Pb(NO$_3$)$_2$ + 0.1 M KCl.
Curve 1: without gelatin.
Curves 2, 3, 4: 0.02, 0.1 and 1 % gelatin.
(after KOLTHOFF and LINGANE).

These maxima can generally be suppressed by the addition of very small quantities of substances which are adsorbed on to the surface of the electrode (gelatin, albumin, methyl cellulose, naphthols, thymol, dyestuffs like methyl red, fuchsin, etc.). Too large a concentration of the suppressor lowers the limiting current (see Fig. 152). 0.01 % of gelatin is usually enough to suppress the maximum without having too much effect on the size of the limiting current.

TABLE I

MEAN SURFACE AREAS AND THICKNESSES OF THE DIFFUSION LAYER δ_0 FOR SOME ELECTRODES

Electrode	Area [cm²]	δ_0 [μ]
Rotating platinum electrode (600 revs/min)	0.2	3
Fixed platinum electrode in a solution stirred at 600 revs/min	0.2	250–500
Dropping mercury electrode	0.02	40–60
Rotating dropping mercury electrode	0.08	10–15
Rotating mercury electrode (1000 revs/min)	1.0	10

Preparation and treatment of the electrodes

Mercury electrode

Only the mercury electrode has the advantage of giving a perfectly well-defined and easily renewed surface. Clean distilled mercury must be used.

Mercury amalgams may be used in the same way.

The bright platinum electrode

The bright platinum electrode is the most important of the various solid microelectrodes which have been proposed.

Great care must be taken to keep the surface of this electrode clean: it becomes covered with a platinum oxide film under oxidizing conditions, and with a film of hydrogen under very reducing conditions, and can also adsorb other substances. The best way to prepare the surface for potentiometry is to rub it with fine emery paper and rinse with distilled water; this has a slight effect on the geometric surface. Chemical or electrochemical cleaning methods may also be used, such as oxidizing with $14\ N\ HNO_3$, reducing with $SnCl_2$ in $6\ N\ HCl$, or oxidation under controlled conditions of potential or current.

Platinum is oxidized in acidic medium at potentials above 1 V. Under more oxidizing conditions, therefore, one has in effect a platinum oxide electrode, and it is best to give the electrode an oxidizing treatment before using it. The oxide film is not redissolved until the potential falls below 0.6 V, so a reducing treatment is the best preparation for working at potentials below 1 V.

The hydrogen which is adsorbed under very reducing conditions may prove troublesome, and should be removed by oxidation.

The platinized platinum electrode

This is obtained by platinum-plating a smooth platinum electrode, using a smooth platinum anode (a platinum crucible will do very well).

The plating bath is made up of 1 g of platinum tetrachloride and 8 mg of lead acetate in 30 ml of water, and the plating is carried out with a current density of 0.06 A/cm² for 5 minutes. It is best to renew the surface before every determination. The old deposit of platinum black is removed by treatment with hot dilute aqua regia, and then the electrode is cleaned in hot chromic acid.

The platinized platinum electrode presents the same difficulties as the polished platinum electrode, and is even more sensitive to adsorption phenomena. When the platinum plating is carried out under very well defined conditions, a very reproducible surface is obtained.

Graphite electrode

The graphite electrode may be prepared like the platinum electrode, by sealing the graphite into a glass tube. The seal is fragile: wax or varnish may be used to prevent leaks. Graphite electrodes are very porous and easily poisoned by adsorption.

Alternatively, a long graphite rod (a spectrographic electrode is suitable) is dipped into an inert varnish, and the end is broken off. The electrode with the freshly broken end may then be used to determine a curve. In order to renew the surface for a new determination, a few millimetres are filed off the end. Under these conditions the surface area of the electrode varies by about 5 %.

Silver electrode

A silver wire is welded into a glass tube, and partially covered by an inert varnish. The surface is renewed by polishing or by means of nitric acid. Electrochemical silver plating of a platinum electrode gives a more reproducible surface area.

Lead dioxide electrode

A platinum electrode is covered with a film of PbO_2 by anodic oxidation of a solution of a lead salt.

Reference electrodes and comparison electrodes

A reference electrode is an electrode whose potential changes very little and is known to within 1 mV or 0.1 mV. Such precision in only obtained if great care is taken. The current passing through the electrode must be very small. Such electrodes are described in the standard text-books on the subject; the best known are the calomel, silver chloride, and hydrogen electrodes.

Such accuracy is not needed in practice for the study of electrochemical reactions; it is enough if the electrode potential does not vary more than 5–10 mV during the whole determination, though the reference electrode may be expected to pass an appreciable current. We will call such electrodes 'comparison electrodes'.

The electrode reaction at the surface of such electrodes should be fast and not limited by diffusion (concentrated solution or sparingly soluble reactant). It is also desirable that the surface area should be large compared to that of the indicator electrode.

The most widely used comparison electrodes are based on the same electrochemical systems as the reference electrodes: calomel, mercurous sulphate, silver chloride, etc. But, in principle, any electrode at whose surface a fast electrochemical reaction may take place may be used. For example, a platinum wire dipping into a fairly concentrated iodine–iodide solution and joined to the cell by a junction gives an electrode whose potential is constant.

It has been suggested that a glass electrode should be used as a comparison electrode in solutions of constant pH. The glass electrode circuit must not draw any current because of the high resistance of the glass wall (1 to 100 $M\Omega$).

Calomel electrode

This consists of mercury in contact with mercurous chloride and a potassium chloride solution of constant concentration. The electrode reaction is

$$2\,Hg\downarrow + 2\,Cl^- - 2e \rightleftharpoons Hg_2Cl_2\downarrow$$

The equilibrium potential is

$$E_{eq} = E_0 - 0.058 \log |Cl^-|$$

and depends on the activity of chloride in the solution. Two main types of calomel electrode are used: the 'saturated' calomel electrode, in which a saturated solution of potassium chloride is used, and the 'normal' calomel electrode in which the electrolyte is a normal solution of potassium chloride.

Preparation. Grind some calomel powder with mercury in a mortar, moistening with a little potassium chloride solution. Put some mercury at the bottom of a small tube, place the calomel–mercury paste on top of it, and fill up with normal or saturated potassium chloride solution. The electrical contact is made by means of a platinum wire dipping into the mercury. The calomel electrode must be joined to the electrolysis cell by a liquid junction.

It may be mentioned that in polarography this is often simply replaced by a mercury anode of large surface (a pool of mercury at the bottom of the cell) in the presence of chloride in the solution. The oxidation of the mercury at this electrode automatically saturates the solution with calomel near the electrode.

Silver–silver chloride electrode

This consists of a silver wire dipping into a solution of a chloride; the solution is automatically saturated with silver chloride near the electrode (for very precise work the electrode may be electrolytically covered with silver chloride).

The electrode reaction is

$$Ag\downarrow + Cl^- - e \rightleftharpoons AgCl\downarrow$$

and the potential is

$$E = E_0 - 0.058 \log |Cl^-|$$

The potential is thus constant if the activity of chloride is constant.

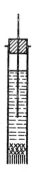

Fig. 153. Comparison electrode.
The solutions are separated by an agar plug on a sintered glass disc.

The silver wire may be dipped directly into the solution under investigation, if this contains chloride at a constant activity. If not, and in particular when the presence of chloride is undesirable, it should be connected to the cell by a junction.

TABLE II

POTENTIAL OF COMPARISON ELECTRODES WITH RESPECT TO THE NORMAL
HYDROGEN ELECTRODE

Electrodes	*Temperature*	
	25° C	*20° C*
Saturated calomel electrode	+ 0.24 V	+ 0.25 V
Normal calomel electrode	+ 0.28 V	+ 0.28 V
Hg, Hg_2SO_4, saturated K_2SO_4	+ 0.65 V	–
Hg, HgO, N NaOH	+ 0.14 V	–
Ag, AgCl, M KCl	+ 0.22 V	+ 0.22 V

REFERENCES

General books

[1] E. MÜLLER, *Elektrometrische Massanalyse*, Steinkopf, Dresden, 1942, 9th ed., p. 90.
[2] O. H. MÜLLER, *The Polarographic Method of Analysis*, Mack, Easton, 1946, 2nd ed., p. 26.
[3] J. HEYROVSKY, *Polarographisches Praktikum*, Göttingen, 1948, p. 23.
[4] I. M. KOLTHOFF and J. J. LINGANE, *Polarography*, Interscience, New York, 1952, 2nd ed., p. 297.
[5] P. DELAHAY, *New Instrumental Methods in Electrochemistry*, Interscience, New York, 1954, p. 369.
[6] L. MEITES, *Polarographic Techniques*, Interscience, New York, 1955, p. 7.
[7] C. R. N. STROUTS, J. H. GILFILLAN and H. N. WILSON, *Analytical Chemistry*, Clarendon Press, Oxford, 1955, vol. II, p. 561.
[8] M. QUINTIN, *Techniques électrochimiques appliquées à l'étude des solutions*, Centre de Documentation Universitaire, Paris, 1955, p. 182.
[9] E. C. POTTER, *Electrochemistry*, Cleaver-Hume, London, 1956, p. 203.
[10] G. W. C. MILNER, *Polarography*, Longmans-Green, London, 1957, p. 83.
[11] J. J. LINGANE, *Electroanalytical Chemistry*, Interscience, New York, 1958, 2nd ed., p. 31–241.

Description of circuits

[12] R. N. ADAMS, C. N. REILLEY and N. H. FURMAN, *Anal. Chem.*, 25 (1953) 1161.
[13] P. ARTHUR, P. A. LEWIS and N. A. LLOYD, *Anal. Chem.*, 26 (1954) 1853.
[14] M. M. NICHOLSON, *Anal. Chem.*, 27 (1955) 1364.
[15] W. JACKSON JR. and P. J. ELVING, *Anal. Chem.*, 28 (1956) 378.
[16] J. BADOZ–LAMBLING, *Anal. Chim. Acta*, 16 (1957) 285.
[17] R. N. ADAMS and J. D. VOORHIES, *Anal. Chem.*, 29 (1957) 1690.
[18] M. ISHIBASHI and T. FUJINAGA, *Anal. Chim. Acta*, 18 (1958) 112.
[19] D. T. SAWYER, R. L. PECSOK and K. K. JENSEN, *Anal. Chem.*, 30 (1958) 481.
[20] S. OKA, *Anal. Chem.*, 30 (1958) 1635.
[21] E. LEWARTOWICZ, *9th meeting of the C.I.T.C.E., Paris, 1957*, Butterworths, London, 1959.
[22] E. LEWARTOWICZ, *Polarographische Berichte*, 5 (1957) 2.
[23] T. TAKAHASKI and E. NIKI, *Talanta*, 1 (1958) 177.

Rate at which the steady state is established

[24] D. B. JULIAN and W. R. RUBY, *J. Am. Chem. Soc.*, 72 (1950) 4719.
[25] J. WEBER, *Chem. listy*, 52 (1958) 1249.
[26] J. KUTA and I. SMOLER, *Chem. listy*, 52 (1958) 1259.

Electrolytic cells

[27] R. G. BATES, *Electrometric pH determinations*, Wiley, New York, 1954, p. 40.

Silica gel

[28] W. N. CARSON JR., *Anal. Chem.*, 25 (1953) 467.

Cellophane

[29] L. Serak, *Collection Czechoslov. Chem. Communs.*, 18 (1953) 439.

Elimination of dissolved oxygen

[30] H. A. Laitinen and L. W. Burdett, *Anal. Chem.*, 22 (1950) 833.
[31] L. Meites and T. Meites, *Anal. Chem.*, 23 (1951) 1194.
[32] K. Koyama and C. E. Michelson, *Anal. Chem.*, 29 (1957) 115.

Solid microelectrodes

[33] I. M. Kolthoff and J. J. Lingane, *Polarography*, Interscience, New York, 1952.

—, *amalgamated platinum*

[34] T. L. Marple and L. B. Rogers, *Anal. Chem.*, 25 (1953) 1351.
[35] K. W. Gardiner and L. W. Rogers, *Anal. Chem.*, 25 (1953) 1393.

—, *platinum – gold – copper*

[36] S. S. Lord and L. B. Rogers, *Anal. Chem.*, 26 (1952) 284.

—, *gold*

[37] F. Baumann and I. Shain, *Anal. Chem.*, 29 (1953) 303.

—, *platinized platinum*

[38] J. Coupez, *Anal. Chim. Acta*, 16 (1957) 582.
[39] R. Rosset and B. Trémillon, *Bull. soc. chim.*, 135 (1959) 139.

—, *graphite*

[40] V. F. Gaylor, A. L. Conrad and J. H. Landerl, *Anal. Chem.*, 29 (1957) 224.

—, *hanging mercury drop*

[41] H. Gerischer, *Z. physik. Chem.*, 202 (1953) 302.
[42] T. Berzins and P. Delahay, *J. Am. Chem. Soc.*, 77 (1955) 6448.
[43] W. Kemula and Z. Kublik, *Roczniki Chem.*, 30 (1956) 1005.
[44] W. Kemula and Z. Kublik, *Anal. Chim. Acta*, 18 (1958) 104.
[45] G. W. Smith and V. Stark, *J. Phys. Chem.*, 62 (1958) 195.
[46] W. Kemula, Z. Galus and Z. Kublik, *Nature*, 182 (1958) 1228.

Mercury pool

[47] P. Arthur, J. C. Komyathy, R. Y. Maness, and H. W. Vaughn, *Anal. Chem.*, 27 (1955) 895.
[48] D. J. Rosie and W. D. Cooke, *Anal. Chem.*, 27 (1955) 1360.
[49] J. W. Ross, R. D. de Mars and I. Shain, *Anal. Chem.*, 28 (1956) 1768.
[50] P. V. Peurifoy and W. G. Schrenk, *Anal. Chem.*, 29 (1957) 410.

Other electrodes

[51] O. H. Müller, *J. Am. Chem. Soc.*, 69 (1957) 2992.
[52] Y. S. Lyalikov and V. I. Karmazin, *Zavodskaya Lab.*, 14 (1948) 138, 144.
[53] Y. S. Lyalikov and R. I. Glazer, *Zavodskaya Lab.*, 15 (1949) 909.
[54] S. N. Flengas, *J. Chem. Soc.*, (1956) 534.
[55] J. G. Nikelly and W. D. Cooke, *Anal. Chem.*, 28 (1956) 243.
[56] J. G. Nikelly and W. D. Cooke, *Proc. XVth Intern. Congr. Pure and Appl. Chem.*, Lisbon, 1956, Vol. I, p. 839.

Rotating solid electrodes

[57] W. Stoll and H. Berback, *Monatsh. Chem.*, 84 (1953) 1179.
[58] J. W. Sargent, A. F. Clifford and W. R. Lemmon, *Anal. Chem.*, 25 (1953) 1727.
[59] E. R. Nightingale Jr., *Anal. Chim. Acta*, 16 (1957) 493.

—, *platinum*

[60] W. Nernst and E. S. Merriam, *Z. phys. Chem.*, 52 (1905) 235.
[61] H. A. Laitinen and I. M. Kolthoff, *J. Phys. Chem.*, 45 (1941) 1079.
[62] J. T. Stock, *Metallurgia*, 36 (1947) 51.
[63] T. Kambara, T. Tsukamoto and I. Tachi, *J. Electrochem. Soc. Japan*, 18 (1950) 356, 386.
[64] J. M. Kolthoff and D. L. Leussing, *Z. anorg. Chem.*, 262 (1950) 160.
[65] I. M. Kolthoff and J. Jordan, *J. Am. Chem. Soc.*, 74 (1952) 382.
[66] I. M. Kolthoff, J. Jordan and A. Heyndrick, *Anal. Chem.*, 25 (1953) 884.
[67] K. W. Gardiner and L. B. Rogers, *Anal. Chem.*, 25 (1953) 1393.
[68] I. Shain and A. L. Crittenden, *Anal. Chem.*, 26 (1954) 281.
[69] I. Bozsai, *Magyar Kém. Folyóirat*, 61 (1955) 305.

[70] J. K. JOHANNESSON, *Chem. Ind.*, (1956) 1141.
[71] M. MALINEK and B. REHAK, *Z. anal. Chem.*, 150 (1956) 329.
[72] I. M. KOLTHOFF and E. R. NIGHTINGALE JR., *Anal. Chim. Acta*, 17 (1957) 329.
[73] J. HASHIMOTO, *J. Chem. Soc. Japan*, 78 (1957) 1729.
[74] M. B. BARDIN and Y. S. LYALIKOV, *Zhur. Anal. Khim. S.S.S.R.*, 12 (1958) 405.
[75] J. HASHIMOTO, *J. Chem. Soc. Japan*, 79 (1958) 583.

—, *gold*

[76] F. BAUMANN and I. SHAIN, *Anal. Chem.*, 29 (1957) 303.
[77] H. KHALIFA and A. M. DAESS, *Z. anal. Chem.*, 159 (1958) 272.

—, *aluminium*

[78] J. K. JOHANNESSON, *Chem. Ind.*, (1957) 480.

—, *silver amalgam*

[79] W. D. COOKE, *Anal. Chem.*, 25 (1953) 215.

Vibrating solid electrodes

—, *platinum*

[80] E. D. HARRIS and A. J. LINDSEY, *Nature*, 162 (1948) 413.
[81] S. ROSENBERG, J. C. PERRONE and P. L. KIRK, *Anal. Chem.*, 22 (1950) 1186.
[82] E. D. HARRIS, *Analyst*, 76 (1951) 647, 650.
[83] A. J. LINDSEY, *J. Phys. Chem.*, 56 (1952) 439.
[84] E. R. ROBERTS and J. S. MEEK, *Analyst*, 77 (1952) 43.
[85] I. P. ALIMARIN and Z. A. GALLAĬ, *Zavodskaya Lab.*, 21 (1955) 244.
[86] A. J. LINDSEY, *Anal. Chim. Acta*, 13 (1955) 200.
[87] L. JENSOVSKY, *Chem. listy*, 50 (1956) 1313.
[88] Z. ZAGORSKI and S. OLSZANSKI, *Proc. Polarog. Conf.*, Warsaw, 1956, p. 253.

—, *graphite*

[89] J. C. MARONI, E. AUTHIER-CABIBEL and B. TREMILLON, *Bull. soc. chim.*, (1959) 127.

Rotating mercury electrode

[90] T. S. LEE, *J. Am. Chem. Soc.*, 74 (1952) 5001.

Streaming mercury electrode

[91] J. HEYROVSKY and J. FOREJT, *Z. phys. Chem.*, 193 (1943) 77.
[92] A. RIUS, J. LLOPIS and S. POLO, *Anales fis. y quim. (Madrid)*, 43 (1947) 1074.
[93] A. RIUS, *Principles and applications of the streaming mercury electrode*, Bermejo, Madrid, 1949 (in Spanish).
[94] P. LÉVÊQUE, *J. Chim. phys.*, 49 (1952) 269.
[95] A. RIUS, J. LLOPIS and A. SANCHEZ-ROBLES, *Proc. 7th C.I.T.C.E. Congr., Lindau 1956*, Butterworths, London, 1957.

Rotating hanging mercury drop

[96] E. BARENDRECHT, *Nature*, 181 (1958) 764.

Other electrodes in which the mercury surface is renewed

[97] H. CORIOU, J. GUÉRON, H. HÉRING and P. LÉVÊQUE, *J. Chim. phys.*, 48 (1951) 55.
[98] M. P. SIMONNIN and M. QUINTIN, *Compt. rend.*, 237 (1953) 1409.
[99] M. P. SIMONNIN and M. QUINTIN, *Compt. rend.*, 238 (1954) 892.
[100] V. S. GRIFFITHS and W. J. PARKER, *Anal. Chim. Acta*, 14 (1956) 194.

Convection electrode

[101] I. M. KOLTHOFF and J. JORDAN, *J. Am. Chem. Soc.*, 75 (1953) 4869.

Pseudo-steady state

See the section on classical polarography in Chapter VIII.

Vibrating dropping mercury electrode

[102] D. A. BERMAN, P. R. SAUNDERS and R. J. WINZLER, *Anal. Chem.*, 23 (1951) 1040.
[103] I. M. KOLTHOFF, Y. OKINAKA and T. FUJINAGA, *Anal. Chim. Acta*, 18 (1958) 295.

Rotating dropping mercury electrode

[104] W. STRICKS and I. M. KOLTHOFF, *J. Am. Chem. Soc.*, 78 (1956) 1085.
[105] N. TANAKA, *J. Japan Chem.*, 10 (1956) 814.
[106] Y. OKINAKA and I. M. KOLTHOFF, *J. Am. Chem. Soc.*, 79 (1957) 3326.
[107] I. M. KOLTHOFF and Y. OKINAKA, *Anal. Chim. Acta*, 18 (1958) 83.

[108] N. TANAKA, T. KOIZUMI, T. MURAYAMA, N. KODAMA and Y. SAKUMA, *Anal. Chim. Acta*, 18 (1958) 97.

Polarographic maxima
[109] A. N. FRUMKIN and B. LEVICH, *J. Phys. Chem. U.S.S.R.*, 21 (1947) 1183.
[110] T. A. KRJUKOVA, *J. Phys. Chem. U.S.S.R.*, 21 (1947) 365.
[111] G. F. SMITH, *Chem. Ind. (London)*, (1949) 619.
[112] H. S. CAMPBELL, *Trans. Faraday Soc.*, 50 (1954) 1351.
[113] M. DILLINGER, *Chem. zvesti*, 11 (1957) 693.
[114] M. VON STACKELBERG, *Rev. polarog.*, 5 (1957) 132.

Dropping amalgam electrodes
[115] J. J. LINGANE, *J. Am. Chem. Soc.*, 61 (1939) 976.
[116] J. HEYROVSKY and M. KALOUSEK, *Collection Czechoslov. Chem. Communs*, 11 (1939) 464.
[117] M. VON STACKELBERG and M. VON FREYHOLD, *Z. Elektrochem.*, 46 (1940) 120.
[118] N. H. FURMAN and W. C. COOPER, *J. Am. Chem. Soc.*, 72 (1950) 5667.

Electrode films

—, *platinum*
[119] I. M. KOLTHOFF and N. TANAKA, *Anal. Chem.*, 26 (1954) 632.
[120] J. W. ROSS and I. SHAIN, *Anal. Chem.*, 28 (1956) 548.
[121] G. A. HARLOW, C. M. NOBLE and G. E. A. WYLD, *Anal. Chem.*, 28 (1956) 784.
[122] F. ANSON and J. J. LINGANE, *J. Am. Chem. Soc.*, 79 (1957) 4961.
[123] J. J. LINGANE, C. H. LANGFORD and F. C. ANSON, *Anal. Chim. Acta*, 16 (1957) 165.

—, *platinum – gold*
[124] F. BAUMANN and I. SHAIN, *Anal. Chem.*, 29 (1957) 303.

—, *platinum – gold – palladium*
[125] J. K. LEE, R. N. ADAMS and C. E. BRICKER, *Anal. Chim. Acta*, 17 (1957) 321.

Pretreatment
[126] L. B. ROGERS, *Anal. Chem.*, 21 (1949) 777.
[127] I. M. KOLTHOFF and J. F. COETZEE, *J. Am. Chem. Soc.*, 79 (1957) 1852.

—, *gold – graphite – platinum*
[128] S. S. LORD Jr. and L. B. ROGERS, *Anal. Chem.*, 26 (1954) 284.

—, *graphite*
[129] V. F. GAYLOR and P. J. ELVING, *Anal. Chem.*, 25 (1953) 1078.

—, *pretreatment by alternating current*
[130] M. M. NICHOLSON, *J. Am. Chem. Soc.*, 76 (1954) 2539.
[131] H. V. DRUSHEL and J. F. MILLER, *Anal. Chim, Acta*, 15 (1956) 389.

Reference electrodes

Descriptions of reference electrodes may be found in the following works.
[132] S. GLASSTONE, *Introduction to Electrochemistry*, Van Nostrand, New York, 1947.
[133] E. C. POTTER, *Electrochemistry*, Cleaver-Hume, London, 1956.
[134] J. J. LINGANE, *Electroanalytical Chemistry*, Interscience, New York, 2nd ed., 1958.
[135] R. G. BATES, *Electrometric pH determinations*, Wiley, New York, 1954.

Chapter VII

POTENTIOMETRY

As the name indicates, this method is concerned with the measurement of potentials.

1. The determination of the equilibrium potential of a system gives a measure of its oxidizing or reducing power. This can be used in dealing with chemical redox reactions and fast electrochemical reactions. A list of the most important standard oxidation potentials is given at the end of the book. In the first part of this chapter we will discuss the significance of the potentials assumed by the electrodes.

2. The potential of an electrode through which a current i is passing (where i may be zero) is a function of the concentration of the substance or substances undergoing electrolysis. Measurements of the electrode potential therefore allow the concentration of a substance to be found, or the variation of this concentration to be followed during the course of a chemical reaction. This may be used to follow a reaction under industrial conditions, or to determine the end point of a titration. The latter case represents the most important application of potentiometry, and may be used for two purposes:

(a) for analysis. When the reaction is known, a potentiometric titration allows unknown concentrations to be determined by the additions of known quantities of solutions of known concentration. The added reactant may also be prepared by coulometry. The principles of potentiometric titration are dealt with in the second part of this chapter. Details of the very numerous applications may be found in a text-book of analytical chemistry.

(b) On the other hand, potentiometry may be used to determine the unknown reaction coefficients of reactions between substances present in known concentrations; the values of they potential may also be used to calculate the equilibrium constant of the reaction. Further details of this aspect may be found in general text-books.

3. Membrane potentials (in particular the potential of the glass electrode) will not be discussed here, since they do not involve the exchange of electrons between a metallic electrode and a solution (*i.e.* an electrochemical reaction).

In this chapter we will consider potentiometry under stationary conditions, where for a given current and a given concentration the potential does not vary with time. The determination of potentials in non-stationary states is treated in Chapter XII. The relation in the steady state between the current through an electrode (which may be zero), the electrode potential, and the concentration of the electroactive substances has already been discussed in preceding chapters.

In the first part of this chapter we will discuss the significance of the measurement of E, where the other variables (i and c) are fixed, and in the second part, we will discuss the curves of potential versus concentration, at a constant (perhaps zero) current which are used in potentiometric titrations.

The electrode which gives information about the concentration or nature of substances capable of exchanging electrons by means of its potential is called the *indicator electrode*. Some electrodes assume a potential which is independent of the composition of the solution. They are used as reference electrodes or comparison electrodes.

We will distinguish two cases: 1) the electrode is not attacked by the solution (inert or indifferent), *i.e.* it does not take part in any chemical or electrochemical reaction under the experimental conditions; 2) the electrode is attacked. It may be oxidized (generally metal electrodes) or reduced (oxide or salt) during the experiment.

We will first examine the case where the operating current is zero (classical potentiometry).

Inert electrodes

The only role of such an electrode is to provide or accept electrons. It must be conducting. Electrodes of gold, bright platinum, graphite and platinum coated with PbO_2, fulfill these conditions up to very high potentials (see electrodes, Chapter VI). Mercury, silver and other metals also act as inert electrodes at sufficiently low potentials.

As has been shown in Chapter I, the potential of an inert electrode immersed in a solution is given from the current–potential curves of the various dissolved substances in contact with the electrode.

Fast redox systems

Let us consider the current–potential curve for the ferricyanide–ferrocyanide system (curve 1, Fig.154).

For each value of the current up to the limiting diffusion current there is a unique value for the electrode potential. In particular, if the current is zero (open circuit), the electrode assumes the equilibrium potential

$$E_{eq} = E_0 + 0.058 \log \frac{|Fe(CN)_6{}^{3-}|}{|Fe(CN)_6{}^{4-}|}$$

where the activities of the ferricyanide and ferrocyanide ions are the same near the electrode as in the bulk of the solution, since the net chemical reaction is zero. In fact, curve 1 of Fig.154 is due to the sum of the two reactions

$$Fe(CN)_6{}^{3-} + e \rightarrow Fe(CN)_6{}^{4-}$$

and

$$Fe(CN)_6{}^{4-} - e \rightarrow Fe(CN)_6{}^{3-}$$

which occur at rates of i_{cat} and i_{an} respectively. The overall reaction is the oxidation of ferrocyanide if $|i_{an}| > |i_{cat}|$, and the reduction of ferricyanide if $|i_{an}| < |i_{cat}|$, and the overall velocity of the reaction is $i = i_{an} + i_{cat}$. At the equilibrium potential, $i = i_{an} + i_{cat} = 0$. When the system is a fast one, $|i_{an}| (= |i_{cat}|)$ is large, the exchange of electrons is fast, and the electrode soon reaches the equilibrium potential. If, moreover, the electrode potential is displaced temporarily, it quickly returns to its equilibrium value, thanks to the rapid exchange of electrons. The measured potential is thus stable.

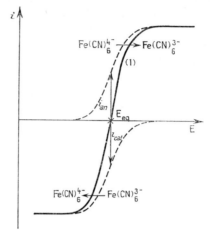

Fig. 154. Equilibrium potential of a fast system.

If $|Ox|$ and $|Red|$ vary during a reaction, the equilibrium potential varies too, which allows the reaction to be followed.

Mixed potentials

Certain substances which belong to different redox systems, and which do not react chemically with each other, may nevertheless exchange electrons at an electrode at an appreciable rate. Take for example a mixture of dichromate and thiocyanate ions. Both substances form part of very slow systems ($Cr_2O_7{}^{2-}/Cr^{3+}$ and $SCN^-/SO_4{}^{2-}$), and the chemical reaction between them is also very slow, so that they can co-exist in solution. The current–potential curve (Fig. 155) shows however that the rate of electron exchange at the electrode is high, and in fact a stable equilibrium potential $E_{\lambda'}$ is rapidly attained.

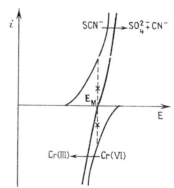

Fig. 155. Mixed potential (after GAUGUIN [21]).

Such potentials resulting from the reaction of substances belonging to different redox systems are called mixed potentials. In principle, the mixed potential may be used to follow a reaction which produces only one of the electroactive substances (in the case given here, either dichromate or thiocyanate); but it is only rarely that this finds any practical application.

Non-electroactive substances. Residual current

The current–potential curve of a solution of a non-electroactive substance such as sodium perchlorate corresponds to the oxidation and reduction of the solvent (Fig. 156). An electrode in such a solution will in principle assume an equilibrium potential E at which the oxidation and reduction reactions balance, assuming the overall current to be zero.

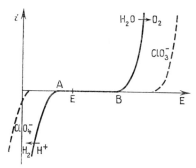

Fig. 156. Non-electroactive substances.

A very small current, the residual current, exists in the potential range from A to B; it is not visible on the scale used in Fig.156. This is due to the electrolysis of trace impurities (including oxygen) which are always present, to the oxidation and reduction of H_2O, the reduction of traces of H^+ or the oxidation of traces of OH^-. The precise value of the current varies with the relationship between E and the various equilibrium potentials.

Experiment shows that the potential E, which is a mixed potential, is established very slowly and is not stable owing to various disturbing factors such as the stirring of the solution.

Slow system

Slow systems, for which the current–potential curve is as shown in Fig. 157 for As(III)/As(V), are very common. The rate of electron exchange is very low, so the equilibrium potential is attained slowly and the measured potential is not stable. It is therefore difficult to follow the variation of such an equilibrium potential in the course of a reaction. Moreover, the residual current is superimposed on the small current due to As(III) and As(V).

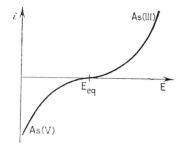

Fig. 157. Slow system (after COURSIER [17–20]).

Limit potential

A special kind of mixed potential is found when one of the two components of a fast system is present in very small quantities. This is nearly always the case near the end point of a reaction.

Let us take the ferricyanide–ferrocyanide system as an example. When the concentration of the ferrocyanide decreases, its current–potential curve varies as shown in Fig.158. When the concentration of ferrocyanide becomes small enough, the curve corresponding to the oxidation of $Fe(CN)_6^{4-}$ falls below the residual current curve. A rather unstable mixed potential is therefore measured. At this potential the value of the residual current is equal and opposite in sign to the value of the reduction current of the ferricyanide.

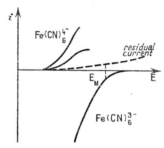

Fig. 158. Limit potential.

Similar phenomena are found when the concentration of ferricyanide in the presence of ferrocyanide becomes very small. Such potentials are called limit potentials.

Addition of the antagonist

As we have just seen, an inert electrode placed in a solution of ferrocyanide will assume a rather unstable limit potential, which does not allow the activity of $Fe(CN)_6^{4-}$ during the course of a reaction to be followed.

If ferricyanide is added to the solution, a stable electrode potential given by

$$E_{eq} = E_0 + 0.058 \log \frac{|Fe(CN)_6^{3-}|}{|Fe(CN)_6^{4-}|}$$

is obtained, and if the ferricyanide does not take part in the reaction which it is wished to follow, its activity remains constant so that the measured potential

$$E_{eq} = A - 0.058 \log |Fe(CN)_6^{4-}|$$

gives a measure of the activity of ferrocyanide in the solution.

The influence of dissolved oxygen

Oxygen dissolved in water can also give rise to mixed potentials. Thus thiosulphate is a part of a slow system $(S_2O_3^{2-}/S_4O_6^{2-})$, and a solution of thiosulphate from which the air has not been excluded will contain $S_2O_3^{2-}$ and O_2 as the only electroactive substances (Fig.159). The mixed potential E_M depends on the concentration of thiosulphate and of oxygen.

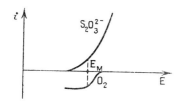

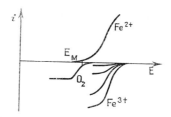

Fig. 159. Mixed potential with oxygen (after COURSIER[17-20]).

Fig. 160. Limit potential with oxygen.

With a fast system such as Fe^{3+}/Fe^{2+}, when the concentration of Fe^{3+} becomes very small the dissolved oxygen becomes electroactive in place of the Fe^{3+}, and a Fe^{2+}/O_2 mixed potential is produced (Fig.160).

The effect of the nature and surface of the electrode

The nature and surface area of the electrode have no influence on the measured value of the potential, as long as it is the equilibrium potential which is measured. The value of a mixed potential does vary with the nature of the electrode, however, since the current–potential curves are involved here, and they depend on the electrode.

Hydrogen electrode

The systems

$$2 H^+ + 2e \rightleftharpoons H_2$$
$$2 H_2O + 2e \rightleftharpoons H_2 + 2 OH^-$$
$$2 HB + 2e \rightleftharpoons H_2 + 2 B^-$$

are fast at a platinized platinum electrode, and for all three cases the potential assumed by the electrode is

$$E = -0.058 \text{ pH} \quad \text{(see p.63)}$$

This electrode may thus be used to determine the pH of the solution.

Inspection of the current–potential curves on page 65 allows us to predict the limits of usefulness of the hydrogen electrode. The rate at which the equilibrium potential is obtained is greater when the corresponding anode and cathode currents are greater, *i.e.* when the intersection of the curve with the potential axis is steeper (see Chapter IX).

For $|H^+| < 5 \times 10^{-5}$, the limiting diffusion current of H^+ becomes less than the usual residual current, and the equilibrium potential is ill-defined and not reproducible. The same is true for $|OH^-| < 10^{-4}$. Between these two limits (pH 4 to 10), therefore, the pH can only be measured in buffer solutions.

The hydrogen electrode is rather inconvenient to use in practice: its preparation is tedious and entails a number of precautions; it cannot be used in oxidizing or reducing solutions; the platinum black is poisoned by a large number of substances; the bubbling of hydrogen may change the composition of the solution (driving off CO_2, NH_3, etc.).

Works describing the various types of hydrogen electrodes are given in the reference list at the end of this chapter.

Reactive electrodes

Such electrodes are themselves capable of undergoing oxidation or reduction reactions; so in order to determine the potential of these electrodes, the current–potential curves of the electrode as well as of the various substances in solution must be considered.

Fast systems

Consider a silver electrode dipping into a solution of Ag$^+$ ions. The curves are given in Fig. 161. The indicator reaction is

$$Ag^+ + e \rightleftharpoons Ag \downarrow$$

This is a fast system. The equilibrium potential is

$$E_{eq} = E_0 + 0.058 \log |Ag^+|$$

The electrode thus gives an indication of the activity of Ag$^+$ ions in solution. A certain number of other metals also behave in this way, e.g. Hg and Cu.

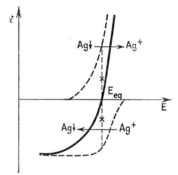

Fig. 161. Equilibrium potential of the system Ag$\downarrow$/Ag$^+$.

Slow systems

For many metals, the system $M^{n+} + ne \rightleftharpoons M\downarrow$ is slow, and the equilibrium potential is thus established slowly. It is difficult to use such metals as indicator electrodes.

Very electronegative metals

Consider a zinc electrode dipping into a solution of Zn^{2+} ions. The current–potential curves for the various systems present are given in Fig. 162.

It will be seen that the reduction of H$_2$O occurs before that of Zn^{2+}, so the measured potential is a mixed potential for Zn/H$_2$O; the zinc electrode cannot therefore be used as an indicator of the activity of Zn^{2+} ions. If the zinc electrode is replaced by a zinc amalgam electrode, the current–potential curves are displaced (Fig. 163). The reaction at the indicator electrode is now

$$Zn^{2+} + Hg \downarrow + 2e \rightleftharpoons Zn(Hg)$$

and the equilibrium potential is

$$E_{eq} = E_0 + 0.029 \log \frac{|Zn^{2+}|}{|Zn(Hg)|}$$

where $|Zn(Hg)|$ is the activity of the zinc in the amalgam.

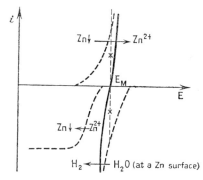

Fig. 162. Mixed potential found at a zinc electrode (theoretical curves).

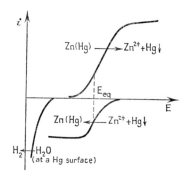

Fig. 163. Equilibrium potential found at a zinc amalgam electrode.

The concentration of zinc in the amalgam is constant, so that

$$E = A + 0.029 \log |Zn^{2+}|$$

Complex redox systems. Potentiometric indicators

A potentiometric indicator is an electroactive substance giving a potential related to the concentration of non-electroactive substances, and thus enabling the concentration of the latter to be determined.

Let us consider for example the complex redox system

$$AB + e \rightleftharpoons B + C$$

whose equilibrium potential is given by

$$E_{eq} = E_1 + 0.058 \log \frac{|AB|}{|B|\,|C|} = E_1 + 0.058 \log \frac{|AB|}{|C|} - 0.058 \log |B|$$

For given concentrations of AB and C, $E_{eq} = A - 0.058 \log |B|$. The system AB/C thus serves as an indicator for B, *e.g.* to follow the course of a reaction in which B is formed (see p. 55).

We will give some examples.

Quinhydrone indicator electrode for H+

Quinhydrone, $C_6H_4(OH)_2 \cdot C_6H_4O_2$, dissociates in the presence of water to give a molecule of hydroquinone, $HO-C_6H_4-OH$, and one of quinone, $O=C_6H_4=O$. This mixture of hydroquinone and quinone forms a redox system which also involves protons

$$O=C_6H_4=O + 2 H^+ + 2e \rightleftharpoons HO-C_6H_4-OH$$

The system is fast enough to allow the equilibrium potential to be measured

$$E_{eq} = E_0 + 0.029 \log \frac{|O=C_6H_4=O|\,|H^+|^2}{|HO-C_6H_4-OH|}$$

But the ratio $|O=C_6H_4=O|/|HO-C_6H_4-OH|$ is equal to 1, since these two substances are produced in equimolecular amounts by the decomposition of quinhydrone, so

$$E = E_0 - 0.058 \text{ pH}$$

Quinhydrone is thus a potentiometric indicator of the pH.

In order to determine the pH of a solution, a little quinhydrone is dissolved in it, and the potential is measured with a platinum or gold electrode.

These measurements are possible below a pH of about 8. In more alkaline media hydroquinone may be oxidized by the air, and also, being a weak acid, it begins to dissociate into $HO-C_6H_4-O^-$ and then to $(O-C_6H_4-O)^{2-}$.

The current–potential curves for this system are shown in Fig. 82 and 83. The other possible reactions are

$$O=C_6H_4=O + 2\,H_2O + 2e \rightleftharpoons HO-C_6H_4-OH + 2\,OH^-$$

and in a buffer solution

$$O=C_6H_4=O + 2\,HB + 2e \rightleftharpoons HO-C_6H_4-OH + 2\,B^-$$

For all these systems

$$E_{eq} = E_0 - 0.058 \text{ pH} \quad \text{(see p. 77)}$$

Electrode indicating the concentration of EDTA (Y^{4-})

Consider the fast redox system

$$HgY^{2-} + 2e \rightleftharpoons Hg\downarrow + Y^{4-}$$

where HgY^{2-} represents the complex of Hg^{2+} with Y^{4-} (see p. oo). The equilibrium potential of a mercury electrode in contact with a solution containing HgY^{2-} and Y^{4-} is

$$E_{eq} = E_0 + 0.029 \log \frac{|HgY^{2-}|}{|Y^{4-}|}$$

If HgY^{2-} is constant, the measured potential gives an indication of the concentration of EDTA

$$E_{eq} = A - 0.029 \log |Y^{4-}|$$

It is thus possible by these means to follow reactions involving Y^{4-}, *e.g.* the titration of a large number of ions with EDTA.

Electrodes covered with a sparingly soluble substance

(a) Consider a silver electrode covered by silver chloride. We have the fast redox system

$$AgCl\downarrow + e \rightleftharpoons Ag\downarrow + Cl^-$$

with

$$E_{eq} = E_1 - 0.058 \log |Cl^-|$$

A silver wire covered with silver chloride gives a potential which is indicative of the activity of Cl^- in the solution. Experiment has shown that a silver wire without any covering will give the same effects when dipped into a solution of chloride ion, doubtless because the wire is covered with a layer of silver chloride by oxidation by the air.

(*b*) If a silver electrode is dipped into a solution of a sulphide in the presence of air, it is covered with a layer of the very insoluble silver sulphide. This gives rise to the fast redox system

$$Ag_2S\downarrow + 2e \rightleftharpoons 2\ Ag\downarrow + S^{2-}$$

with

$$E_{eq} = E_2 - 0.029 \log |S^{2-}|$$

The electrode thus gives a measure of the sulphide ion concentration, and can be used to follow reactions involving this ion, *e.g.* $Cu^{2+} + S^{2-} \rightarrow Cu\ S\downarrow$

(*c*) If an antimony electrode is dipped into an aqueous solution in the presence of air, a layer of antimony oxide is formed, which is very insoluble between pH 2 and 8. The redox system in this case is

$$Sb(OH)_3\downarrow + 3\ H^+ + 3e \rightleftharpoons Sb\downarrow + 3\ H_2O$$

$$E_{eq} = E_3 - 0.058\ pH$$

This electrode thus gives a measure of the pH of the solution.

The above arguments about indicator electrodes only hold if the equations derived for the equilibrium potential do not change. Thus the concentration of the electro-active substance (quinone, hydroquinone, HgY^{2-}) must not change, or the sparingly soluble substance (AgCl, Ag_2S, $Sb(OH)_3$) must saturate the solution near the electrode. No chemical reaction must therefore occur with any of the other substances in solution so as to change the relevant concentrations or render the sparingly soluble substances soluble (acid–base reactions or complex formation, etc.).

Also, no other oxidant or reductant (the solvent included) should have an effect on the determination of the equilibrium potential at the electrode in question.

'Mediator' systems

For example, the system As(III)/As(V) is slow and the equilibrium potential is only attained very slowly. But the chemical reaction

$$As(III) + I_3^- \rightleftharpoons As(V) + 3\ I^-$$

is fast. If a little iodine and iodide is added to the solution, the chemical equilibrium is attained very rapidly. The solution then contains the fast iodine–iodide system, whose equilibrium potential can easily be measured. Now since the two systems As(III)/As(V) and I_3^-/I^- are in chemical equilibrium, their equilibrium potentials are equal, so the measured potential gives the equilibrium potential of As(III)/As)V) too.

The following conditions must be fulfilled:

1) The amount of the system added, in this case I_3^-/I^-, must be so small that the chemical reaction which occurs does not change the relative amounts of As(III) and As(V) appreciably.

2) The standard oxidation potential of the 'mediator' system must not be too far from the equilibrium potential to be determined. If it is, when the chemical equilibrium is attained one of the components of the mediator system (I_3^- or I^-) will be present in very low concentration, and a limit potential may be obtained in place of the desired equilibrium potential (see p. 158).

Constant-current potentiometry

It may be useful to pass a very small current through the electrode. The electrode potential is then often very stable, much more so than the equilibrium potential, especially with slow systems. This potential can give very valuable information.

Fast systems

If only the reductant is present, the potential is given by

$$E = E_{\frac{1}{2}} + \frac{0.058}{n} \log \frac{i}{i_{Red} - i}$$

and when $i = i_\varepsilon$, which is negligible compared to i_{Red},

$$E_\varepsilon = E_{\frac{1}{2}} + \frac{0.058}{n} \log \frac{i_\varepsilon}{k_{Red}} - \frac{0.058}{n} \log |Red|$$

Similarly, when only the oxidant is present and a small cathode current $- i_\varepsilon$ is imposed, then

$$E_\varepsilon = E_{\frac{1}{2}} + \frac{0.058}{n} \log \frac{k_{Ox}}{i_\varepsilon} + \frac{0.058}{n} \log |Ox|$$

When both the oxidant and reductant are present, the potential for i_ε and $- i_\varepsilon$ is nearly the same as the equilibrium potential, as long as i_ε is negligible compared to i_{Ox} and i_{Red}.

Slow systems

Now, for $i = i_\varepsilon$ the equation is

$$E_A = E_{\frac{1}{2}\ an} + \frac{0.058}{\beta n} \log \frac{i_\varepsilon}{k_{Red}} - \frac{0.058}{\beta n} \log |Red|$$

and for $i = - i_\varepsilon$

$$E_C = E_{\frac{1}{2}\ cat} + \frac{0.058}{\alpha n} \log \frac{k_{Ox}}{i_\varepsilon} + \frac{0.058}{\alpha n} \log |Ox|$$

The same remarks apply as for fast systems.

Speed of a system

The ratio of the potential difference $E_A - E_C$ to $\Delta i = 2i_\varepsilon$, as Δi tends to zero, is the slope of the current–potential curve for zero current, and is a measure of the speed of the system.

II. POTENTIOMETRIC TITRATIONS

Potentiometry may be used to follow a titration, and in particular to determine its end point. Such a titration is called a potentiometric titration, and comprises:

1) A titration reaction, which is produced by the addition of known quantities of a reactant, either as a solution from a burette (volumetric analysis) or as prepared by electrolysis (coulometry). In both cases, a chemical reaction is produced between the substance to be determined and the reactant. The substance to be determined may also be oxidized or reduced directly by electrolysis (direct coulometry).

2) One or more indicator reactions, which are electrochemical reactions produced at the indicator electrodes. If the indicator reactions involve the substance to be determined, or the reactant, or the reaction products, the measured potential will vary during the course of the reaction, and the end point will be indicated by a singular point in the curve of voltage against quantity of reactant added.

The quantities of substances oxidized or reduced in the indicator reactions must be negligible compared to those involved in the titration reaction.

Potentiometry is thus one of the methods which can be used to determine the end point of a reaction, whether it be in volumetric analysis, in coulometric analysis, in following a slow reaction, or in the course of a preparative reaction.

Variations of the potential during a chemical reaction

We have seen in Chapter III how the current–potential curves change during a chemical reaction. The potential variations for a given current may be found from the intersections of the various curves with a line parallel to the potential axis; if the current is zero, this line is the potential axis itself. We have seen that the potential varies with the concentration according to a logarithmic relationship. During the titration the potential varies very little to begin with, and then near the end point it changes very abruptly, as the logarithm of the concentrations undergoes a rapid variation. The problem in general is then to detect this sharp potential change; and measurements must be made close to the end point. This assumes of course that the reaction is nearly quantitative.

We will describe here only the electrode indications during the reactions, giving several examples. Information on their application to titrations will be found in textbooks of quantitative analytical chemistry.

Different types of potentiometric titrations

The basic types are as follows:
1. Potentiometry with zero current.
   (a) one indicator electrode, one reference electrode;
   (b) two indicator electrodes of different kinds.
2. Potentiometry with a constant non-zero current.
   (a) one indicator electrode, one reference electrode.
   (b) two indicator electrodes, usually of the same kind.

Potentiometric titrations where the current is zero

(a) Titrations using only one indicator electrode

We will suppose in this case that an indicator electrode is dipped into the solution and that its potential is determined when the current flowing is zero or negligibly small.

Redox reactions. Inert indicator electrode

The determination of ferrous salts by ceric salts. The titration reaction is

$$Fe^{2+} + Ce^{4+} \rightarrow Fe^{3+} + Ce^{3+}$$

which is a fast chemical reaction. The systems Fe^{2+}/Fe^{3+} and Ce^{4+}/Ce^{3+} are also fairly fast, *e.g.* at a platinum electrode. Before the end point, considerable amounts of Fe^{2+} and Fe^{3+} are present, so the electrode rapidly attains a stable potential given by

$$E_{eq} = E_1 + 0.058 \log \frac{|Fe^{3+}|}{|Fe^{2+}|} = E_1 + 0.058 \log \frac{1-x}{x}$$

where x is the fraction of Ce^{4+} added.

In the immediate vicinity of the end point the concentration of Fe^{2+} becomes very small, so as we have seen this ion ceases to be electroactive. The only substances present in appreciable amounts are Fe^{3+} and Ce^{3+}, and the rather unstable mixed potential of Fe^{3+}/Ce^{3+} is measured.

Once the end point is well past, the solution contains appreciable amounts of Ce^{3+} and Ce^{4+}, and the stable equilibrium potential

$$E_{eq} = E_2 + 0.058 \log \frac{|Ce^{4+}|}{|Ce^{3+}|} = E_2 + 0.058 \log (x-1)$$

is obtained.

The dotted part of the curve of Fig. 164 indicates the region where the potential is not measurable in practice. Usually this does not matter, as one drop of the titrating solution is enough to bring the system from A to B for solutions which are not too dilute.

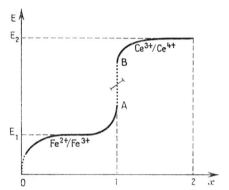

Fig. 164. The reaction $Fe^{2+} + Ce^{4+} \rightarrow Fe^{3+} + Ce^{3+}$.

Determination of ferrous ions by permanganate. This titration is based on the fast chemical reaction

$$5\ Fe^{2+} + MnO_4^- + 8\ H^+ \rightarrow 5\ Fe^{3+} + Mn^{2+} + 4\ H_2O$$

Before the end point the equilibrium potential of the system Fe^{2+}/Fe^{3+} is measured, as long as the concentrations of both Fe^{2+} and Fe^{3+} are more than 10^{-4} to 10^{-5}. After the end point the system MnO_4^-/Mn^{2+} is present in the solution; it will be seen from the curves of Fig. 165 that Mn^{2+} is not electroactive, so in the absence of any other reductants the oxidation of water is the indicator reaction, and the mixed potential of MnO_4^-/H_2O is measured.

In the immediate vicinity of the end point the potential measured is the mixed potential of Fe^{3+}/H_2O, which is not very stable.

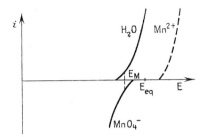

Fig. 165. The mixed potential of MnO_4^-/H_2O.

The titration curve is shown in Fig. 166. The full lines represent the potentials which may be observed, and the dotted lines the unstable mixed potentials. The broken line represents the equilibrium potentials of the system MnO_4^-/Mn^{2+}, which can be calculated but not measured. The calculated equilibrium potential at the end point is represented by the point C, $E_{eq} = (5 E_2 + E_1)/6$. In practice, this potential is not reached until considerably after the end point (the point D).

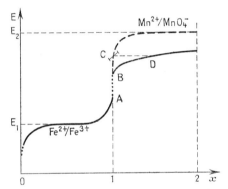

Fig. 166. The reaction $5 Fe^{2+} + MnO_4^- + 8 H^+ \rightarrow 5 Fe^{3+} + Mn^{2+} + 4 H_2O$
at a platinum electrode (after COURSIER [17–20]).

Precipitation reactions

Determination of silver salts. Silver indicator electrode. The titration reaction is

$$Ag^+ + X^- \rightarrow AgX\downarrow$$

where X^- may be Cl^-, Br^-, I^-, SCN^-, etc. The indicator reaction is

$$Ag^+ + e \rightleftharpoons Ag\downarrow$$

We have seen that when a silver electrode dips into a solution of silver ions, the potential measured is the equilibrium potential

$$E_{eq} = 0.80 \text{ V} + 0.058 \log |Ag^+|$$

If C_0 is the initial concentration of Ag^+ ions to be determined and xC_0 is the concentration of X^- added, then the equation becomes

$$E_{eq} = 0.80 \text{ V} + 0.058 \log C_0 (1 - x)$$

It follows that the potential changes sharply near $x = 1$ (Fig. 167).

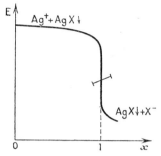

Fig. 167. The reaction $Ag^+ + X^- \rightarrow AgX\downarrow$ at a silver electrode.

The same electrode reaction may be used in the titration of solutions of X^-. The indicator reaction before the end point is now

$$AgX\downarrow + e \rightleftharpoons Ag\downarrow + X^-$$

since experiment has shown that the silver electrode is covered with $AgX\downarrow$ from the start of the titration. The potential is then

$$E_{eq} = 0.80 \text{ V} + 0.058 \log s - 0.058 \log C_0 (1 - x)$$

if C_0 is the initial concentration of X^-, xC_0 the added concentration of Ag^+ and s is the solubility product $|Ag^+| \, |X^-|$.

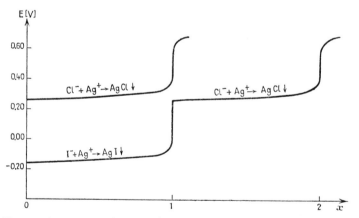

Fig. 168. The reactions $I^- + Ag^+ \rightarrow AgI\downarrow$ and $Cl^- + Ag^+ \rightarrow AgCl\downarrow$ at a silver electrode.

Fig. 168 shows the titration curves for decinormal chloride and iodide solutions and for the two together. Potentiometric titration thus allows a mixture of Cl^- and I^- to be titrated so as to indicate the end points of the reactions

$$I^- + Ag^+ \rightarrow AgI\downarrow \quad \text{and} \quad Cl^- + Ag^+ \rightarrow AgCl\downarrow$$

separately. After the final end point, the indicator reaction is $Ag^+ + e \rightarrow Ag\downarrow$, since the solution contains Ag^+ ions.

Precipitation and complex-formation reactions

Determination of cyanide by means of silver salts. Silver indicator electrode. The chemical reactions on which the titration is based are

$$2\ CN^- + Ag^+ \rightarrow Ag(CN)_2^- \qquad \frac{|Ag^+|\,|CN^-|^2}{|Ag(CN)_2^-|} = K$$

followed by

$$Ag(CN)_2^- + Ag^+ \rightarrow Ag[Ag(CN)_2]\downarrow \qquad |Ag^+|\,|Ag(CN)_2^-| = s$$

The potential assumed by a silver electrode dipping into a solution of cyanide is a mixed potential, but as soon as a small amount of silver is added, $Ag(CN)_2^-$ is formed and the indicator reaction is

$$Ag(CN)_2^- + e \rightleftharpoons Ag\downarrow + 2\ CN^-$$

The equilibrium potential is then given by

$$E_{eq} = 0.80\ V + 0.058\ \log K + 0.058\ \log \frac{|Ag(CN)_2^-|}{|CN^-|^2}$$

$$= 0.80\ V + 0.058\ \log K + 0.058\ \log \frac{x}{C_0\,(1 - 2x)^2}$$

if C_0 is the initial cyanide concentration, and xC_0 is the concentration of Ag^+ added. The potential changes sharply at $x = \frac{1}{2}$ (Fig. 169). When $x = \frac{1}{2} + \varepsilon$, the precipitation of $Ag[Ag(CN)_2]$ starts; the indicator reaction is then

$$Ag[Ag(CN)_2]\downarrow + 2e \rightarrow 2\ Ag\downarrow + 2\ CN^-$$

with

$$E = 0.80\ V + 0.058\ \log s - 0.058\ \log |CN^-|$$

$$= 0.80\ V + 0.058\ \log s - 0.058\ \log C_0\,(1 - x)$$

The potential again changes abruptly when $x = 1$, indicating that the last traces of cyanide have disappeared. After the second end point, the indicator reaction is

$$Ag^+ + e \rightarrow Ag\downarrow$$

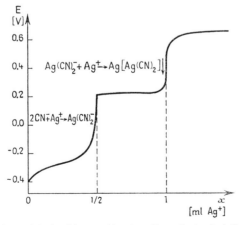

Fig. 169. Reactions of Ag^+ with cyanide at a silver electrode (after GAUGUIN [21]).

Use of indicators in potentiometric titrations

Titrations with EDTA. Mercury electrode. Consider a mercury electrode in contact with a solution containing mercuric ions; then, in principle, we have the electrochemical reaction

$$Hg\downarrow - 2e \rightleftharpoons Hg^{2+} \quad \text{with} \quad E_{eq} = E_0 + 0.029 \log |Hg^{2+}| \tag{1}$$

If EDTA (Y^{4-}) is added to the solution, the equilibrium

$$Hg^{2+} + Y^{4-} \rightleftharpoons HgY^{2-} \quad \text{with} \quad \frac{|Hg||Y^{4-}|}{|HgY^{2-}|} = K$$

is set up. The redox system is then

$$Hg\downarrow + Y^{4-} - 2e \rightleftharpoons HgY^{2-} \quad \text{with} \quad E_{eq} = E_1 + 0.029 \log \frac{|HgY^{2-}|}{|Y^{4-}|} \tag{2}$$

If a reaction involving Y^{4-}, *e.g.*

$$M^{2+} + Y^{4-} \rightleftharpoons MY^{2-} \quad \text{with} \quad \frac{|M^{2+}||Y^{4-}|}{|MY^{2-}|} = K'$$

occurs in the solution, a new redox system may appear in the solution (we assume that M^{2+} is not electroactive)

$$Hg\downarrow + MY^{2-} - 2e \rightleftharpoons HgY^{2-} + M^{2+}$$

with

$$E_{eq} = E_2 + 0.029 \log \frac{|HgY^{2-}||M^{2+}|}{|MY^{2-}|} \tag{3}$$

$$E_2 = E_0 + 0.029 \log K - 0.029 \log K'$$

The equilibrium potential is thus governed by one of three equations (1, 2 or 3) according to the conditions, so the electrode can be used to indicate various concentrations.

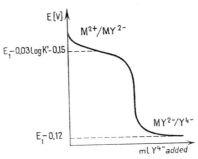

Fig. 170. The reaction $M^{2+} + Y^{4-} \rightarrow MY^{2-}$ at a mercury electrode; $C_0 = 0.1$.

1st case: The complex HgY^{2-} is more stable than the complex MY^{2-}; $K \ll K'$; M^{2+} cannot react with HgY^{2-}.

A little HgY^{2-} is added to the solution of M^{2+} to be titrated; the concentration of the former does not vary during the titration. The solution then contains M^{2+} and HgY^{2-}, and Y^{4-} is added to bring about the reaction

$$M^{2+} + Y^{4-} \rightarrow MY^{2-}$$

The potential assumed by the mercury electrode is

$$E_{eq} = E_2 + 0.029 \log \frac{|HgY^{2-}| \, |M^{2+}|}{|MY^{2-}|} \qquad (3)$$

If $|HgY^{2-}| = 10^{-5}$, this equation becomes

$$E_{eq} = E_2 - 0.15 + 0.029 \log \frac{|M^{2+}|}{|MY^{2-}|}$$

After the end point the solution contains HgY^{2-}, MY^{2-} and excess Y^{4-}, so

$$E_{eq} = E_1 + 0.029 \log \frac{|HgY^{2-}|}{|Y^{4-}|} \qquad (2)$$

$$E_{eq} = E_1 - 0.15 - 0.029 \log |Y^{4-}|$$

The titration curve is given in Fig. 170.
The mercury electrode may be replaced by an 'amalgamated' platinum electrode, or a gold amalgam electrode [22].

2nd case: The complex HgY^{2-} is less stable than MY^{2-} $(K \gg K')$ and cannot therefore exist in the presence of M^{2+}. Hg^{2+} can then be added to the solution. The solution now contains M^{2+} and Hg^{2+}. The chemical reaction

$$M^{2+} + Y^{4-} \rightarrow MY^{2-}$$

occurs, and the potential measured at the mercury electrode is given by

$$E_{eq} = E_0 + 0.029 \log |Hg^{2+}| \qquad (1)$$

At the end point of the titration, Hg^{2+} disappears to give HgY^{2-}. If the amount of Hg^{2+} added was very small, its disappearance is accompanied by a sharp change in the potential.
    Examples of this second case have been described for other systems. For example, the system Fe^{3+}/Fe^{2+} has been proposed [62] as indicator for F^- during the reaction

$$Pb^{2+} + Cl^- + F^- \rightarrow PbClF \downarrow$$

Other indicators. A large number of substances, added in traces, have been proposed as indicators, *e.g.* $IO_3^- + I^-$ for the titration of a base with an acid; the reaction

$$IO_3^- + 6 H^+ + 5 I^- \rightarrow 3 I_2 + 3 H_2O$$

does not occur in alkaline solution. The IO_3^- ion is not electroactive at a platinum electrode in neutral and alkaline media, so at the start of the titration a mixed potential is measured. As soon as excess H^+ ions are present, iodine is formed, and the stable equilibrium potential of the fast system I_2/I^- is measured; this is very different from the mixed potential. Conversely, iodine has been suggested as indicator for the neutralization of an acid by a base.

Back titrations

If a titration does not involve any electroactive substances, it is still possible to determine the end point of the reaction by potentiometry, by back-titrating with an electroactive substance (see p. 59).

(b) Potentiometric titrations with two indicator electrodes

This method uses two indicator electrodes of different natures or of different surface areas, and the potential difference between them is followed during the titration. Usually the two electrodes are made of two suitable metals. The method is based on the fact that a mixed potential varies with the nature and surface of the electrode.

Redox reactions

Two fast systems. If the substance to be determined and the titrant both belong to fast systems, then both before and after the end point equilibrium potentials will be measured, and both electrodes will register the same potential. Near the end point, however, where the concentrations of certain substances are very low, a mixed potential is measured which depends on the nature of the electrode and a potential difference thus appears between the two electrodes.

An example is the titration of ferrous iron with vanadium (V).

$$Fe(II) + V(V) \rightarrow Fe(III) + V(IV)$$

The potential difference between a platinum electrode and a graphite electrode for this reaction is shown in Fig. 171.

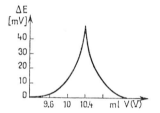

Fig. 171. Determination of Fe^{2+} by means of a potentiometric titration with V(V). Two indicator electrodes: platinum and graphite (after COURSIER [17-20]).

Only one of the systems is fast. Many examples of this have been given by the originators of this method, who have also studied many pairs of electrodes: Pt/Pd, Pt/Rh, W, etc. [63].

In this case either the substance to be determined or the titrant belongs to a fast system; the corresponding potential is an equilibrium potential. The other substance

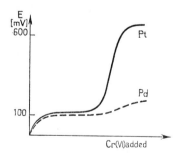

Fig. 172. The reaction
$3 Fe(II) + Cr(VI) \rightarrow 3 Fe(III) + Cr(III)$
(after WILLARD and FENWICK [36]).

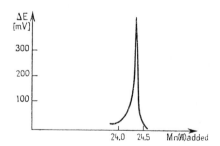

Fig. 173. The reaction:
$5 Fe(II) + Mn(VII) \rightarrow 5 Fe(III) + Mn(II)$
(after WILLARD and FENWICK [36]).

belongs to a system which is so slow that the potential measured is a mixed potential; this is so for a number of common reagents, such as MnO_4^-/Mn^{2+}, $Cr_2O_7^{2-}/Cr^{3+}$, etc.

Thus, during the titration of ferrous iron with dichromate, first the equilibrium potential of the system Fe^{2+}/Fe^{3+} is measured, and later the mixed potential of $Cr_2O_7^{2-}/H_2O$. We have shown the potential curves during the titration for a platinum electrode and for a palladium electrode in Fig. 172. A potential difference appears between the electrodes at the end point and thereafter.

The curve for the titration of Fe^{2+} with decinormal permanganate with electrodes of platinum and rhodium-plated platinum is shown in Fig. 173. At the end point there is a very sharp potential peak of height 400 mV.

Other reactions

Reactions other than redox reactions may also be followed in this way by choosing one of the electrodes so as to give an equilibrium potential, if that is possible (e.g. a metal M in the presence of M^{n+}).

For example, the titration of Cu^{2+} with EDTA has been followed in this way[64]. The argentometry of chloride, bromide and iodide can also be followed with two electrodes: one of silver, the other of silver amalgam.

Use of potentiometric indicators. Acid–base reactions may be followed with two electrodes, especially if indicators such as H_2O_2 are added[63].

Back-titrations. These may be used if the forward reaction is slow, or if they give a better indication of the end point.

Properties of the method

The use of two electrodes of different natures has the advantage that the experimental set-up is simple, but the stability of the potentials is rarely good. The method using two indicator electrodes with a slight current is also simple and does not suffer from this inconvenience.

Potentiometric titrations with a constant current

Classical potentiometry, where the current is zero, is in general not applicable to the following cases where the electrode potential is very slow in reaching a steady value:

1. Slow systems.

2. Fast systems where only the oxidant or the reductant is present in solution, i.e. acid–base reactions, precipitation and complex-formation reactions.

The other half of the redox system cannot be added to give an equilibrium potential which can be rapidly measured, if it can also take part in the titration reaction.

On the other hand, if a constant finite current is used the electrode potential rapidly reaches a stable value, which allows the potential changes occuring during the reaction to be followed. The end point is often indicated by a sharp change in the potential. The phenomena occuring can be treated in terms of the current–potential curves.

The current must be small, so that the amounts of the substances electrolyzed are negligible compared to the quantity of the substance to be determined.

One indicator electrode and one reference electrode may be used, or two indicator electrodes such as two small platinum electrodes.

Many examples of these two different methodes have been given by WILLARD, FENWICK and VAN NAME [35, 36, 37].

Theoretical example

Let us consider the case of an oxidant A, which can be reduced according to the equation

$$A + e \rightarrow C$$

and to which a substance B is added:

$$A + B \rightarrow AB \qquad \frac{|A| |B|}{|AB|} = K$$

The current–potential curves for this case have been studied on page 46; we will suppose here that B is not electroactive, and C is absent (Fig. 174).

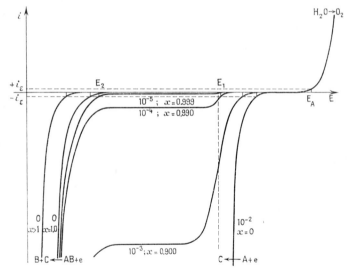

Fig. 174. The reaction $A + B \rightarrow AB$ ($|A| = 10^{-2}$)
(cf. Figs. 50 and 60).

The values of x corresponding to the concentrations xC_0 of B added, and the concentrations of A assuming that the chemical reaction is quantitative, are indicated beside the curves of Fig. 174. The initial concentration of A is taken to be $C_0 = 10^{-2}$.

1st case. One indicator electrode and one electrode of practically constant potential. Let us suppose that the indicator electrode is the cathode, and that the current at this electrode is $- i_\varepsilon$. The current at the other electrode is then $+ i_\varepsilon$, and this electrode has the constant potential E_A. (The conditions would be similar if a reference electrode had been chosen as the anode). For a fast system the equation of the cathode curve is

$$E = E_{\frac{1}{2}} + 0.058 \log \frac{i_A - i}{i}$$

where

$$i_A = - k_A |A|_s$$

The potential E_1 corresponding to the current $- i_\varepsilon$ is therefore

$$E_1 = E_{\frac{1}{2}} + 0.058 \log \frac{k_A}{i_\varepsilon} + 0.058 \log |A|_s$$

During the reaction, $|A|_s$ decreases: $|A|_s = (1 - x)C_0$, where x is the fraction of B added

$$E_1 = E_{\frac{1}{2}} + 0.058 \log \frac{k_A}{i_\varepsilon} + 0.058 \log C_0 (1 - x)$$

It will be seen that the limiting diffusion current of A decreases during the reaction, and that in the example chosen $|i_A|$ becomes smaller than $|i|$ when $|A| = 10^{-5}$. At this moment the potential changes abruptly from E_1 $(x = 0.99)$ to E_2, where the latter potential corresponds to the cathode reaction

$$AB + e \rightarrow C + B$$

with

$$E_{eq} = E_0' + 0.058 \log \frac{|B| |C|}{|AB|} \qquad E_0' = E_0 + 0.058 \log K$$

The electrode potential is now given by

$$E = E_0' + 0.058 \log \frac{k_B k_C}{k_{AB}} + 0.058 \log \frac{i - i_{AB}}{i^2}$$

and for $i = - i_\varepsilon$

$$E_2 = E_0' + 0.058 \log k_B k_C - 0.116 \log i_\varepsilon + 0.058 \log C_0$$

It will be noticed that the potential jump takes place slightly before the end point, since it occurs for $i_A = i_\varepsilon$ and not $i_A = 0$. For this error to be negligible, the concentration of A at that moment must be negligible compared to its initial concentration, e.g. 10^{-5} as compared to an initial concentration of 10^{-2} N. The curve thus obtained is very similar to that for a titration where the current is zero, and the smaller i_ε the greater the similarity (see Fig. 175).

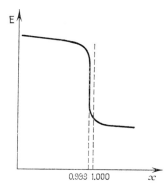

Fig. 175. Potentiometry with a constant current, with one indicator electrode and one electrode whose potential is constant. The reaction A + B → AB.

2nd case. Two indicator electrodes. Let us consider the same system as in the previous case, but with $|C| = 10^{-2}$. The current–potential curves are shown in Fig. 176. We have seen that C can be oxidized according to the equations

$$C - e \rightleftharpoons A$$

and

$$C + B - e \rightleftharpoons AB$$

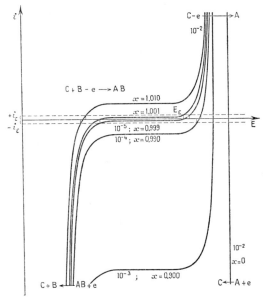

Fig. 176. The reaction $A + B \rightarrow AB$ ($|A| = 10^{-2}$, $|C| = 10^{-2}$)
(cf. Figs. 52 and 61).

Let us suppose that a constant current is imposed at the two electrodes, $+ i_\varepsilon$ at the anode and $- i_\varepsilon$ at the cathode. It will be seen that the potential of electrode 1, which acts as the cathode, is at first very little different from the equilibrium potential of the system

$$A + e \rightarrow C \quad \text{with} \quad E_{eq} = E_0 + 0.058 \log \frac{|A|}{|C|}$$

Then, just before the end point, when $|i_A| = k_A C_0(1 - x)$ is less than or equal to $|i_\varepsilon|$, it becomes nearly equal to the equilibrium potential of the system

$$AB + e \rightleftharpoons B + C \quad \text{with} \quad E = E_1 + 0.058 \log \frac{|AB|}{|B||C|}$$

and

$$E_1 = E_0 + 0.058 \log K$$

This behaviour is represented by curve 1 in Fig. 177. This curve is nearly the same as that obtained during a titration where the current is zero; the deviation of the value of x at which the sudden change in voltage from 1 occurs increases with $|i_\varepsilon|$, however.

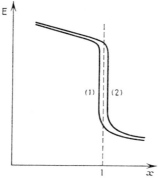

Fig. 177. Constant-current potentiometry with two indicator electrodes, for the reaction A + B → AB. Curve 1: cathode curve. Curve 2: anode curve.

The second electrode, which acts as the anode, first assumes a potential near the equilibrium potential of the first system, so at the end point the potential E_ε corresponds to the oxidation of C only at a current i_ε. After the end point, in the presence of B, C is oxidized according to the equation

$$B + C - e \rightarrow AB$$

at a potential near $E_1 = E_0 + 0.058 \log K$. The current is limited by the diffusion of B: $i_B = k_B C_0(x - 1)$. As soon as i_B becomes equal to i_ε, the potential jumps sharply from E_ε to a value near the equilibrium potential of the system AB $\rightleftharpoons$ B + C − e.

The potential difference between the two electrodes, $E_A - E_C$, thus varies during the reaction; this variation is plotted in Fig. 178. The peak is sharper as i_ε is smaller.

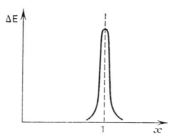

Fig. 178. Constant-current potentiometry with two indicator electrodes, for the reaction A + B → AB.

Various examples of potentiometric titrations

We give here various examples, in order to show how the current–potential curves derived in Chapter III can be used to obtain the titration curves for the following different types of potentiometry:

1) zero-current, with one indicator electrode.
2) zero-current, with two indicator electrodes.
3) constant-current, with one indicator electrode.
4) constant-current, with two identical or different indicator electrodes.

The indicator electrodes may be inert or reactive. The electrochemical systems may be fast or slow. The chemical reactions must be fast, and may be an acid–base, redox, complex-formation or precipitation reaction.

Precipitation of silver bromide

The current–potential curves at a silver electrode during the reaction

$$Ag^+ + Br^- \rightarrow AgBr\downarrow \qquad |Ag^+||Br^-| = 10^{-12}$$

are shown in Fig. 179 (see p. 79).

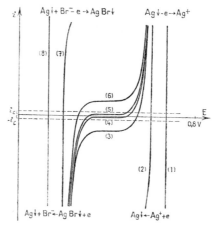

Fig. 179. The reaction $Ag^+ + Br^- \rightarrow AgBr\downarrow$ at a silver electrode
(theoretical curves).

One silver indicator electrode and one reference electrode. No current. The titration curve
representing the equilibrium potential of the system

$$Ag^+ + e \rightleftharpoons Ag\downarrow$$

or, equally well, that of

$$AgBr\downarrow + e \rightleftharpoons Br^- + Ag\downarrow$$

given in either case by

$$E_{eq} = 0.80 \text{ V} + 0.058 \log|Ag^+| = 0.80 \text{ V} + 0.058 \log C_0 (1 - x)$$

is shown in curve (1), Fig. 180 for $C_0 = 10^{-2}$.

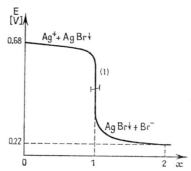

Fig. 180. The potentiometric titration $Ag^+ + Br^- \rightarrow AgBr\downarrow$ at a silver indicator
electrode; no current.

One silver indicator electrode and one reference electrode. Current $= i_\varepsilon$. When the oxidation current is set at $+ i_\varepsilon$, the electrode potential will be very close to the equilibrium potential of the system $Ag\downarrow - e \rightarrow Ag^+$

$$E_{eq} = E_0 + 0.058 \log |Ag^+|$$

right up to the end point: curves (1), (2) and (3), Fig. 180 and 181. After the end point, a new oxidation reaction is possible

$$Ag\downarrow + Br^- - e \rightarrow AgBr\downarrow$$

with

$$E = E_1 - 0.058 \log |Br^-| \qquad E_1 = E_0 + 0.058 \log s$$

When the limiting diffusion current for Br^- corresponding to this reaction exceeds i_ε, this reaction will occur at the electrode, which will assume an appropriate potential. It may be mentioned that this potential jump will occur when $i_{Br^-} = i_\varepsilon$, *i.e.* rather after the end point: curve (2) (Fig. 181).

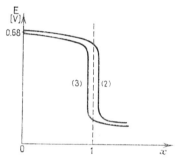

Fig. 181. Potentiometric titrations $Ag^+ + Br^- \rightarrow AgBr\downarrow$ at a silver indicator electrode. Curve (2): current $= + i_\varepsilon$; curve (3): current $= - i_\varepsilon$.

We have supposed in Fig. 179, which gives the current–potential curves for the indicator electrode which plays the role of the anode, that a little AgBr is deposited on the electrode itself.

If the current is made $i = - i_\varepsilon$, the silver electrode acts as a cathode, and at first the electrochemical reaction

$$Ag^+ + e \rightarrow Ag\downarrow$$

occurs at this electrode. The electrode potential is very near the equilibrium potential

$$E_{eq} = E_0 + 0.058 \log |Ag^+|$$

When Ag^+ becomes small enough, the diffusion current of Ag^+ is less than i_ε, and the electrode assumes the much lower potential corresponding to the reaction

$$AgBr\downarrow + e \rightarrow Ag\downarrow + Br^-$$

Experiment shows that a little silver bromide does always get deposited on the electrode by stirring.

The potential jump occurs slightly before the end point: curve (3) of **Fig. 181**.

Two indicator electrodes, current i_ε. One electrode acts as a cathode, the other as an anode, as has been indicated in curves (2) and (3) of Fig. 181. The variation of the potential difference between the two electrodes, ΔE, during the reaction is shown as curve 4, Fig. 182.

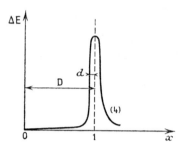

Fig. 182. The potentiometric titration $Ag^+ + Br^- \rightarrow AgBr\downarrow$.
Two silver electrodes, current i_ε.

Accuracy. The distance shown as d in Fig. 182 must be negligible compared to D. Now d/D is the ratio of i_ε to the initial diffusion current of Ag^+; if the initial concentration is $10^{-2} N$, and if i_ε is the limiting diffusion current corresponding to $|Ag^+| = 10^{-5}$, the error will be 0.1 %, which is negligible.

Oxidation of ferrous salts by ceric salts

The chemical reaction is

$$Fe^{2+} + Ce^{4+} \rightarrow Fe^{3+} + Ce^{3+}$$

The ideal current–potential curves are shown in Fig. 183. The theoretical titration curves are given below:

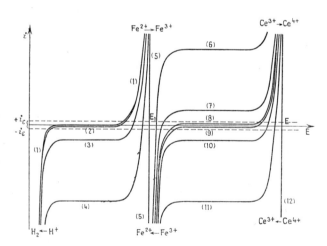

Fig. 183. The reaction $Fe^{2+} + Ce^{4+} \rightarrow Fe^{3+} + Ce^{3+}$ (theoretical curves).

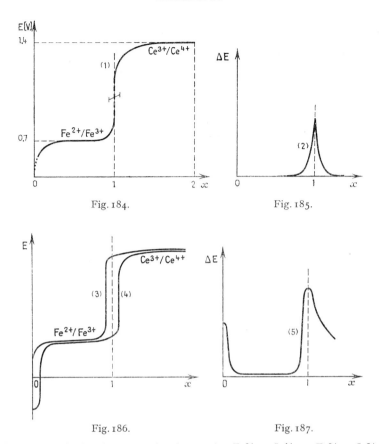

Fig. 184.   Fig. 185.

Fig. 186.   Fig. 187.

Potentiometric titration curves for the reaction $Fe^{2+} + Ce^{4+} \rightarrow Fe^{3+} + Ce^{3+}$.

Curve (1): zero-current potentiometry, one indicator electrode.
Curve (2): zero-current potentiometry, two indicator electrodes of different kinds.
Curve (3): constant-current potentiometry, one indicator anode.
Curve (4): constant-current potentiometry, one indicator cathode.
Curve (5): constant-current potentiometry, two identical indicator electrodes.

The reaction of mercury (II) with EDTA

The chemical reaction is

$$Hg^{2+} + Y^{4-} \rightarrow HgY^{2-} \qquad \text{(see p. 62)}$$

The electrochemical reactions at a mercury electrode are shown in Fig. 188. Before the end point, the reactions are

$$Hg\downarrow - 2e \rightleftharpoons Hg^{2+}$$

and

$$HgY^{2-} + 2e \rightarrow Hg + Y^{4-}$$

at the end point

$$Hg\downarrow - 2e \rightarrow Hg^{2+}$$

and

$$HgY^{2-} + 2e \rightarrow Hg + Y^{4-}$$

References p. 188–190

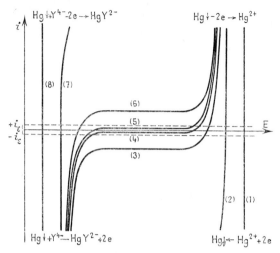

Fig. 188. The reaction $Hg^{2+} + Y^{4-} \rightarrow HgY^{2-}$ at a mercury electrode
(idealized curves).

and after the end point

$$Hg\downarrow + Y^{4-} - 2e \rightleftharpoons HgY^{2-}$$

and

$$Hg\downarrow - 2e \rightarrow Hg^{2+}$$

The titration curves are given in Fig. 189, 190 and 191.

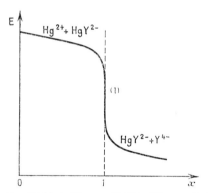

Fig. 189. The reaction $Hg^{2+} + Y^{4-} \rightarrow HgY^{2-}$. Mercury indicator electrode.
Zero current.

Constant-current titrations with potentiometric indicators

(a) We have seen on page 62 that a mercury electrode is an indicator of the concentration of EDTA (Y^{4-}). If a mercury electrode is placed in the solution of a substance which is to be determined by titration with EDTA

$$M^{2+} + Y^{4-} \rightarrow MY^{2-} \qquad K'$$

the titration may be followed.

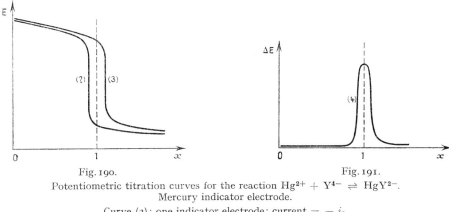

Fig. 190.   Fig. 191.

Potentiometric titration curves for the reaction $Hg^{2+} + Y^{4-} \rightleftarrows HgY^{2-}$.
Mercury indicator electrode.

Curve (2): one indicator electrode; current $= -i_\varepsilon$.
Curve (3): one indicator electrode; current $= +i_\varepsilon$.
Curve (4): two indicator electrodes; current $= |i_\varepsilon|$.

The possible electrochemical reactions at the electrode (see Fig. 192) are

$$Hg\downarrow - 2e \qquad \rightarrow Hg^{2+} \qquad\qquad E_0$$

$$Hg\downarrow + MY^{2-} - 2e \rightarrow HgY^{2-} + M^{2+} \qquad E_2 = E_0 + 0.029 \log \frac{K}{K'}$$

$$Hg\downarrow + Y^{4-} - 2e \qquad \rightarrow HgY^{2-} \qquad E_1 = E_0 + 0.029 \log K$$

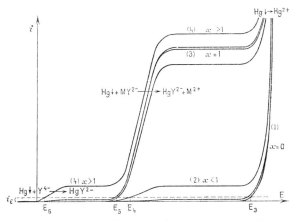

Fig. 192. The reaction $M^{2+} + Y^{4-} \rightarrow MY^{2-}$ at a mercury indicator electrode
(theoretical curves).

If the potential of the mercury electrode with respect to an electrode of fixed potential is followed, for $i = i_\varepsilon$, the titration curve of Fig. 193 is obtained.

(b) HgY^{2-} may be added to the initial solution, and the potential difference between two mercury electrodes at a constant current $|i_\varepsilon|$ can be followed. Apart from the three reactions mentioned for the previous case, the possible electrochemical reactions are, at the cathode

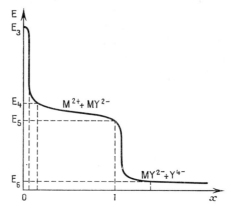

Fig. 193. Constant-current potentiometric titration curves at a mercury indicator electrode, for the reaction $M^{2+} + Y^{4-} \rightarrow MY^{2-}$ (theoretical curves).

$$HgY^{2-} + M^{2+} + 2e \rightarrow Hg{\downarrow} + MY^{2-} \qquad E_2$$

$$HgY^{2-} + 2e \rightarrow Hg{\downarrow} + Y^{4-} \qquad\qquad E_1$$

(see Fig. 194). The variation of the potential of the two electrodes during the titration and the potential difference between the two electrodes are shown in Figs. 195 and 196.

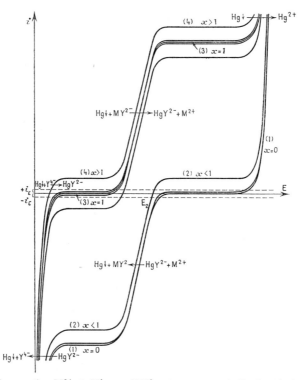

Fig. 194. The reaction $M^{2+} + Y^{4-} \rightarrow MY^{2-}$ at a mercury indicator electrode, in the presence of HgY^{2-} (theoretical curves).

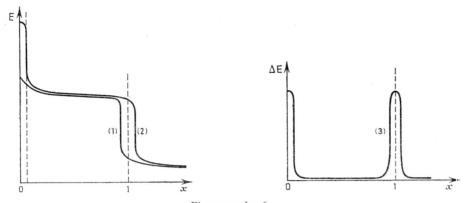

Fig. 195 and 196.
Constant-current potentiometric titration curves for the reaction $M^{2+} + Y^{4-} \rightarrow MY^{2-}$ at a mercury indicator electrode in the presence of HgY^{2-}. Curve (1): indicator cathode; curve (2): indicator anode; curve (3): two indicator electrodes (theoretical curves).

Other examples. It was suggested as long ago as 1923 that potentiometric titrations with an indicator could be used for acid–base titrations[63].

Potentiometric titrations with a variable current. It can be shown that the potential jump may still occur, although less sharply, if the current varies during the titration (see Chapter IX).

The reaction is realized electrochemically, by direct coulometry. This case is treated in Chapter X.

Micropotentiometry. See the references 47 and 56 on p. 189.

Characteristics of the various methods of potentiometric titration

Range of application

In zero-current potentiometry the equilibrium potential of a fast system (more rarely a mixed potential) must be determined. Most slow systems cannot be followed in this way, except with potentiometric indicators. Constant-current potentiometry, on the other hand, allows a large number of slow redox systems to be used when the substance to be determined or the reactant can be oxidized or reduced electrochemically, or when an indicator system can be found.

Accuracy

The chemical reactions must be sufficiently quantitative, although non-quantitative reactions can sometimes be used by stopping at the experimentally determined potential of the equivalent point, by back titration or by pretitration (see Chapter IX).

The accuracy of the determination may be limited by the volumetric or coulometric methods used.

Sensitivity

The sensitivity of the method is limited by the accuracy of the measurement of potentials at low concentrations. Below 10^{-5} N, the residual current interferes with the determination. This is true for zero-current potentiometry. Similarly, the current in constant-current potentiometry cannot be fixed at less than the residual current, which is of the order of the limiting current for a 10^{-5} N solution. A 10^{-2} N solution can therefore be titrated with an accuracy of 0.1 %, and a 10^{-3} N solution with an accuracy of 1 %.

The conditions are different for the determination of a solid deposited on an electrode (usually by coulometry, see Chapter X), but the residual current is still disturbing and still limits the accuracy of the determination. We will see below that it is possible to eliminate the influence of the residual current to a certain extent, thus allowing very dilute solutions to be titrated with sufficient accuracy (see Chapter IX).

III. INSTRUMENTATION

In potentiometry the potential difference between two electrodes must be measured. It makes no difference in principle whether the potential of only one electrode varies (one indicator electrode and one comparison electrode), or whether that of both varies (two indicator electrodes).

Electrical equipment

Zero-current potentiometry

The potential difference is measured with a millivoltmeter. The input resistance of the instrument is very large ($> 10^{12}$ Ω), and the current flowing through the measuring circuit is negligible (Fig. 197).

Constant-current potentiometry

Here the potential difference between two electrodes through which a known current passes is measured. The measurement is made in the same way as in the pre-

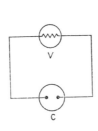

Fig. 197.

C = electrolysis cell
V = millivoltmeter (high input resistance).

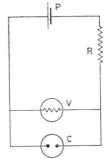

Fig. 198.

C = electrolysis cell
P = voltage source (battery)
R = resistance
V = millivoltmeter.

vious case. A current which is practically independent of what happens in the electro-lysis cell is obtained from a sufficiently constant source of high voltage (battery or stabilized power supply) and a large resistance in series with the cell (see Chapter VI). A variation of 5 % in the current during the titration has a negligible effect on the titration curve (see Chapter IX). For the circuit as a whole, $V = \Delta E - Ri$, where V is the voltage of the voltage supply, ΔE the potential difference between the elec-trodes, R the total resistance of the circuit and i the current, so that

$$i = \frac{V - \Delta E}{R}$$

If ΔE varies by 500 mV throughout the titration, i will be constant to within $\pm 5\%$ if $V = 10$ V. A resistance of 10 MΩ will then give a current of about 1 μA. It is not always necessary to check the value of the current with a galvanometer.

Variable-current potentiometry is discussed in Chapter IX.

Potential measurements during the titration

The end point in potentiometric titrations is determined by finding where the poten-tial difference between the electrodes changes more or less abruptly. The titration may be plotted point by point or recorded. In the latter case a recording millivolt-meter with a high input resistance is generally used, which gives a plot of voltage against time. The reactant must be introduced at a constant rate, using a constant-flow burette for volumetric analysis and an amperostat in coulometry. The electrode potential must reach equilibrium quickly, which is not always the case with equili-brium potentials.

But it is not necessary to plot the whole curve to determine the position of the end point: it is enough to observe the movement of the millivoltmeter needle. Auto-matic titrimeters stop the addition of the reactant at the end point, which is indicated by a sharp change in the potential: an electromagnetic valve shuts off the burette in volumetric analysis, and the electrolysis circuit is broken in coulometry.

If the potential difference does not change very sharply, the end point may still be found by finding the point of inflection of the titration curve. Instruments are available which record the differential curve, which gives an easily located maximum.

In a number of automatic titrimeters, the potential at the end point must be determined in advance. The potentiometer of a bridge circuit is then set to this value. As long as the measured potential is greater than this value (or less), a relay keeps the tap of the burette open or the electrolysis circuit closed. At the end point, the current through the relay changes sign and the titration is stopped.

REFERENCES

Determination of oxidation potentials

[1] S. GLASSTONE, *Introduction to Electrochemistry*, Van Nostrand, New York, 1942.
[2] R. WURMSER, *Oxydations et réductions*, Les Presses Universitaires, Paris, 1930.

Determination of coefficients and constants

[3] G. CHARLOT and R. GAUGUIN, *Les méthodes d'analyse des réactions en solution*, Masson, Paris, 1951.

General works, potentiometric titrations

[4] I. M. KOLTHOFF and H. A. LAITINEN, *pH and Electrotitrations*, Wiley, New York, 1944.
[5] P. DELAHAY, *New Instrumental Methods in Electrochemistry*, Interscience, New York, 1954.
[6] J. J. LINGANE, *Electroanalytical Chemistry*, Interscience, New York, 2nd ed., 1958.
[7] H. A. LAITINEN, in W. G. BERL (ed.), *Physical Method in Chemical Analysis*, Vol. II, Academic Press, New York, 1951.
[8] E. MÜLLER, *Elektrometrische Massanalyse*, Steinkopff, Leipzig, 6th ed., 1942.
[9] E. ABRAHAMCZIK, in HOUBEN-WEIL, *Methoden der Organischen Chemie*, G. Thieme, Leipzig, 4th ed., 1955.
[10] G. CHARLOT and D. BÉZIER, *Analyse quantitative minérale*, Masson, Paris, 1955 (english edition, Methuen, Wiley, 1957).

—, *hydrogen electrode*

[11] W. M. CLARK, *The Determination of Hydrogen Ions*, William and Wilkins, Baltimore, 1922.

—, *reviews*

[12] N. H. FURMAN, *Ind. Eng. Chem., Anal. Ed.*, 14 (1942) 367.
[13] N. H. FURMAN, *Anal. Chem.*, 22 (1950) 33.
[14] N. H. FURMAN, *Anal. Chem.*, 23 (1951) 21.
[15] N. H. FURMAN, *Anal. Chem.*, 26 (1954) 84.
[16] C. N. REILLEY, *Anal. Chem.*, 28 (1956) 671.

Zero-current potentiometry with one indicator electrode

—, *theory based on current–potential curves*

[17] J. COURSIER, *Thesis*, Masson, Paris, 1954.
[18] J. COURSIER, *Ann. Chim.*, 9 (1954) 353.
[19] J. COURSIER, *Anal. Chim. Acta*, 7 (1952) 77, 585.
[20] J. COURSIER, *Anal. Chim. Acta*, 10 (1954) 182.
[21] R. GAUGUIN, *J. Chim. phys.*, 42 (1945) 34.

—, *electrodes of gold amalgam and mercury*

[22] C. N. REILLEY, R. W. SCHMID and D. W. LAMSON, *Anal. Chem.*, 30 (1958) 953.

Reference electrodes without junction

[23] E. BISHOP, *Analyst*, 77 (1952) 672.

Zero-current potentiometry with two indicator electrodes

[24] H. WILLARD and F. FENWICK, *J. Am. Chem. Soc.*, 44 (1922) 2504.
[25] R. G. VAN NAME and F. FENWICK, *J. Am. Chem. Soc.*, 47 (1925) 9.
[26] N. H. FURMAN and E. B. WILSON JR., *J. Am. Chem. Soc.*, 50 (1928) 277.
[27] E. MÜLLER and H. KOGERT, *Z. physik. Chem.*, 136 (1928) 436.
[28] B. KAMIENSKI, *Z. physik. Chem.*, 145 (1929) 48.
[29] R. M. FUOSS, *Ind. Eng. Chem., Anal. Ed.*, 1 (1929) 125.
[30] M. L. HOLT and L. KAHLENBERG, *Trans. Am. Electrochem. Soc.*, 57 (1930) 361.

—, *theory*

[31] J. COURSIER, *Anal. Chim. Acta*, 10 (1954) 265.
[32] I. M. KOLTHOFF, *Anal. Chem.*, 26 (1954) 1685.

—, *silver and silver amalgam*

[33] E. G. COGBILL and J. J. KIRKLAND, *Anal. Chem.*, 57 (1955) 1611.

—, *platinum, tungsten*

[34] I. M. KOLTHOFF and E. R. NIGHTINGALE JR., *Anal. Chim. Acta*, 19 (1958) 593.

Constant-current potentiometry

[35] P. DUTOIT and G. VON WEISSE, *J. Chim. phys.*, 9 (1911) 578, 608, 630.
[36] H. H. WILLARD and F. FENWICK, *J. Am. Chem. Soc.*, 44 (1922) 2504, 2516.

37 H. H. WILLARD and F. FENWICK, *J. Am. Chem. Soc.*, 45 (1923) 84, 623, 715, 928.
38 R. G. VAN NAME and F. FENWICK, *J. Am. Chem. Soc.*, 47 (1925) 19.
39 C. BERTIN, *Anal. Chim. Acta*. 5 (1951) 1.
40 C. N. REILLEY, W. D. COOKE and F. FURMAN, *Anal. Chem.*, 23 (1951) 1223.
41 R. GAUGUIN, *Anal. Chim. Acta*, 5 (1951) 200.
42 R. GAUGUIN, G. CHARLOT, C. BERTIN and J. BADOZ, *Anal. Chim. Acta*, 7 (1952) 360.
43 G. DUYKAERTS, *Anal. Chim. Acta*, 8 (1953) 57.
44 M. TEGZE, *Acta Chim. Acad. Sci. Hung.*, 3 (1953) 391.
45 R. N. ADAMS, *Anal. Chem.*, 26 (1954) 1933.
46 N. TANAKA, I. T. OIWA and M. KODAMA, *Anal. Chem.*, 28 (1956) 1955.
47 E. BISHOP, *Microchim. Acta*, (1956) 619.
48 C. O. HUBER and I. SHAIN, *Anal. Chem.*, 29 (1957) 1178.
49 N. Y. KHLOPIN and L. G. GEIN, *Zhur. Anal. Khim. S.S.S.R.*, 12 (1957) 561.
50 I. M. KOLTHOFF and E. R. NIGHTINGALE JR., *Anal. Chim. Acta*, 17 (1957) 329.
51 J. K. LEE and R. N. ADAMS, *Anal. Chem.*, 30 (1958) 240.
52 R. GAUGUIN, *Anal. Chim. Acta*, 18 (1958) 29.
53 E. BISHOP, *Analyst*, 83 (1958) 211.
54 E. R. NIGHTINGALE JR., *Anal. Chim. Acta*, 19 (1958) 587.

——, *review*

55 N. TANAKA, *Japan Analyst*, 4 (1955) 640.

Micropotentiometry

56 J. T. STOCK, *Analyst*, 73 (1948) 321.

Potentiometric indicators

57 S. SIGGIA and D. W. EICHLIN, *Anal. Chem.*, 27 (1955) 1745.
58 C. N. REILLEY, W. G. SCRIBNER and C. TEMPLE, *Anal. Chem.*, 28 (1956) 450.
59 C. N. REILLEY and W. W. PORTERFIELD, *Anal. Chem.*, 28 (1956) 443.
60 C. N. REILLEY and R. W. SCHMID, *Anal. Chem.*, 30 (1958) 947.
61 C. N. REILLEY, R. W. SCHMID and D. W. LAMSON, *Anal. Chem.*, 30 (1958) 953.
62 L. FARKAS and L. URI, *Anal. Chem.*, 20 (1948) 237.
63 H. H. WILLARD and F. FENWICK, *J. Am. Chem. Soc.*, 45 (1923) 714.
64 L. M. BUDANOVA and O. P. PLATANOVA, *Zavodskaya Lab.*, 21 (1955) 1294.

Instrumentation

——, *general works*

65 P. DELAHAY, *Instrumental Analysis*, Macmillan, New York, 1957.
66 C. R. N. STROUTS, J. H. GILFILLAN and N. H. WILSON, *Analytical Chemistry*, Clarendon, Oxford, 1955, Vol. II, p. 561.
67 M. QUINTIN, *Techniques électrochimiques appliquées à l'étude des solutions*, Centre de Documentation Universitaire, Paris, 1955, p. 182.
68 E. C. POTTER, *Electrochemistry, Principles and Applications*, Cleaver-Hume, London, 1956, p. 203.
69 J. J. LINGANE, *Electroanalytical Chemistry*, Interscience, New York, 1958, p. 31–241.

——, *electrical circuit*

70 E. ABRAHAMCZIK, in HOUBEN-WEIL, *Methoden der Organischen Chemie*, G. Thieme, Leipzig, 4th ed., 1955, p. 138.
71 I. SHAIN and C. O. HUBER, *Anal. Chem.*, 30 (1958) 1286.

——, *automatic instruments*

72 J. J. LINGANE, *Electroanalytical Chemistry*, Interscience, New York, 1958, 2nd ed., p. 158.

——, *applications*

73 G. D. PATTERSON JR., *Anal. Chem.*, 29 (1957) 610.
74 J. E. DUBOIS and W. WALISH, *Compt. rend.*, 242 (1956) 1161, 1289.
75 J. E. DUBOIS, M. ASHWORTH and W. WALISH, *Compt. rend.*, 242 (1956) 1452.
76 M. LELEU and M. LECHEVALLIER, *Electron. ind.*, (1957) 183.

——, *for constant-current potentiometry*

77 A. MAC INNES, YANG CHIA-CHIH and A. R. PRAY, *J. Phys. Chem.*, 61 (1957) 662.
78 I. SHAIN and C. O. HUBER, *Anal. Chem.*, 30 (1958) 1286.

Potentiometric titrations

—, *recording*

[79] H. ZIEGEL, *Trans. Am. Electrochem. Soc.*, 26 (1914) 91.
[80] E. A. KEELER, *Ind. Eng. Chem.*, 14 (1922) 395.
[81] G. GUTZEIT and C. DEVAUD, *Arch. sci. phys. et nat.*, 11 (1929) 67.
[82] W. KORDATZKI and P. WULFF, *Chem. Fabr.*, 3 (1930) 329, 342.
[83] W. KORDATZKI and P. WULFF, *Z. Anal. Chem.*, 89 (1932) 241.
[84] J. M. G. BAREDDO and J. K. TAYLOR, *Trans. Electrochem. Soc.*, 92 (1947) 437.
[85] E. F. MUELLER, *Ind. Eng. Chem., Anal. Ed.*, 12 (1940) 171.
[86] A. KROGH, *J. Chem. Soc.*, (1931) 2436.
[87] A. KROGH, *Ind. Eng. Chem., Anal. Ed.*, 7 (1935) 130.
[88] R. H. MÜLLER, *Ind. Eng. Chem., Anal. Ed.*, 18 (1946) 23 (adv. sect.).
[89] J. J. LINGANE, *Anal. Chem.*, 20 (1948) 285.
[90] H. A. ROBINSON, *Trans. Electrochem. Soc.*, 2 (1947) 445.

—, *titration to a predetermined end point*

[91] H. VOGELS, *Bull. sci. roy. Belg.*, 19 (1943) 452.
[92] W. E. SHENK and F. FENWICK, *Ind. Eng. Chem., Anal. Ed.*, 7 (1935) 194.
[93] D. J. POMPEO, C. J. PENTHER and K. E. HALLIKAINEN, *Instruments*, 16 (1943) 402.
[94] R. H. MÜLLER and J. J. LINGANE, *Anal. Chem.*, 20 (1948) 795.
[95] J. J. LINGANE, *Anal. Chem.*, 20 (1948) 285, 797.
[96] J. J. LINGANE, *Anal. Chem.*, 21 (1949) 407.
[97] R. C. HAWES, A. STRICKLER and T. H. PETTERSON, *Elec. Mfg.* 47 (1951) 76.
[98] M. T. KELLEY and E. B. WAGNER, *Oak Ridge* 7 (apr. 20, 1955).
[99] J. T. STOCK, *Analyst*, 84 (1958) 982.

—, *differential potentiometry*

[100] P. DELAHAY, *Anal. Chem.*, 20 (1948) 1212.
[101] P. DELAHAY, *Anal. Chim. Acta*, 1 (1947) 19.

Using the curve dE/dV as a function of reactant added

[102] R. C. HAWES, A. STRICKLER and T. H. PETTERSON, *Elec. Mfg.*, 47 (1951) 76, 212.
[103] W. N. CARSON, *Anal. Chem.*, 25 (1953) 1733.
[104] C. F. JACOBSEN and J. LEONIS, *Compt. rend. trav. lab. Carlsberg., Ser. Chim.*, 27 (1951) 333.
[105] D. A. MAC INNES and M. DOLE, *J. Am. Chem. Soc.*, 51 (1929) 1119.
[106] H. H. BAKER and R. H. MÜLLER, *Trans. Electrochem. Soc.*, 76 (1939) 75.
[107] P. DELAHAY, *Bull. soc. chim. Belg.*, 56 (1947) 7.
[108] P. DELAHAY, *Anal. Chem.*, 20 (1948) 1212, 1215.
[109] T. TAKAHASHI, E. NIKI and K. KIMOTO, *Japan Analyst*, 3 (1956) 236.

—, *plotting the second derivative*

[110] H. B. MALMSTADT and E. R. FETT, *Anal. Chem.*, 26 (1954) 1348.
[111] H. B. MALMSTADT and E. R. FETT, *Anal. Chem.*, 27 (1955) 1757.

Chapter VIII

AMPEROMETRY

As the name indicates, this method entails the determination of the nett current passing through the electrolysis cell.

1. The current is a function of the concentration of the electroactive substances and of the potential. Under certain standardized conditions, it is possible to determine the concentration of the electrolyzed substances by measuring the current. Such determinations are usually classed under the name of polarography, especially when a dropping mercury electrode is used.

2. Measurement of the current may be used to follow the concentration changes during a chemical or electrochemical reaction; for example it may be used to control the course of a reaction or to follow a titration, and in particular to determine its end point. Such titrations are called amperometric titrations, and may be volumetric or coulometric according to whether the reactant is added in known amounts from a burette or by electrolysis.

3. Conversely, knowing the composition of the solution, this method may be used to determine the reaction coefficients and the equilibrium constant of the reactions.

In this chapter we will discuss: (*a*) the measurement of concentrations under standard conditions (classical polarography); (*b*) amperometric titrations.

As in the previous chapter, we will only consider the steady state where, for a given potential and a given concentration, the current does not vary with time. The measurement of the current in the non-stationary state is discussed in Chapter XII.

1. ELECTRODE INDICATIONS

The indications supplied by the electrodes are governed by an equation of the form $f(E, i, C) = 0$, where C is the concentration of the electroactive substance. The form of this equation is known for the case where the solution contains an indifferent electrolyte and where the conditions at the electrodes approach a steady state. When the potential is constant, the equation becomes $f(i, C) = 0$; and when the current reaches its limiting value the simple law $i_{red} = k_{red} |\text{Red}|$ or $i_{ox} = -k_{ox} |\text{Ox}|$ holds, and a slight change in the applied potential leaves the current practically unchanged. Under these conditions, the current is proportional to the concentration of the electrolyzed substances in the solution.

Application to quantitative analysis. Classical polarography

This is a very important method which is the subject of a number of books. Only the general principles will be given here.

Principle

The oxidation or reduction occurs at an electrode called the indicator electrode; the other electrode usually has a fixed potential. The current–potential curves then only differ from the current–voltage curves by Ri, the ohmic drop in the cell. In both cases, the value of the limiting diffusion current, i_{ox} or i_{red}, is proportional to the concentration of the substance oxidized or reduced at the indicator electrode. A calibration is carried out with solutions of known concentrations, and the unknown concentration can then be deduced.

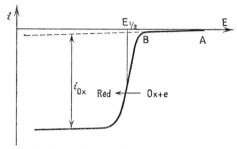

Fig. 199. Current–potential curve for the electrochemical reaction Ox + e → Red.

In a polarographic determination, the substance to be determined is electrolyzed at the indicator electrode. The voltage applied between the electrodes is varied, and the current–potential curve for the indicator electrode is thus traced (Fig. 199). The value of the limiting current is then measured, and under suitable conditions this is proportional to the concentration of the substance oxidized or reduced at the indicator electrode

$$i_D = k_D . C$$

If several oxidants or reductants are present, a curve like that of Fig. 200 is obtained. When the various half-wave potentials are sufficiently far from each other a series of distinct steps is obtained, and the concentrations of the various substances may be determined from the heights of the corresponding steps.

The value of the constant k_{ox} or k_{red} naturally depends on the geometry and size of the cell and electrode used; it is therefore always necessary to calibrate the equipment at some stage with a solution of known concentration.

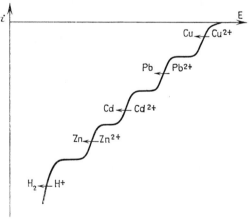

Fig. 200. Successive reactions.

The law $i_{red} = - k_{red} |Red|$ only holds for low concentrations, usually in the range 10 to 1000 p.p.m. It is also necessary that the overall concentration of the electrolyzed substance should not change appreciably during the determination. The current must therefore be small, and since the current density must be fairly large to give limiting currents, the surface area of the indicator electrode must be very small. The currents met with in classical polarography are of the order of 10^{-4} to 10^{-8} A.

The residual current (the current obtained when no electroactive substances are present in the solution, see p. 129) should in principle be subtracted from the total current measured.

The most widely used indicator electrode for polarography is the dropping mercury electrode. Its advantages are: (a) good reproducibility of the diffusion conditions (pseudo-steady state, see p. 144); (b) constant renewal of the electrode surface; (c) the large overvoltage of hydrogen on mercury which allows the reduction of a large number of substances, including certain cations the reduced forms of which metals form amalgams with mercury. The disadvantages are: (a) the anodic dissolution of mercury, $Hg\downarrow - 2e \rightarrow Hg^{2+}$, which limits the useful potential range to $+ 0.70$ V under the best conditions, i.e. in the absence of ions which form complexes or precipitates with Hg(I) or Hg(II). In molar chloride solution the oxidation potential of mercury is only 0.30 V (b) the large residual current (see Chapter VI); (c) the existance of polarographic maxima (see Chapter VI).

For the other types of electrode, see Chapter VI. Unlike the usual convention in electrolysis, in polarography the cathodic current is usually plotted upwards, and more reducing (lower) potentials to the right. The potential of the calomel electrode is often taken as the origin.

Influence of chemical reactions

We have seen in Chapter III and IV the influence of acid–base, complex-formation, precipitation, and redox reactions on the form of the current–potential curves.

Such effects (especially that of the pH and of complexing agents) can be used to improve the selectivity of polarographic determinations by displacing the half-wave potentials. Fig. 201 shows the reduction of Tl^+ and Pb^{2+}: in 0.1 M HCl the two curves cannot be distinguished (curve 1) and it is not possible to determine the two ions separately; in the presence of an excess of OH^- ions, which have a different effect on the two ions, two distinct steps are obtained (curve 2).

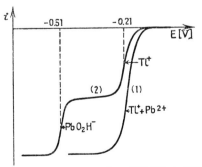

Fig. 201. Polarography of Pb(II) + Tl(I).
Curve (1): reduction of $Pb^{2+} + Tl^+$ in 0.1 N HCl.
Curve (2): reduction of $PbO_2H^- + Tl^+$ in an alkaline medium (see KOLTHOFF and LINGANE [5]).

Amperometric indicators

We may give the name of amperometric indicators to oxidants or reductants which allow the concentration of non-electroactive substances to be determined by the measurement of a current (see p. 56).

Consider a redox system involving more than two substances, *e.g.*

$$AB + e \rightleftharpoons B + C$$

Let us suppose that we add some C to a solution of B, which is not electroactive, and whose concentration we wish to determine. The current–potential curves for the oxidation of C have the form shown in Fig. 202. The limiting diffusion current is proportional to the concentration of B if C is present in excess (see Chapter III).

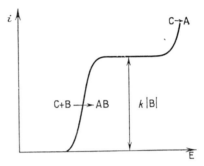

Fig. 202. C as an indicator of the concentration of B.

Many examples exist of determinations of this type at dropping mercury electrode and at other metallic electrodes (see amperometric titrations):

Mercury electrode as an indicator of the concentration of halides

$$2\,Hg\downarrow + 2\,X^- - 2e \rightleftharpoons Hg_2X_2\downarrow$$

or of EDTA

$$Hg\downarrow + Y^{4-} - 2e \rightleftharpoons HgY^{2-}$$

Silver electrode as an indicator of the concentration of halides

$$Ag\downarrow + X^- - e \rightarrow AgX, \quad \text{etc.}$$

Fig. 86, p. 81, shows the use of a mercury electrode to indicate successively the CN^-, I^-, Br^- and Cl^- ions.

Parasitic phenomena

Influence of dissolved oxygen. The reduction of oxygen may be superimposed on the electrochemical reaction used for the determination, and thus give difficulties in the potential range in which this reduction occurs. The potential range varies from electrode to electrode (see Chapter IV); for a mercury cathode, it starts at 0.25 V. The oxygen can be removed by bubbling nitrogen through the solution (see p. 140).

Certain other factors can also disturb polarographic determinations: temperature variations, the residual current, adsorption, formation of films on the electrode, etc. These questions have all been discussed in Chapter V.

Characteristics of the method

Field of application. Polarography allows certain determinations, especially of organic substances, to be made which are not possible by any other method. It is sometimes the simplest method to use for the determination of inorganic substances (*e.g.* a mixture of Zn^{2+} and Cd^{2+}). It is also useful for the repetitive determination of many elements.

Under favourable conditions several elements can be determined at the same time; and the one operation can give both qualitative and quantitative results: the values of the half-wave potentials are often characteristic of the substances to be determined, and the step heights give a measure of their concentrations. The methods lends itself to automation since preliminary chemical separations are sometimes unnecessary, or considerably reduced in extent.

Selectivity. This depends on the half-wave potentials of the substances, which must differ by at least 250 mV in order to give a separation. As we have seen, the selectivity can sometimes be improved by displacing the curves by chemical means.

Sensitivity. This is limited only by the size and reproducibility of the residual current, and is usually 10^{-5} to 10^{-6} N. In micropolarography, where very small volumes are treated with the aid of special equipment (*e.g.* 0.01 ml), very small quantities can be determined, *e.g.* 0.01 μg of zinc.

Accuracy. This is of the order of 2 or 3 per cent (rarely 1 per cent), for concentrations of 10^{-3} to 10^{-4} N, though certain precautions have to be taken, *e.g.* the temperature must be kept constant. The method is most useful for the determination of small amounts of substances, for the accuracy is often still 5 % for concentrations of 10^{-5} N.

Differential polarography and derivative polarography

Normal polarography does not give a good accuracy when it is wished to determine the concentration of a small amount of a substance B in the presence of considerably more of a substance A, which is reduced before B, since the limiting diffusion current of B is determined as the difference of two large quantities (Fig. 203). Three methods may be used to solve this problem to a certain extent.

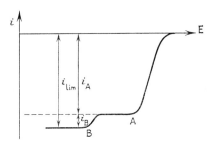

Fig. 203. Differential polarography.

Use of a counter-current. A counter-current slightly less than i_A, the limiting current of A, is passed through the electrolysis circuit. The current is then not much greater than i_B, so a greater galvanometer sensitivity can be used in determining it.

Differential polarography. The concentration of A is first determined, and a second cell is filled with a solution containing the same concentration of A, but no B. One dropping mercury electrode is placed in each cell, and the two are synchronized, i.e. they have the same dropping time and the two drops of mercury are detached simultaneously. The two electrolysis circuits are arranged so that the currents are opposed. The resulting current is then due only to B; the effect of A has been eliminated.

Derivative polarography. The curve $di/dE = f(E)$ can be obtained directly, with the aid of suitable electronic equipment

$$\frac{di}{dE} = \frac{nF}{RT} \cdot \frac{\exp\left[\frac{nF}{RT}(E - E_{\frac{1}{2}})\right]}{\left\{1 + \exp\left[\frac{nF}{RT}(E - E_{\frac{1}{2}})\right]\right\}^2} \quad \text{and} \quad \left(\frac{di}{dE}\right)_{\text{max}} = -\frac{2.303\, n i_D}{0.0591 \times 4}$$

The half-wave potential $E_{\frac{1}{2}}$, which corresponds to a point of inflection of the current–potential curve, gives a maximum in the derived curve. The height of this maximum is proportional to the concentration of the substance to be determined (Fig. 204)

$$(di/dE)_{\text{max}} = k'C$$

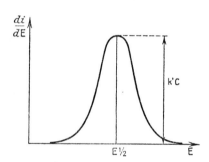

Fig. 204. Derivative polarography.

It is easy to see that since i_A is constant in the potential range in which the reduction step of B occurs, $di_A/dE = 0$, while in this same range i_B is increasing so that its derivative is positive. Measuring the derivative of the total reduction current thus eliminates the influence of A. This method also has the advantage of allowing determinations when the half-wave potentials are very close.

Other methods may be used to get curves similar to the differentiated curve of the polarographic step, and have the same advantages as this method (see a.c.-modulated polarography, Chapter XII).

Instrumentation

The general methods of determining the current–potential curves are described in Chapter VI. All details concerning the special case of classical polarography (plotting the curves at a dropping mercury electrode): description of the cells, circuits, equipment, etc., are given in the references 1–63 of this Chapter.

II. AMPEROMETRIC TITRATIONS

We have seen that the measurement of the current may be used to determine concentrations. This method may also be used to follow the concentrations during a reaction, in particular during a titration. An amperometric titration thus consists in following the variation of the current during a chemical reaction (volumetric analysis or coulometry).

There are thus two reaction systems in this case:
(a) the chemical titration reaction, which is often quantitative;
(b) the electrochemical reactions at the indicator electrode, which must involve negligible amounts of the substances to be determined compared to the titration reaction.

In a volumetric titration the reactant is added in known amounts from a burette, while in a coulometric titration it is formed in known amounts by electrolysis (see Chapter X). It is also possible to follow the variation of concentration during an electrochemical reaction (direct coulometry).

There are two main types of amperometric titrations:
1. with one indicator electrode and one reference electrode;
2. with two indicator electrodes, of the same or different natures.

The electrodes may be inert or reactive. In both cases, a suitably chosen constant voltage is applied between the two electrodes. Sometimes it is possible to short-circuit the electrodes, thus giving zero voltage between them. If one indicator and one reference electrode are used, in this case the former is thus given the same potential as the latter, if we neglect the ohmic drop.

Titration with one indicator electrode

The titration curves

These curves, showing the current as a function of the reactant added in volumetric analysis or of the quantity of electricity in coulometry, are usually made up of straight lines if the reaction is quantitative, since the current is proportional to the concentration. Let us consider for example the chemical titration reaction

$$A + B \rightarrow AB$$

If A is an oxidant, the indicator reaction may be of the form $A + e \rightarrow C$ (Fig. 205). At the potential E_1, applied to the indicator electrode, the current measured is the diffusion current of $A: i_A = - k_A |A|$. The concentration of A may thus be followed during the chemical reaction, thanks to the indicator reaction (Fig. 206). Fig. 207 and 208 show what happens when C is also present.

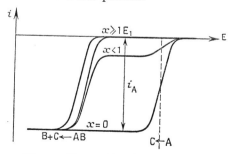

Fig. 205. The reaction $A + B \rightarrow AB$.

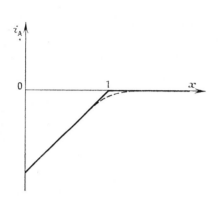

Fig. 206. Amperometric titration curve for the reaction A + B → AB, at a potential E_1.

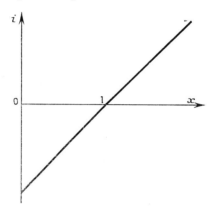

Fig. 207. The reaction A + B → AB in the presence of C.

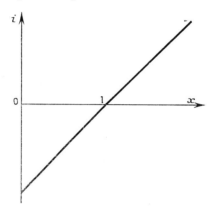

Fig. 208. Amperometric titration curve for the reaction A + B → AB in the presence of an excess of C, at a potential E_1.

Other types of titration reactions are possible; *e.g.* A + B → C + D. The current–potential curves for the reduction of A and the oxidation of B are shown in Fig. 209. At the potential E_1, A is reduced and B is oxidized. Thus, before the end point the current corresponds to the reduction of A and after the end point to the oxidation of B; it changes sign near the end point (Fig. 210).

We may mention the following properties of titration curves of this kind:

1. If the reactant is added in solution (volumetric analysis) the current must be corrected for the dilution which occurs during the titration. If V is the initial volume and v the volume of B added, the current must be multiplied by the factor $(V+v)/V$.

2. This method can still be used if the reaction is not really quantitative, giving a titration curve as shown by the dotted line in Fig. 206. If measurements are made with an excess of A and an excess of B, the two straight lines are defined, and their point of intersection gives the end point. Consecutive non-quantitative reactions can also be followed.

3. The end point can be determined with great accuracy if a large number of points are taken to define the straight lines.

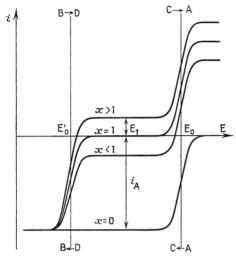

Fig. 209. The reaction A + B → C + D.

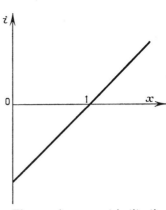

Fig. 210. Amperometric titration
curve for the reaction A + B →
C + D at a potential E_1.

Examples

Only the substance to be titrated is reduced at the electrode. Consider the titration reaction
$Pb^{2+} + SO_4^{2-} \rightarrow PbSO_4\downarrow$. The current–potential curves at a dropping mercury electrode in the absence of oxygen are shown in Fig. 211. It will be seen that if the potential of the indicator electrode is fixed at E_1, the reaction

$$Pb^{2+} + Hg\downarrow + 2e \rightarrow Pb(Hg) \quad \text{with} \quad i = -k_{Pb^{2+}} \cdot |Pb^{2+}|$$

will occur, giving the titration curve shown in Fig. 212.

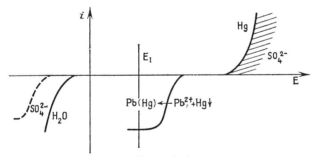

Fig. 211. Theoretical curves.

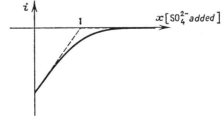

Fig. 212. The reaction $Pb^{2+} + SO_4^{2-} \rightarrow PbSO_4\downarrow$ at a mercury electrode
(after MAJER[57], see KOLTHOFF and PAN[58]).

Only the reactant is reduced at the electrode. Consider the titration of arsenious acid with bromate

$$3 HAsO_2 + BrO_3^- + 3 H_2O \rightarrow 3 H_3AsO_4 + Br^-$$

After the end point the reaction becomes

$$BrO_3^- + 5 Br^- + 6 H^+ \rightarrow 3 Br_2 + 3 H_2O$$

The current–potential curves at a rotating or vibrating platinum electrode are given in Fig. 213. It is convenient to fix the potential of the indicator electrode at E_1; this

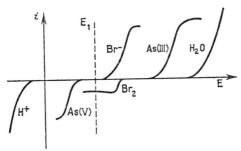

Fig. 213. Theoretical curves.

may be done by connecting the platinum electrode directly to a calomel reference electrode, with only a galvanometer in between. Under these conditions the only possible electrochemical reaction is

$$Br_2 + 2e \rightarrow 2 Br^-$$

so the titration curve is as shown in Fig. 214. The current is zero until the end point.

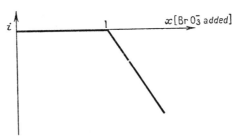

Fig. 214. The reactions $3 As(III) + Br(V) \rightarrow 3 As(V) + Br^-$ and $5 Br^- + Br(V) \rightarrow 3 Br_2$ at a platinum electrode (after KOLTHOFF and LINGANE[5], p. 947).

Both the substance to be determined and the reactant are reduced at the electrode. Consider the titration reaction

$$2 Pb^{2+} + Cr_2O_7^{2-} + H_2O \rightarrow 2 PbCrO_4\downarrow + 2 H^+$$

at a dropping mercury electrode. The current–potential curves are given in Fig. 215. At the potential E_1, the possible electrochemical reactions are

$$Pb^{2+} + Hg\downarrow + 2e \rightarrow Pb(Hg)$$

and

$$Cr_2O_7^{2-} + 6 H^+ + 6e \rightarrow 2 Cr^{3+} + 3 H_2O$$

giving the titration curve shown in Fig. 216. Only Pb^{2+} is reduced before the end point, and only $Cr_2O_7^{2-}$ after (Fig. 217).

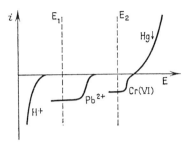

Fig. 215. Theoretical curves.

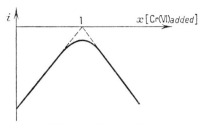

Fig. 216. The reaction
$Pb^{2+} + CrO_4^{2-} \rightarrow PbCrO_4\downarrow$ at a mercury electrode (after KOLTHOFF and PAN [59]).

Complex formation. Consider the titration of bismuth (III) with EDTA

$$Bi^{3+} + Y^{4-} \rightarrow BiY^-$$

The possible electrochemical reactions are

$$Bi^{3+} + 3e \rightarrow Bi\downarrow$$
$$BiY^- + 3e \rightarrow Bi\downarrow + Y^{4-}$$

The current–potential curves are given in Fig. 217. At a potential E_1, only the first reaction occurs and the titration curve is then as shown in Fig. 218.

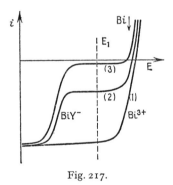

Fig. 217.

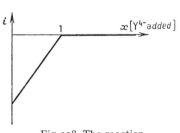

Fig. 218. The reaction
$Bi^{3+} + Y^{4-} \rightarrow BiY^-$.

Consecutive titrations. (The titration of Pb^{2+} and Ba^{2+} with dichromate). The titration reactions are

$$2\,Pb^{2+} + Cr_2O_7^{2-} + H_2O \rightarrow 2\,PbCrO_4\downarrow + 2\,H^+ \tag{1}$$
$$2\,Ba^{2+} + Cr_2O_7^{2-} + H_2O \rightarrow 2\,BaCrO_4\downarrow + 2\,H^+ \tag{2}$$

At first only reaction (1) occurs, and then both, and finally only reaction (2), which is not quantitative.

The current–potential curves for the electrochemical reactions are shown in Fig. 215: Ba^{2+} is not electroactive. If the potential is fixed at E_2, the electrode reaction is

$$Cr_2O_7^{2-} + 14\,H^+ + 6e \rightarrow 2\,Cr^{3+} + 7\,H_2O$$

which occurs after the end point. The titration curve is given in Fig. 219 (curve 1).
As long as reactions (1) and (2) occur, the current is zero, and only the sum $Pb^{2+} +$
Ba^{2+} can be determined. But if the indicator electrode potential is fixed at E_1, the
indicator reaction $Pb^{2+} + Hg\downarrow + 2e \rightarrow Pb(Hg)$ may occur during reaction (1).
During reaction (2) no electroactive substance is present, so the current is zero; and
after the second end point the indicator reaction is the reduction of dichromate, so
the whole titration curve is given by curve 2, Fig. 219. Reaction (2) begins before
reaction (1) is quite complete, and moreover the second reaction is not quantitative;
but the theoretical end points may be obtained by producing the straight lines (broken
lines in figure).

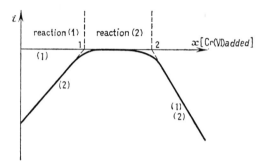

Fig. 219. The reactions $Pb^{2+} + CrO_4^{2-} \rightarrow PbCrO_4\downarrow$ (1)
and $Ba^{2+} + CrO_4^{2-} \rightarrow BaCrO_4\downarrow$ (2)
at a mercury electrode (after KOLTHOFF and GREGOR[60]).

The current changes sign at the end point. (The titration of Ti^{3+} with Fe^{3+}.) The titration
reactions are

$$Ti^{3+} + Fe^{3+} \rightarrow Ti^{4+} + Fe^{2+}$$

At a potential E_1 the indicator reactions are

$$Ti^{3+} - e \rightarrow Ti^{4+}$$

before the end point, and

$$Fe^{3+} + e \rightarrow Fe^{2+}$$

after. The current–potential curves are shown in Fig. 220. At first Ti^{3+} is oxidized, so
the current is positive. When the Ti^{3+} has all gone, Fe^{3+} can exist in solution; the

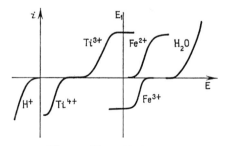

Fig. 220. Theoretical curves.

electrode now acts as a cathode. The end point corresponds to the point where the current changes sign. The titration curve is shown in Fig. 221.

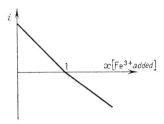

Fig. 221. The reaction $Ti^{3+} + Fe^{3+} \rightarrow Ti^{4+} + Fe^{2+}$ at a platinum electrode.

The electrode is reactive. (Titration of a silver salt with chloride.) The titration reaction is

$$Ag^+ + Cl^- \rightarrow AgCl\downarrow$$

The current–potential curves at a silver electrode are shown in Fig. 222. It will be seen that if the electrode potential is fixed at E_1, two electrochemical reactions are possible

$$Ag^+ + e \rightarrow Ag\downarrow$$

before the end point and

$$Ag\downarrow + Cl^- - e \rightarrow AgCl\downarrow$$

after. The titration curve is then given by curve 1, Fig. 223. At the potential E_2 the only possible indicator reaction is $Ag^+ + e \rightarrow Ag\downarrow$, giving the titration curve 2, Fig. 223.

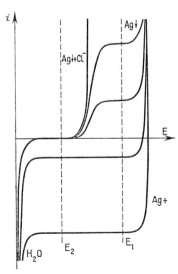

Fig. 222. Theoretical curves.

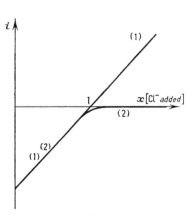

Fig. 223. The reaction
$Ag^+ + Cl^- \rightarrow AgCl\downarrow$
at a silver electrode.

Titration without any chemical reaction. An oxidant and a reductant which do not react with each other may be respectively reduced and oxidized at a given potential. Thus, Cu(II) and Sn(II) give the current-potential curves shown in Fig. 224 in a tartrate buffer of pH 4. There is no chemical reaction. If the potential of the indicator electrode is fixed at E_1, the current is given by

$$i = i_{Sn} - i_{Cu} = k_{Sn}\,|\,Sn(II)\,| - k_{Cu}\,|\,Cu(II)\,|$$

If a solution of Cu(II) of known concentration is added to a solution of Sn(II), the titration curve of Fig. 225 is obtained, with $i = 0$ when $|\,Cu(II)\,|/|\,Sn(II).\, = k_{Sn}/k_{Cu}$. The titration is thus possible if a preliminary calibration is carried out to determine the value of k_{Sn}/k_{Cu} under the conditions used.

Fig. 224 and 225. Titration without any chemical reaction (after LINGANE[73]).

Simplified methods

Let us consider for example the amperometric titration of arsenious acid with bromate (Fig. 214, p. 200). If the reaction is sufficiently quantitative, the current remains practically zero up to the end point, and if the galvanometer is sufficiently sensitive it will give an appreciable deflection when a very small amount of bromate is added after the end point. The appearance of current thus indicates the end point.

Under these conditions it is no longer necessary to determine the titration curve, so all the precautions needed to ensure that the law $i_D = k_D \cdot C$ is obeyed are unnecessary: the stirring need not be very regular, the temperature may vary, the electrodes need not be in exactly the same condition during the whole titration. A platinum electrode can then be used as the indicator electrode (see this Chapter, *Instrumentation*, p. 218).

A further simplification may be introduced by using a second electrode (which may be a reactive metal) whose potential is such as to give a galvanic cell with the platinum electrode.

Amperometric titrations with two indicator electrodes
Principle

In the previous case, the electrolysis was carried out with one indicator electrode and one reference electrode. The potential of the reference electrode remained constant whatever the current, so if a potential difference was applied between the electrodes, the indicator was given a practically constant potential.

In this case the two electrodes are plunged directly into the solution and a potential difference ΔE is applied between them. The current–potential curves at these two electrodes depend on the nature and the surface area of each one. These curves may be used to predict the current changes occurring during a titration.

The potential of one of the electrodes is practically constant

This is so when the potential of one of the electrodes corresponds to the electrolysis of a substance which does not take part in the reaction, *e.g.* the solvent, or chloride ion in the presence of a silver electrode, or any other substance added to the solution with the intention of producing a constant potential at the electrode in question. This case is very similar to that of one indicator electrode and one reference electrode.

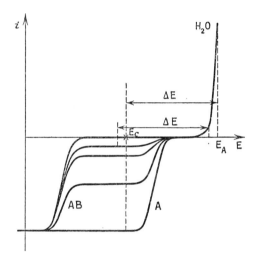

Fig. 226. The reaction A + B → AB.

Consider for example the chemical reaction A + B → AB. A is reducible: A + e → C. The current–potential curves for this reaction have already been discussed (see p. 174), and are given again in Fig. 226. Only one electrochemical oxidation reaction is possible, that of the solvent

$$2 \, H_2O - 4e \rightarrow O_2 + 4 \, H^+$$

If a given potential difference ΔE is applied between the electrodes, the electrode which acts as anode will assume the potential E_A, corresponding to the current i, while the other electrode will have the potential E_C and the current $- i$.

The relationship $i = - k_A \, |A|$ holds as long as the potential E_C remains in the range in which the diffusion of A is limiting. Now the system is under the restraint

$$\Delta E = E_C - E_A = \text{constant}$$

Since the anodic part of the current-potential curve is nearly vertical, E_A does not vary much as i decreases, so E_C remains fairly constant too. Under these conditions, the current is proportional to the concentration of A (Fig. 227).

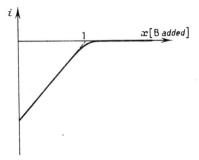

Fig. 227. The reaction A + B → AB.

Both electrodes are indicator electrodes

Let us again consider the example of the titration of A with B, but suppose that this time the solution contains both A and C, with A + e → C (fast system). When a potential difference ΔE is applied between the two electrodes (Fig. 228), the current is limited by the anodic or the cathodic reaction, depending on which has the smaller limiting diffusion current. The conditions are chosen so that the limiting current is that of the substance whose concentration is to be followed, *i.e.* A or B. An excess of C must be used, so that the reaction C − e → A never limits the current. Before the end point, the current is limited by the diffusion of A, with the reaction A + e → C at the cathode, and the reaction C − e → A at the anode. At the end point, the current is zero. After the end point, the current at the anode corresponds to the reaction B + C − e → AB, and the current is limited by B; the reaction at the cathode is then AB + e → B + C.

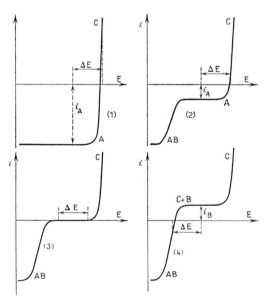

Fig. 228. The reaction A + B → AB with an excess of C (see Fig. 176).
Curve (1): $x = 0$. Curve (2): $x < 1$. Curve (3): $x = 1$. Curve (4): $x > 1$.

The same electrode acts as the anode before and after the end point, but in one case it is an indicator electrode, and in the other case its potential is nearly constant. The titration curve is therefore as shown in Fig. 229.

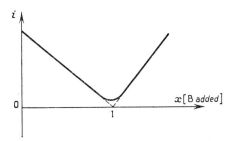

Fig. 229. The reaction A + B → AB with an excess of C.
Two indicator electrodes.

Simplified methods

The remarks made on this subject for titrations with a single indicator electrode also apply here. If the titration reaction is quantitative, the end point may be found by determining where the current is zero, and it is no longer necessary to plot the whole titration curve. It does not matter whether this consists of straight lines or not, so there is no need to take those precautions which are necessary to ensure that the current is proportional to the concentrations.

The titration becomes very simple under these conditions, especially with two indicator electrodes (see this Chapter, *Instrumentation*, p. 218).

The case where ΔE is small (see the theory of Chapter IX)

If a very small potential difference ΔE is applied between the two electrodes, current only flows when both the oxidant and the reductant of a fast system are present, *e.g.*

$$A + e \rightleftharpoons C \qquad (or\ AB + e \rightleftharpoons B + C)$$

The current is zero when either of the components of the fast system are absent.

The current is thus determined by the same reactions as metnioned above, but the potential of the indicator electrode no longer corresponds to the state where diffusion is limiting. This has the effect of reducing the current observed, and gives a non-linear variation of the current (Fig. 230). The current is always zero at the end point. It is therefore enough to observe the variations in the current near the end

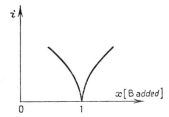

Fig. 230. ΔE is small ('Dead-stop end point').

point in order to determine its position. A sensitive galvanometer is used, which allows the moment at which $i = 0$ to be determined with accuracy (the 'dead-stop end point' method, see Fig. 230).

ΔE need often be no more than 10 to 15 mV. Since the current is no longer proportional to the concentration, it is no longer necessary to have such regular stirring, or such a constant temperature or electrode surface, etc.

On the other hand, it is necessary that the reaction should be quantitative, so that the current shows a sharp minimum at the end point.

Examples

The titration of Fe^{2+} with dichromate at a platinum electrode.

(*a*) Consider the titration of Fe^{2+} with dichromate in the presence of an excess of Fe^{3+}. The current–potential curves change during the titration as shown in Fig. 231.

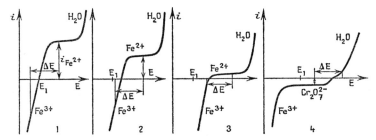

Fig. 231. The reaction $3\,Fe(II) + Cr(VI) \rightarrow 3\,Fe(III) + Cr(III)$ in the presence of an excess of Fe(III). Curves 1, 2 and 3 before the end point; curve 4 after the end point (*cf.* Fig. 93).

If a potential difference ΔE is applied between the electrodes, the titration curve is as shown in Fig. 232. Before the end point Fe^{2+} is oxidized at the anode, and Fe^{3+} is reduced at the cathode; the current decreases as $|Fe^{2+}|$ decreases. After the end point water is oxidized at the anode and dichromate is reduced at the cathode; the current is limited by the concentration of dichromate, and therefore increases with the dichromate concentration.

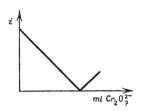

Fig. 232. The reaction $3\,Fe(II) + Cr(VI) \rightarrow 3\,Fe(III) + Cr(III)$ in the presence of an excess of Fe(III). Two indicator electrodes (theoretical curves).

(*b*) If the same titration is carried out in the absence of Fe^{3+}, the current–potential curves are given by Fig. 233. Before the end point, the current increases at first as Fe^{3+} appears, reaches a maximum where $k_{Fe^{3+}}|Fe^{3+}| = k_{Fe^{2+}}|Fe^{2+}|$, and decre-

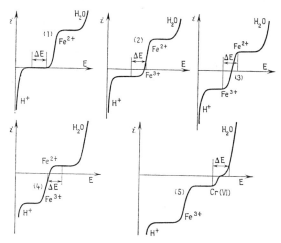

Fig. 233. The reaction 3 Fe(II) + Cr(VI) → 3 Fe(III) + Cr(III).
Curves 1, 2, 3 and 4 before the end point; curve 5 after the end point (theoretical curves).

ases as Fe^{2+} disappears. After the end point, the current increases again with the excess of dichromate (Figs. 234 and 235).

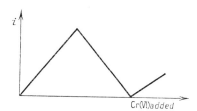

Fig. 234. The reaction
3 Fe(II) + Cr(VI) → 3 Fe(III) + Cr(III).
Two indicator electrodes; ΔE fairly large.

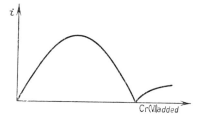

Fig. 235. The reaction
3 Fe(II) + Cr(VI) → 3 Fe(III) + Cr(III).
Two indicator electrodes; ΔE small.

Titration of Ag^+ with bromide ion at a silver electrode. The titration reaction is

$$Ag^+ + Br^- \rightarrow AgBr\downarrow$$

The current–potential curves during the reaction are shown in Fig. 236, on the assumption that there is a little $AgBr\downarrow$ on the electrode, as has been found to be the case. The titration curves are shown in Fig. 237.

The titration of Fe^{2+} with Ce^{4+}. The titration reaction is

$$Fe^{2+} + Ce^{4+} \rightarrow Fe^{3+} + Ce^{3+}$$

The current–potential curves are shown in Fig. 238, and the titration curves with one indicator electrode, two indicator electrodes and large ΔE, and two indicator electrodes and small ΔE, are shown in Figs. 239, 240 and 241.

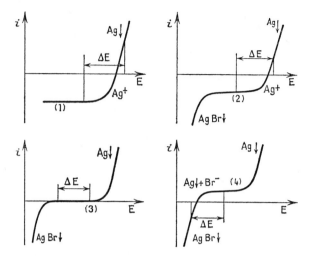

Fig. 236. The reaction $Ag^+ + Br^- \rightarrow AgBr\downarrow$ (see Fig. 84).
Curve (1): $x = 0$; curve (2): $x < 1$; curve (3): $x = 1$; curve (4): $x > 1$.

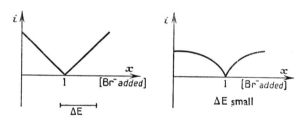

Fig. 237. The reaction $Ag^+ + Br^- \rightarrow AgBr\downarrow$ Two silver electrodes.

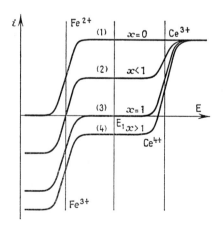

Fig. 238. The reaction
$Fe^{2+} + Ce^{4+} \rightarrow Fe^{3+} + Ce^{3+}$
(theoretical curves).

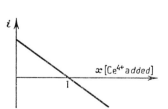

Fig. 239. The reaction
$Fe^{2+} + Ce^{4+} \rightarrow Fe^{3+} + Ce^{3+}$.
One indicator electrode.

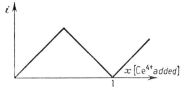

Fig. 240. The reaction Fe^{2+}, $Ce^{4+} \rightarrow$ Fe^{3+}, Ce^{3+}. Two indicator electrodes, ΔE large.

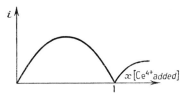

Fig. 241. The reaction Fe^{2+}, $Ce^{4+} \rightarrow$ Fe^{3+}, Ce^{3+}. Two indicator electrodes, ΔE small.

Titration of Hg(II) with EDTA (see p. 213). The chemical reaction is

$$Hg^{2+} + Y^{4-} \rightarrow HgY^{2-}$$

The current–potential curves at a mercury electrode are shown in Fig. 242, and the titration curves in Figs. 243 and 244.

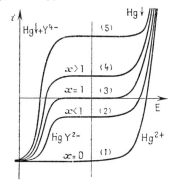

Fig. 242. The reaction $Hg^{2+} + Y^{4-} \rightarrow HgY^{2-}$.

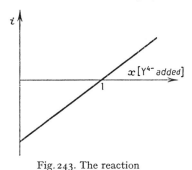

Fig. 243. The reaction $Hg^{2+} + Y^{4-} \rightarrow HgY^{2-}$. One mercury indicator electrode.

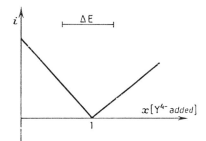

Fig. 244. The reaction $Hg^{2+} + Y^{4-} \rightarrow HgY^{2-}$. Two mercury electrodes.

Acid–base titration. Strong acid–strong base give the reaction

$$H^+ + OH^- \rightarrow H_2O$$

while weak acid–strong base give

$$HB + OH^- \rightarrow B^- + H_2O$$

The reaction

$$4 OH^- - 4e \rightarrow O_2 + 2 H_2O$$

occurs at a platinum indicator electrode, and this may be used to follow the concentration of OH^- ions during the titration (Fig. 245).

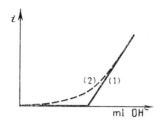

Fig. 245. (1) The reaction $H^+ + OH^- \rightarrow H_2O$.
(2) The reaction $HBO_2 + OH^- \rightarrow BO_2^- + H_2O$
Bright platinum electrode, $E = 1.45$ V; platinized platinum electrode, $E = 1.15$ V.

Titration of uranium (VI) in the presence of ferric ions. The solution is first reduced, *e.g.* with zinc, to give Fe^{2+}, U^{3+} and U^{4+}. The mixture is then titrated with permanganate. The chemical reactions are

$$5 \text{ U(III)} + \text{Mn(VII)} \rightarrow 5 \text{ U(IV)} + \text{Mn(II)} \tag{1}$$

$$5 \text{ U(IV)} + 2 \text{ Mn(VII)} \rightarrow 5 \text{ U(VI)} + 2 \text{ Mn(II)} \tag{2}$$

$$5 \text{ Fe(II)} + \text{Mn(VII)} \rightarrow 5 \text{ Fe(III)} + \text{Mn(II)} \tag{3}$$

in that order. The reactions are followed with two indicator electrodes with a small potential difference between them. We have seen that under these conditions current only flows if both the oxidant and the reductant of a fast system are present. The systems U^{3+}/U^{4+} and Fe^{2+}/Fe^{3+} are fast, and the systems U^{4+}/UO_2^{2+} and MnO_4^-/Mn^{2+}

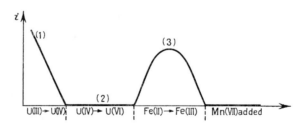

Fig. 246. The reactions
$$5 \text{ U(III)} + \text{Mn(VII)} \rightarrow 5 \text{ U(IV)} + \text{Mn(II)} \tag{1}$$
$$5 \text{ U(IV)} + 2 \text{ Mn(VII)} \rightarrow 5 \text{ U(VI)} + 2 \text{ Mn(II)} \tag{2}$$
$$5 \text{ Fe(II)} + \text{Mn(VII)} \rightarrow 5 \text{ Fe(III)} + \text{Mn(II)} \tag{3}$$
Two indicator electrodes (after SMIT and KLINKHAMER[76]).

are slow. The titration curve is therefore as shown in Fig. 246. It will be seen from this curve that the volume of reagent consumed over portion (2) of the curve is a measure of the uranium concentration, and that used over portion (3) gives the concentration of the iron.

Titrations with amperometric indicators

We have seen that the current–potential curves corresponding to the redox system

$$AB + e \rightleftharpoons C + B$$

depend on the concentration of B, even though B by itself may not be electroactive. C, AB, or the two together can be used as indicators for B; in particular, they may be used to follow the concentration of B or of MB during the reaction

$$M + B \rightarrow MB$$

(see Chapter III, p. 56 and Figs. 56 to 61). We will give some examples of such titrations.

Titrations with EDTA (see p. 57). Consider the titration of a cation with EDTA

$$M^{2+} + Y^{4-} \rightarrow MY^{2-}$$

where M^{2+} and Y^{4-} are not electroactive.

(*a*) This reaction may be followed by amperometry with one indicator electrode: a mercury electrode indicating the concentration of Y^{4-}. The possible electrochemical reactions at the mercury electrode are

$$Hg\downarrow - 2e \rightarrow Hg^{2+} \tag{4}$$

$$Hg\downarrow + MY^{2-} - 2e \rightarrow HgY^{2-} + M^{2+} \tag{5}$$

$$Hg\downarrow + Y^{4-} - 2e \rightarrow HgY^{2-} \tag{6}$$

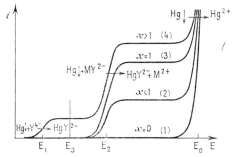

Fig. 247. The reaction $M^{2+} + Y^{4-} \rightarrow MY^{2-}$. Mercury indicator electrode (theoretical curves).

The current–potential curves during the titration are shown in Fig. 247. If the potential is fixed at E_3, only the electrochemical oxidation reaction (6) can occur. The current is therefore determined by the concentration of free Y^{4-}: *i.e.* the current only appears after the end point (Fig. 248).

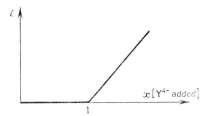

Fig. 248. The reaction $M^{2+} + Y^{4-} \rightarrow MY^{2-}$. Mercury indicator electrode.

(b) HgY^{2-} may be added to the solution of M^{2+} whose concentration is to be determined, in such concentrations that it does not limit the current; it then acts as an indicator at a mercury electrode. The current–potential curves during the titration are shown in Fig. 249, supposing that the complex HgY^{2-} is more stable than the complex MY^{2-}. If one indicator electrode is used, the potential may be fixed at E_3; then before the end point, the electrochemical reaction

$$HgY^{2-} + M^{2+} + 2e \rightarrow Hg\downarrow + MY^{2-}$$

will occur, curves (1) and (2), and after the end point the reaction will be

$$Hg\downarrow + Y^{4-} - 2e \rightarrow HgY^{2-}$$

curve (4). The titration curve in this case is given in Fig. 250. Two indicator electrodes may also be used, with a small potential difference between them. Before the end point we have

$$Hg\downarrow + MY^{2-} - 2e \rightleftharpoons HgY^{2-} + M^{2+}$$

with oxidation at one electrode and reduction at the other. Similarly after the end point, with the system

$$Hg\downarrow + Y^{4-} - 2e \rightleftharpoons HgY^{2-}$$

The titration curve is shown in Fig. 251.

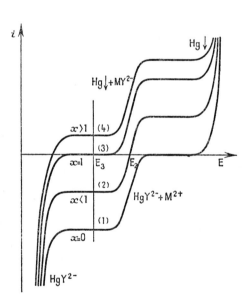

Fig. 249. The reaction $M^{2+} + Y^{4-} \rightarrow MY^{2-}$ at a mercury electrode, in the presence of excess HgY^{2-} (theoretical curves).

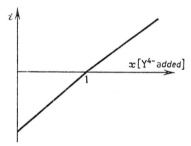

Fig. 250. The reaction $M^{2+} + Y^{4-} \rightarrow MY^{2-}$, in the presence of an excess of HgY^{2-}. One mercury indicator electrode.

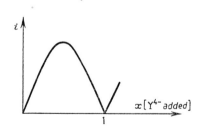

Fig. 251. Two mercury indicator electrodes (ΔE small).

(c) *Back-titration.* It is also possible to add an excess of Y^{4-} to a solution of M^{2+}, and titrate the excess of Y^{4-} with a mercuric salt. The chemical reactions are

$$Y^{4-} + Hg^{2+} \rightarrow HgY^{2-} \tag{7}$$

followed by

$$MY^{2-} + Hg^{2+} \rightarrow HgY^{2-} + M^{2+} \tag{8}$$

supposing that HgY^{2-} is more stable than MY^{2-}. The current–potential curves during these reactions are shown in Fig. 252. At a potential E_3 the titration curve of the excess Y^{4-} is as shown in Fig. 253, if one indicator electrode is used. If two indicator electrodes are used, the titration curve is as shown in Fig. 254.

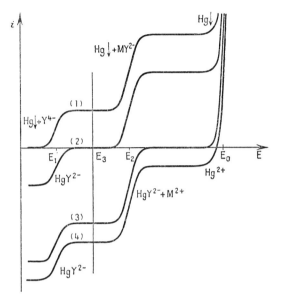

Fig. 252. The reaction M^{2+} + excess $Y^{4-} \rightarrow MY^{2-}$, followed by back-titration of the excess Y^{4-} according to the reaction $Y^{4-} + Hg^{2+} \rightarrow HgY^{2-}$.

Curve (1): at the start of the titration; curve (2): end point of the titration of the excess Y^{4-}; curve (3): end point of the titration of MY^{2-} with Hg^{2+} according to the reaction $MY^{2-} + Hg^{2+} \rightarrow HgY^{2-} + M^{2+}$; curve (4): excess Hg^{2+} (theoretical curves).

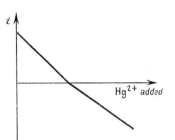

Fig. 253. The reaction M^{2+} + excess $Y^{4-} \rightarrow MY^{2-}$, and back-titration of the excess Y^{4-} according to the equation $Y^{4-} + Hg^{2+} \rightarrow HgY^{2-}$. One mercury indicator electrode.

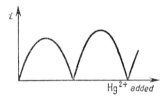

Fig. 254. The reaction M^{2+} + excess $Y^{4-} \rightarrow MY^{2-}$, and back-titration of the excess Y^{4-} according to the equation $Y^{4-} + Hg^{2+} \rightarrow HgY^{2-}$. Two mercury indicator electrodes.

The complex AB is less stable than MB $(K \gg K')$

In order to follow the titration reaction $M + B \rightarrow MB$:

1. C may be used as an indicator, in excess so as not to limit the current. The only possible electrochemical reactions are

$$C - e \rightarrow A \qquad\qquad E_0$$
$$C + B - e \rightarrow AB \qquad\qquad E_1$$

The reaction

$$C + MB - e \rightarrow AB + M$$

is no longer possible, since M reacts with AB

$$AB + M \rightarrow MB + A$$

The current–potential curves are shown in Fig. 255. With one indicator electrode at a potential E_3, the only possible electrochemical reaction is $B + C - e \rightarrow AB$, so the titration curve is as shown in Fig. 258.

2. A may also be used as indicator. The current–potential curves are shown in Fig. 256. With a single indicator electrode, the end point of the reaction $M + B \rightarrow MB$ is shown by a reduction of the current as A starts to disappear as a result of the reaction $A + B \rightarrow AB$ (Fig. 259).

3. The same titration curve may be obtained with two indicator electrodes, if both A and C are added as indicator.

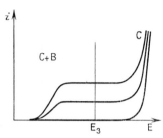

Fig. 255. Indicator: C in excess.
The reaction $M + B \rightarrow MB$, with indicator systems $A + e \rightleftharpoons C$ and $AB + e \rightleftharpoons C + B$. AB is less stable than MB.

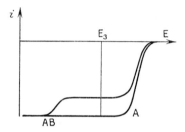

Fig. 256. Indicator: A.
The reaction $M + B \rightarrow MB$, with indicator systems $A + e \rightleftharpoons C$ and $AB + e \rightleftharpoons C + B$. AB is less stable than MB.

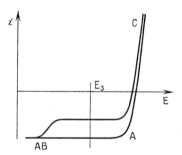

Fig. 257. Indicators: A + excess C.
The reaction $M + B \rightarrow MB$, with indicator systems $A + e \rightleftharpoons C$ and $AB + e \rightleftharpoons C + B$. AB is less stable than MB.

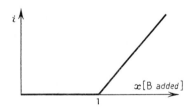

Fig. 258.
The reaction $M + B \rightarrow MB$, with indicator systems $A + e \rightleftharpoons C$ and $AB + e \rightleftharpoons C + B$; AB is less stable than MB.
One indicator electrode (E_3) and excess C as indicator.

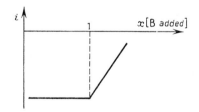

Fig. 259.
The reaction $M + B \rightarrow MB$, with indicator systems $A + e \rightleftharpoons C$ and $AB + e \rightleftharpoons C + B$; AB is less stable than MB.
One indicator electrode (E_3) and A as indicator, or two indicator electrodes $(\Delta E$ large) and A + excess C as indicators.

Examples. Fe^{3+} has been suggested[98-100] as indicator for F^-. This is an example of case 2, with the indicator system

$$FeF^{2+} + e \rightleftharpoons Fe^{2+} + F^-$$

Case 1 would correspond to using Fe^{2+} as indicator, and case 3 to $Fe^{2+} + Fe^{3+}$.

ZnO_2^{2-} has been suggested as indicator[101] for Y^{4-} in the reaction

$$Ca^{2+} + Y^{4-} \rightarrow CaY^{2-}$$

this is also case 2.

Simplified methods

All the methods described above can be used so that only the phenomena near the end point are observed, *i.e.* it is not necessary to plot the whole amperometric titration curve.

Many indicators have been suggested for titrations with 'dead-stop' end points, *e.g.*:

$IO_3^- + I^-$ for the titration of bases with a strong acid[97]. When a pH of 7 is reached, the reaction

$$IO_3^- + 5\,I^- + 6\,H^+ \rightarrow 3\,I_2 + H_2O$$

occurs. Current now passes, as a result of the appearance of the fast system I_3^-/I^-.

I_2 for the titration of acids with bases[97]. The iodine disproportionates at about the same pH (reverse of the above reaction), and the system I_3^-/I^- disappears.

H_2O_2 for acid–base titrations[72, 97].

NO_2^- for argentometric titrations[97].

Titrations with an indicator and two different electrodes

An aluminium electrode can be an indicator of F^-, *e.g.* according to the reaction

$$Al\downarrow + F^- - 3e \rightleftharpoons AlF^{2+}$$

(Fig. 260). The concentration of F^- can thus be followed during titrations[104], *e.g.* the determination of Th^{4+} at a suitable pH. One aluminium indicator electrode and one platinum electrode may be used. If these are short-circuited, so that $\Delta E = 0$, $i = k\,|F^-|$.

CN^- can similarly be followed with one silver electrode and one platinum one[104].

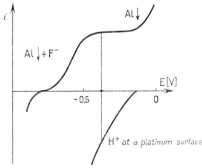

Fig. 260. $Al\downarrow$ as an indicator of F^- (after DUMONTIER-GOUREAU and TRÉMILLON[103]).

Characteristics of amperometric titrations

Range of application

Amperometric titrations may be used in a large number of cases, for if the substance to be determined is not itself electroactive, the reactant or the reaction products may be. By choosing a suitable potential difference, the simple method with two indicator electrodes may be used. The use of amperometric indicators enlarges the range of possibilities considerably. If a reaction is not quantitative, it may often still be followed by operating under ideal electrolytic conditions; if it is quantitative, however, it is often sufficient to determine the moment when the current is zero.

Amperometric titrations have many advantages compared to polarography: they allow much simpler equipment to be used, especially when working with two platinum electrodes. It is then no longer necessary to control the experimental conditions (temperature, diffusion etc.). The results no longer depend on the properties of the apparatus, so calibration is no longer necessary.

Sensitivity. The sensitivity of the method is limited by the existence of the residual current, corresponding to 10^{-5} to 10^{-6} N, or by the fact that the reaction used is not quantitative.

Accuracy. This may be limited by the volumetric or coulometric measurements.

Instrumentation

The electrolysis current is measured during the titration, the potential difference between the two electrodes being kept practically constant, sometimes zero.

Two cases may be distinguished:

1. The end point is determined by extrapolating two straight lines representing the variation of current during the titration. We have seen that the value of the electrolysis current depends to a large extent on the diffusion phenomena at the surface of the electrode, and in particular on whether a steady state has been attained. It is therefore necessary to use such conditions as guarantee the existence of a steady state (see this Chapter, and Chapter V, p. 117).

2. It is sufficient to detect the position of the end point directly (simplified amperometric methods, p. 217), and when this is a well-defined point on the titration curve, where the current either becomes appreciable or becomes zero, the above-mentioned conditions need not be kept.

Fig. 261. Zero voltage between the two electrodes.
C = electrolysis cell; G = microammeter.

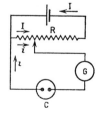

Fig. 262. Constant voltage between the electrodes (see p. 134).

It may be necessary to free the reactant from oxygen, as well as the solution of the substance to be determined.

The voltage to be applied between the electrodes is chosen from a consideration of the current–potential curves, or sometimes empirically.

A virtually constant voltage may be obtained with the aid of the very simple low-resistance circuit shown in Fig. 262 (see also Chapter VI, p. 134); a zero voltage may simply be attained by short-circuiting the electrodes (Fig. 261).

In the latter case the comparison electrode, which is formed by a fast system, imposes its potential on the indicator electrode. The comparison electrode must therefore be chosen so as to produce a suitable potential.

The titration curves can be recorded, as with potentiometric titrations. Automatic titrimeters working on this principle also exist.

The characteristics of the cells, electrodes and measuring equipment have beer given in Chapter VI.

REFERENCES

Polarography, books and review articles

[1] J. HEYROVSKY, *Polarographie*, Springer, Vienna, 1941.
[2] J. HEYROVSKY, *Polarographisches Praktikum*, Springer, Berlin, 1948.
[3] M. VON STACKELBERG, *Polarographische Arbeitsmethoden*, de Gruyter, Berlin, 1950.
[4] O. H. MÜLLER, *The Polarographic Method of Analysis*, Chemical Education Publishers, Easton, Pa., 1951.
[5] I. M. KOLTHOFF and J. J. LINGANE, *Polarography*, Interscience, New York, 1952.
[6] G. W. C. MILLER, *The Principles and Applications of Polarography*, Longmans Green and Co., London, 1957.
[7] D. N. HUME, *Anal. Chem.*, 28 (1956) 625.
[8] D. N. HUME, *Anal. Chem.*, 30 (1958) 675.

Organic compounds. Reviews

[9] S. WAWZONEK, *Anal. Chem.*, 21 (1949) 61.
[10] S. WAWZONEK, *Anal. Chem.*, 26 (1954) 65.
[11] S. WAWZONEK, *Anal. Chem.*, 28 (1956) 638.
[12] S. WAWZONEK, *Anal. Chem.*, 30 (1958) 661.

Complete documentation by Czech workers, 1922–1950

[13] J. HEYROVSKY et al., *Proc. 1st Intern. Polarog. Congr., Prague 1951*.
[14] J. HEYROVSKY and O. H. MÜLLER, *Collection Czechoslov. Chem. Communs.*, 16, 17 (1951–1952) 430, Suppl. I.
[15] J. HEYROVSKY and O. H. MÜLLER, *Collection Czechoslov. Chem. Communs.*, 18 (1953) Suppl. I.
[16] J. HEYROVSKY and O. H. MÜLLER, *Collection Czechoslov. Chem. Communs.*, 19 (1954) Suppl. I.
[17] J. HEYROVSKY and O. H. MÜLLER, *Collection Czechoslov. Chem. Communs.*, 20 (1955) Suppl. I.
[18] J. HEYROVSKY and O. H. MÜLLER, *Collection Czechoslov. Chem. Communs.*, 21 (1956) Suppl. I.

Complete documentation by Italian workers at the Polarography Study Centre of the National Research Council at the University of Padua

—, *author indexes*

[19] G. SEMERANO, *Ricerca sci.*, 19 (1949) Suppl. A.
[20] E. GAGLIARDO, *Ricerca sci.*, 21 (1951) Suppl. A.
[21] M. MENEGUS-SCARPA, *Ricerca sci.*, 23 (1953) Suppl. A.
[22] M. MENEGUS-SCARPA, *Ricerca sci.*, 24 (1954) Suppl. A.
[23] M. MENEGUS-SCARPA, *Ricerca sci.*, 25 (1955) Suppl. A.
[24] B. TOSINI, *Ricerca sci.*, 26 (1956) Suppl. A.
[25] B. TOSINI, *Ricerca sci.*, 27 (1957) Suppl. A.
[26] B. TOSINI, *Ricerca sci.*, 28 (1958) Suppl. A.

—, *subject index*

[27] B. TOSINI, *Ricerca sci.*, 28 (1958) Suppl. A.

Half-wave potentials

[28] P. Zuman, *Collection Czechoslov. Chem. Communs.*, 15 (1950) 1107–1208.
[29] L. Meites, *Polarographic Techniques*, Interscience, New York, 1955.
[30] G. Semerano and L. Griggio, *Ricerca sci.*, 27 (1957) III A (selected values).
[31] K. Schwabe, *Polarographie und chemische Konstitution organischer Verbindungen*, Akademie-Verlag, Berlin, 1957.
[32] E. J. Breda, L. Meites, T. B. Reddy and P. W. West, *Anal. Chim. Acta*, 14 (1956) 390.
[33] J. W. Grenier and L. Meites, *Anal. Chim. Acta*, 14 (1956) 482.

Derivative polarography

[34] J. Heyrovsky and J. Forejt, *Z. physik. Chem.*, 193 (1943) 77.
[35] J. Heyrovsky, *Chem. listy*, 40 (1946) 221.
[36] J. Heyrovsky, *Analyst*, 72 (1947) 229.
[37] J. Heyrovsky, *Anal. Chim. Acta*, 2 (1948) 537.
[38] M. Kalousek, *Collection Czechoslov. Chem. Communs.*, 13 (1948) 105.
[39] P. Lévêque and F. Roth, *J. Chim. phys.*, 46 (1949) 480.
[40] J. Heyrovsky, *Chem. listy*, 43 (1949) 149.
[41] J. Vogel and J. Riha, *J. Chim. phys.*, 47 (1950) 5.
[42] L. Airey and A. A. Smales, *Analyst*, 75 (1950) 287.
[43] J. J. Lingane and R. D. Williams, *J. Am. Chem. Soc.*, 74 (1952) 790.
[44] B. B. Baker and J. D. Morrison, *Anal. Chem.*, 27 (1955) 1306.
[45] T. Fujinaga, *Bull. Inst. Chem. Research, Kyoto Univ.*, 33 (1955) 107.
[46] E. Barendrecht, *Anal. Chim. Acta*, 15 (1956) 484.
[47] M. T. Kelley and D. J. Fisher, *Anal. Chem.*, 30 (1958) 929.

Differential polarography

[48] G. Semerano and L. Riccoboni, *Gazz. chim. ital.*, 72 (1942) 297.
[49] S. Stankoviansky, *Chem. Zvesti*, 2 (1948) 133.

Use of a counter current

[50] D. Ilkovic and G. Semerano, *Collection Czechoslov. Chem. Communs.*, 4 (1932) 176.

Micropolarography

[51] V. Majer, *Mikrochemie*, 18 (1935) 74.
[52] T. Meites and L. Meites, *Anal. Chem.*, 28 (1951) 1893.

—, *amperometric titrations*

General works (see also references 1–6)

[53] J. Heyrovsky, in W. G. Berl, *Physical Methods in Chemical Analysis*, Academic Press, New York, 1951.
[54] G. Charlot and D. Bézier, *Les méthodes électrochimiques d'analyse*, Masson, Paris, 1954.
[55] P. Delahay, *New Instrumental Methods in Electrochemistry*, Interscience, New York, 1954.
[56] J. J. Lingane, *Electroanalytical Chemistry*, Interscience, New York, 2nd Ed., 1958.
[57] V. Majer, *Z. Elektrochem.*, 42 (1936) 120, 123.
[58] I. M. Kolthoff and Y. D. Pan, *J. Am. Chem. Soc.*, 62 (1940) 3332.
[59] I. M. Kolthoff and Y. D. Pan, *J. Am. Chem. Soc.*, 61 (1939) 3402.
[60] I. M. Kolthoff and H. P. Gregor, *Anal. Chem.*, 20 (1948) 541.
[61] J. J. Lingane, *J. Am. Chem. Soc.*, 65 (1943) 866.

Reviews

[62] I. M. Kolthoff, *Anal. Chim. Acta*, 2 (1948) 606.
[63] H. A. Laitinen, *Anal. Chem.*, 21 (1949) 66.
[64] H. A. Laitinen, *Anal. Chem.*, 24 (1952) 46.
[65] T. D. Parks, *Anal. Chim. Acta*, 6 (1952) 553.
[66] H. A. Laitinen, *Anal. Chem.*, 28 (1956) 666.
[67] H. A. Laitinen, *Anal. Chem.*, 30 (1958) 657.

—, *dead-stop end point*

[68] N. H. Furman, *Anal. Chem.*, 26 (1954) 85.
[69] J. T. Stock, *Metallurgia*, 46 (1952) 209.
[70] N. Konopik, *Österr. Chem.*, 54 (1953) 289, 325.
[71] N. Konopik, *Österr. Chem.*, 55 (1954) 127.
[72] H. L. Kies, *Thesis*, Delft, 1956.

Two indicator electrodes

[73] E. SALOMON, *Z. physik. Chem.*, 24 (1897) 55.
[74] C. W. FOULK and A. T. BAWDEN, *J. Am. Chem. Soc.*, 48 (1926) 2045.
[75] B. F. BRANN and M. H. CLAPP, *J. Am. Chem. Soc.*, 51 (1929) 39.
[76] W. N. SMIT and J. KLINKHAMER, *Rec. trav. chim.*, 73 (1954) 1009.
[77] J. T. STOCK, *Metallurgia*, 55 (1957) 48 (review article).

Theory, in terms of current–potential curves (see also ref. 72)

[78] P. DELAHAY, *Anal. Chim. Acta*, 4 (1950) 635.
[79] G. DUYKAERTS, *Anal. Chim. Acta*, 8 (1953) 57.
[80] K. G. STONE and H. G. SCHOLTEN, *Anal. Chem.*, 24 (1952) 671.

Theory, generalization

[81] R. GAUGUIN and G. CHARLOT, *Anal. Chim. Acta*, 8 (1953) 65.
[82] R. GAUGUIN, *Chim. anal.*, 36 (1955) 285.
[83] P. S. FARRINGTON, D. J. MEIER and E. H. SWIFT, *Anal. Chem.*, 25 (1953) 591.
[84] I. M. KOLTHOFF, *Anal. Chem.*, 26 (1954) 1685.
[85] R. H. GALE and E. MOSHER, *Anal. Chem.*, 22 (1950) 942.
[86] L. ERDEY and E. BODOR, *Anal. Chem.*, 24 (1952) 418.
[87] H. L. KIES, *Anal. Chim. Acta*, 6 (1952) 190.
[88] H. L. KIES, *Anal. Chim. Acta*, 10 (1954) 161, 575.
[89] H. L. KIES, *Anal. Chim. Acta*, 11 (1954) 382.
[90] H. L. KIES, *Anal. Chim. Acta*, 18 (1958) 14.
[91] J. H. BRADBURY, *Trans. Faraday Soc.*, 50 (1954) 959.
[92] H. L. KIES and T. S. HIEN, *Z. anal. Chem.*, 148 (1955) 91.
[93] I. M. KOLTHOFF and E. R. NIGHTINGALE JR., *Anal. Chim. Acta*, 17 (1957) 329.

One indicator electrode

Mercury pool

[94] J. G. NIKELLY and W. D. COOKE, *Anal. Chem.*, 28 (1956) 243.
[95] J. G. NIKELLY and W. D. COOKE, *Proc. XV Intern. Congr. Pure Appl. Chem., Lisbon 1956 (Actas do Congresso)*, Lisbon, 1957, p. 839.
[96] W. FURNESS, P. CRAWSHAW and W. C. DAVIES, *Analyst*, 74 (1949) 629.

Amperometric indicators

[97] D. R. CLIPPINGER and C. W. FOULK, *Ind. Eng. Chem., Anal. Ed.*, 11 (1939) 216.
[98] A. RINGBOM, *Tekn. Tid.*, 77 (1947) 755.
[99] A. RINGBOM and B. WILKMAN, *Acta Chem. Scand.*, 3 (1949) 22.
[100] M. SUNDARESAN and M. D. KARKHANAVALA, *Current Sci. (India)*, 23 (1954) 258.
[101] H. A. LAITINEN and R. F. SYMPSON, *Anal. Chem.*, 26 (1954) 556.
[102] G. MICHEL, *Anal. Chim. Acta*, 10 (1954) 87.
[103] A. DUMONTIEU-GOUREU and B. TRÉMILLON, *Bull. soc. chim.*, (1959) 132.

Microamperometry

[104] J. T. STOCK, *Analyst*, 71 (1946) 583.
[105] J. T. STOCK, *Metallurgia*, 37 (1948) 220.

Chapter IX

THE RELATIONSHIP BETWEEN POTENTIOMETRY
AND AMPEROMETRY

I. VOLTAMMETRIC TITRATIONS AT CONSTANT RESISTANCE

We have supposed in the previous chapters that the titrations were carried out either with a constant current (potentiometry) or with a constant potential or voltage (amperometry). It is of course possible to apply a strictly constant current or potential during a titration by means of the appriproate equipment (see p. 133), but in general simple methods are used, which only approximate to these conditions. These

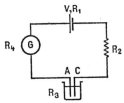

Fig. 263. Electrolysis circuit. Total resistance: $R = R_1 + R_2 + R_3 + R_4$.

circuits may be represented by the generalized circuit diagram of Fig. 263. In such a circuit, an e.m.f. V (with an internal resistance R_1) is applied, which induces a counter-e.m.f. $E_A - E_C$ in the cell. A current i flows through the whole circuit. Ohm's law then gives

$$V - (E_A - E_C) = R|i| \tag{1}$$

In such a set-up, therefore, R is constant and both $E_A - E_C$ and i vary during the titration. If R is small however, $E_A - E_C$ is practically constant, so we then have again the conditions studied in the previous chapter. If on the other hand R is large and V is also fairly large, i can be regarded as constant.

We will discuss the general case of titrations at constant resistance here in order to give an idea of the role of the resistance in these titrations, which we have not done so far.

The electrochemical phenomena at the electrodes during the titration determine a certain relationship between i, $E_A - E_C$ and C

$$f(i, E_A - E_C, C) = 0 \tag{2}$$

The two equations (1) and (2), with three unknowns, i, $E_A - E_C$ and C, allow the form of the titration curve to be deduced. This may be amperometric, $i = f(C)$, or potentiometric, $E_A - E_C = f(C)$.

We will distinguish two cases:

1. one indicator electrode and one electrode with a constant potential;
2. two indicator electrodes.

One indicator electrode

Let us suppose that the cathode is a comparison electrode (E_C = constant), while the anode is an indicator electrode. Eq. (1) becomes

$$E_A = E_C + V - Ri \quad \text{or} \quad E_A = E_1 - Ri \quad \text{or} \quad i = \frac{E_1 - E_A}{R} \tag{3}$$

In such a circuit, therefore, there is a linear relationship between the potential of the anode, E_A, and the current i.

Graphic representation

Eq. (3) gives a straight line of slope $-1/R$ when i is plotted against E (Fig. 264). Eq. (2), which describes the electrochemical phenomena during the titration, gives a current–potential curve which changes during the titration. The intersection of these two curves gives the point M, representing the measured values of i and E at any moment.

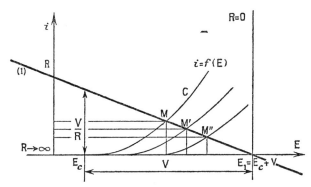

Fig. 264. Titrations at constant resistance.
The point representing the measured values of the current or the potential describes the straight line (1) during the titration.

Since the straight line corresponding to Eq. (3) is usually inclined to the axes, both the current i and the potential E will vary during the titration. The projection of the points M, M', M'', etc., on the potential axis allows the variation of E_A during the titration to be deduced, thus giving the potentiometric titration curve, while projection on the current axis gives the amperometric titration curve.

The current will be zero when

$$E_A = E_C + V = E_1$$

whatever the value of R.

When $R = 0$, the straight line (1) becomes parallel to the current axis, at a potential E_1 (classical amperometry, see Chapter VIII). When R is infinite, the straight line (1) coincides with the potential axis ($i = 0$) (classical potentiometry, Chapter VII). If R and V are both very large, the value of i during the titration, i.e. near E_C, will be finite. Since the slope $1/R$ is small, the current will remain practically constant, $i \sim V/R$ (constant-current potentiometry).

Since the relationship between i and E_A is linear, $E_A = E_1 - Ri$, the amperometric and potentiometric titration curves for a given value of R will have the same form.

Amperometric and potentiometric titration curves at constant resistance

Let us consider the titration of a reducing agent Red, of concentration C_0, with an oxidizing agent Ox. After xC_0 of the titrant has been added, we have $|Ox| = xC_0$, and $|Red| = (1 - x)C_0$.

We will suppose for the sake of simplicity that the system $Ox + ne \rightleftharpoons Red$ is fast. The equation describing the electrochemical phenomena is

$$E_A = E_0 + \frac{0.058}{n} \log \frac{i - i_{Ox}}{i_{Red} - i} \tag{4}$$

where i_{Ox} and i_{Red} are the limiting diffusion currents of Ox and Red

$$i_{Ox} = - k_D |Ox| = - k_D x C_0$$

and

$$i_{Red} = k_D |Red| = k_D (1 - x)C_0$$

assuming $k_{Red} \sim k_{Ox} = k_D$ so that $E_{\frac{1}{2}} \sim E_0$).

Eq. (4) relates the three variables i, E_A and x. The titration curves $i = f(x)$ and $E_A = f(x)$ are obtained by eliminating either E_A or i from Eqs. (3) and (4).

The general equation for the titration curves for $x \leq 1$ is

$$x = \frac{\exp\left[\dfrac{nF}{RT}(E_A - E_0)\right]}{1 + \exp\left[\dfrac{nF}{RT}(E_A - E_0)\right]} - \frac{E_1 - E_A}{Ri_D} = F_1(E) - F_2(E) \tag{5}$$

$$= \frac{\exp\left[\dfrac{nF}{RT}(E_1 - E_0 - Ri)\right]}{1 + \exp\left[\dfrac{nF}{RT}(E_1 - E_0 - Ri)\right]} - \frac{i}{i_D} = F_1(i) - F_2(i) \tag{6}$$

where i_D is the initial limiting diffusion current of Red, $i_D = k_D C_0$.

Limiting cases

(a) *The resistance R is very small.* The term Ri is negligible; it follows from Eq. (3) that E_A is practically constant and equal to E_1. Eq. (6) becomes $x = $ constant $- i/i_D$, and if E_1 has such a value as to obtain the limiting diffusion current of Red ($E_1 \gg E_0$), $x = 1 - i/i_D$. We thus have the amperometric titration curve discussed in the previous chapter, with $i = (1 - x)i_D$.

The potential E_A also varies linearly with x (see remark above):
$E_A = E_1 - R(1 - x)i_D$. During the titration E_A changes by Ri_D. This variation is too small to be used for an accurate titration.

(b) *The total resistance R is very large, and V is not very large.* In general, V is made zero; i then remains infinitely small during the titration. The second term of Eq. (5) is also negligible, and the equation of the potentiometric titration curve becomes

$$E = E_0 + \frac{0.058}{n} \log \frac{x}{1 - x} \tag{8}$$

(zero-current potentiometry).

(c) *R and V are both very large.* The current remains practically constant throughout the titration, and is equal to

$$i_0 = \frac{E_1 - E}{R} \sim \frac{V}{R}$$

The equation of the potentiometric titration curve is now

$$E = E_0 + \frac{0.058}{n} \log \frac{x + i_0/i_D}{1 - (x + i_0/i_D)} \tag{9}$$

(constant-current potentiometry).

In the last two cases, the current is also a bilogarithmic function of x, but the variation of this small current near the end point cannot be used for titrations.

The general case. The influence of the total resistance R on the form of the titration curves. Let us suppose that V has been chosen not too large, so that E_1 corresponds to a limiting diffusion current of Red, the substance to be determined. We will examine the deformation of the amperometric and potentiometric titration curves as R varies from zero to infinity. This may be approximated to in practice by means of a variable resistance (R_2 in Fig. 263).

The general equations (5) and (6) are of the form $x = F_1(E) - F_2(E)$, or $x = F_1(i) - F_2(i)$.

When $F_2 \ll F_1$, *i.e.* when R is large, the titration curves are s-shaped [Eq. (8)]; but when R is small, $F_1 \ll F_2$ and the curves are practically linear [Eq. (7)].

As R increases from zero to infinity, the curves pass progressively from the linear form to the s-shaped, as sketched in Fig. 265 and 266.

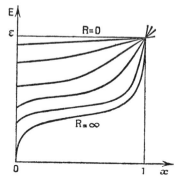 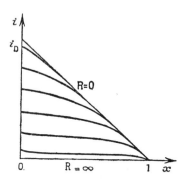

Figs. 265 and 266.
Deformation of constant-resistance potentiometric and amperometric titration curves as R varies from zero to infinity.

Choice of the resistance. For a given resistance, both titration curves have the same form. When R is small, they are practically straight lines, but the variation of E is very small while that of i is maximum. When R is large, the curves are s-shaped; in this case, the variation of i is negligible and that of E is maximum.

At the end point, the variation of E is larger as R is increased, while the variation of i is larger as the resistance becomes smaller.

The resistance should therefore be large for a potentiometric titration, and small for an amperometric titration.

Two indicator electrodes

If the potential difference between the two electrodes is denoted by

$$\Delta E = E_A - E_C$$

Eq. (1) may be written as

$$\Delta E = V - Ri \qquad (10)$$

Graphic representation

Eq. (10) may be represented in the i,E diagram (Fig. 267) as a parallelogram ABCD, where the diagonal AC has a length equal to the applied voltage V, and the sides AD and BC are of slope $-2/R$.

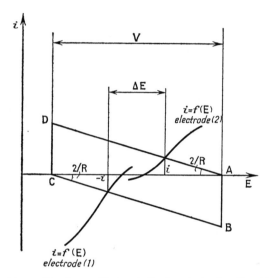

Fig. 267. Constant-resistance titrations with two indicator electrodes. Graphical determination of the variation of the current and the potential.

For a given value of x, at a given moment during the titration, the electrochemical phenomena at the electrodes are represented by two current–potential curves, one corresponding to each electrode. The parallelogram is placed so that the currents at the anode and the cathode are equal and opposite. Then

$$\Delta E = V - 2\frac{R}{2}i = V - Ri$$

As the current–potential curves change during the titration, the parallelogram must be shifted along the potential axis.

When $R = 0$, $\Delta E = V$, and the construction reduces to that of the previous Chapter (p. 205).

When R is infinite, ΔE is equal to the potential difference between the electrodes for $i = 0$ (see Chapter VII).

When $V = 0$ (no applied voltage) the parallelogram reduces to a straight line of slope $-2/R$ shown in Fig. 268, and placed so that the currents at the anode and the cathode are equal and opposite. This represents the operation of the cell as a galvanic cell, which necessitates a favourable disposition of the current–potential curves at the two electrodes. The current which flows is zero if R is very large; it is maximum when $R = 0$, when it corresponds to $\Delta E = 0$. For an intermediate value of the resistance, $|\Delta E| = Ri$.

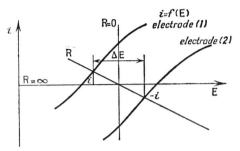

Fig. 268. Constant-resistance titrations with two short-circuited electrodes. Graphical representation of the measurement.

This graphical construction can be used to determine the variation of ΔE or i during the titration, i.e. to plot the potentiometric or amperometric titration curves.

Amperometric and potentiometric titration curves at constant resistance

These are obtained by eliminating ΔE or i from Eq. (10) and the equation which represents the electrochemical phenomena at the electrodes. This second equation, $f(i, \Delta E, x) = 0$, has not been established. It is simply obtained by combining the two equations $f(i, E, x) = 0$ for the two electrodes.

We will establish this relationship for the limiting case when at each moment of the titration the current i and the potential difference between the two electrodes are very small.

It is clear that under these conditions

$$\frac{i}{\Delta E} \sim \left(\frac{di}{dE}\right)_{i=0} \tag{11}$$

i.e. the current is proportional to ΔE, the constant of proportionality being equal to the slope of the current–potential curve near its intersection with the potential axis (the derivative method of REILLEY, COOKE and FURMAN [9]).

The equation $f(i, \Delta E, x) = 0$. Let us suppose that the electrochemical reaction $Ox + ne \rightleftharpoons Red$ only occurs at the two electrodes during the titration, and that the diffusion coefficients of Ox and Red are both equal to k_D. We will also suppose that the titration reaction (which is also a redox reaction) forms xC_0 of Ox and leaves $(1 - x)C_0$ of Red. Differentiation of the general equation $i = f(E)$ leads to the expression

$$\left(\frac{di}{dE}\right)_{i=0} = \frac{(\alpha + \beta)nF}{RT} i_0 C_0 \frac{\frac{i_0}{k_D} x(1 - x) + x^{\frac{\alpha + 2\beta}{\alpha + \beta}} (1 - x)^{\frac{2\alpha + \beta}{\alpha + \beta}}}{\left[\frac{i_0}{k_D} + x^{\frac{\beta}{\alpha + \beta}} (1 - x)^{\frac{\alpha}{\alpha + \beta}}\right]^2} \tag{11}$$

which may be written

$$\left(\frac{di}{dE}\right)_{i=0} = \frac{nF}{RT} i_0 C_0 \frac{x(1-x)}{\frac{i_0}{k_D} + x^{(1-\alpha)}(1-x)^\alpha} \tag{12}$$

since $\alpha + \beta = 1$.

If the system is fast, $i_0 \gg k_D$, so that

$$\left(\frac{dE}{di}\right)_{i=0} = k_D \frac{nF}{RT} C_0 x(1-x) \tag{13}$$

and if the system is slow, $i_0 \ll k_D$, so

$$\left(\frac{di}{dE}\right)_{i=0} = \frac{nF}{RT} i_0 C_0 x^\alpha (1-x)^{(1-\alpha)} \tag{14}$$

If we assume that $\alpha = 0.5$, the derivative passes from the form $x(1-x)$ to the form $\sqrt{x(1-x)}$ on passing from a fast system to a slow one.

Although the equations derived above only hold when both i and ΔE are infinitesimally small, the curves will have more or less the same form when i and ΔE are fairly large.

Amperometric and potentiometric titration curves. Eq. (12) to (14) are of the form

$$\frac{i}{\Delta E} = f(x) \tag{15}$$

On combining Eqs. (10) and (15), we obtain the equation of the titration curves for $x \leqslant 1$

amperometric:

$$i = \frac{V \cdot f(x)}{1 + R \cdot f(x)} \tag{16}$$

potentiometric:

$$\Delta E = \frac{V}{1 + R \cdot f(x)} \tag{17}$$

Limiting cases

a. *The total resistance R is very small.* According to Eq. (17), ΔE remains practically equal to the applied voltage V, but $i \sim V \cdot f(x)$.

The amperometric titration curves shown in Fig. 269 are obtained for redox systems of various speeds and a constant applied voltage V.

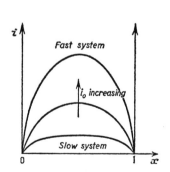

Fig. 269. Amperometric titrations
with two indicator electrodes;
ΔE is small.

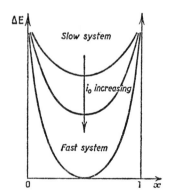

Fig. 270. Potentiometric titrations
with two indicator electrodes;
i = constant.

b. The total resistance R is very large. According to Eq. (16), i remains practically equal to V/R (V must be fairly large if the current is not to be negligible). On the other hand

$$\Delta E \sim \frac{V}{R \cdot f(x)}$$

The constant-current potentiometric titration curves obtained under the same conditions as for Fig. 269 are shown in Fig. 270.

The general case. Influence of the resistance on the shape of the titration curve

We will consider a fast system for the sake of simplicity.

As R increases, the amperometric titration curve becomes flatter. For $x =$ about 0.5, it becomes a straight line parallel to the x axis and of height V/R. But as x tends to 1, the current tends to zero, and the tangent to the curve at $x = 1$ is the same no matter what the value of R. The variation in the shape of the curve as R increases is shown in Fig. 271.

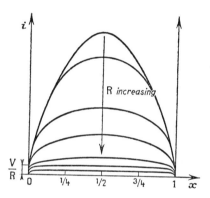

Fig. 271. Amperometric titration curves with two indicator electrodes; ΔE is small. Deformation of the titration curve as R varies from zero to infinity.

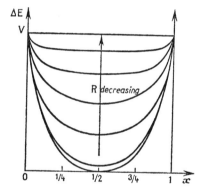

Fig. 272. Potentiometric titration curves with two indicator electrodes; $i=$constant. Deformation of the titration curve as R varies from infinity to zero.

In practice, it may be enough for the experimental curve to rejoin the theoretical curve (for $R = 0$) to within 1% when $x = 0.9$, say. Calculation shows that if $i_D(= k_D C_0)$, the limiting diffusion current of Red, is 100 μA, R must be less than 25 ohms if this condition is to be fulfilled.

As R decreases, it is the potentiometric titration curve which becomes flatter (Fig. 272). Whatever the value of R, $\Delta E \to V$ as $x \to 1$.

Choice of the resistance

The remarks made for the titrations with one indicator electrode apply here too: R should be large for a potentiometric titration and as small as possible for an amperometric titration.

Example. Influence of the resistance on the titration curves of Mn^{2+} with permanganate in a pyrophosphate medium

Mn(II) is oxidized to Mn(III) (pyrophosphate complex) by permanganate according to the overall equation

$$4\,Mn(II) + Mn(VII) \rightleftharpoons 5\,Mn(III)$$

GOFFART, MICHEL and PITANCE[1] have followed this titration reaction with a silver electrode and a platinum electrode. In order to be able to predict the titration curves the phenomena at each electrode during the titration must be known.

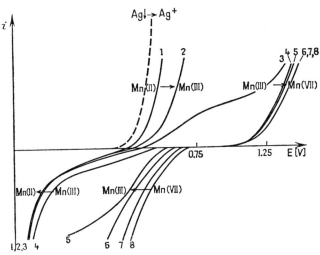

Fig. 273. The reaction $4\,Mn(II) + Mn(VII) \rightarrow 5\,Mn(III)$, pH = 7.8.
Curves 1, 2, 3: before the end point, curve 4: at the end point, curves 5, 6, 7, 8: after the end point (after DUYCKAERTS[2]).

The current–potential curves at the platinum electrode change as shown in Fig. 273 (after DUYCKAERTS[2]). The oxidation curve for silver is placed more or less as shown in the figure. The applied voltage was zero, and the system was used as a galvanic cell, the output voltage being measured. During the whole titration ($x < 1$) the electrochemical reactions are $Ag\downarrow \rightarrow Ag^+ + e$ at the silver anode and $Mn(III) + e \rightarrow Mn(II)$ at the platinum cathode, and the graphic construction shown in Fig. 274 shows that i and ΔE are zero no matter what value R has.

After the end point, the reaction at the anode is still the same, but the reaction at the cathode is now $Mn(VII) + 4e \rightarrow Mn(III)$, so a current i now flows, and there is a potential difference ΔE between the electrodes (Fig. 275).

The change in the amperometric and potentiometric titration curves as R varies is shown in Figs. 276 and 277.

It may be seen from Fig. 277 that when the total resistance is very large, the potential difference between the electrodes becomes appreciable, instead of being zero. This effect is due to the presence of the residual current. In fact, a small current, of the order of magnitude of the residual current, always flows through the cell before

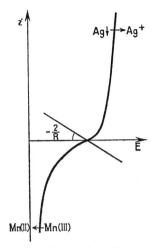

Fig. 274. Before the end point.
The reaction $4\,Mn(II) + Mn(VII) \rightarrow 5\,Mn(III)$.
Constant-resistance titration; one platinum
electrode, and one silver electrode.

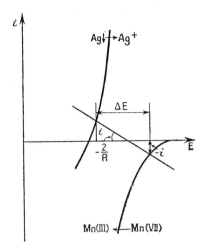

Fig. 275. After the end point.
The reaction $4\,Mn(II) + Mn(VII) \rightarrow 5\,Mn(III)$.
Constant-resistance titration; one platinum
electrode, and one silver electrode.

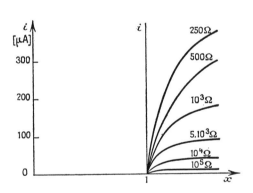

Fig. 276. Amperometric titration curves at
various values of the resistance. The reaction
$4\,Mn(II) + Mn(VII) \rightarrow 5\,Mn(III)$. Platinum
and silver electrodes (after GOFFART, MICHEL
and PITANCE [1]).

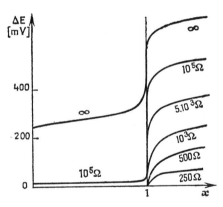

Fig. 277. Potentiometric titration curves at
various values of the resistance. The reaction
$4\,Mn(II) + Mn(VII) \rightarrow 5\,Mn(III)$. Platinum
and silver electrodes (after GOFFART, MICHEL
and PITANCE [1]).

the end point; and this causes a potential difference $\Delta E = Ri$ which increases with R.
It will be seen from Fig. 277 that the end point is sharpest when $R = 10^5\,\Omega$, and that
it is better at $R = 5 \times 10^3\,\Omega$ than at $R = $ infinity.

It may therefore be advisable in a potentiometric titration like this not to use
the very large resistance which is theoretically best, but to use one of moderate value
in order to get the sharpest potential change at the end point.

This remark leads us to consider the role of the residual current, which is the
cause of many of the discrepancies between the theoretical predictions and the experimental observations.

II. LIMIT OF SENSITIVITY OF POTENTIOMETRIC
AND AMPEROMETRIC TITRATIONS

A number of effects lead to errors in the determination of the potential or the current during a titration: (1) the residual current introduces a systematic error; (2) various other effects lead to a certain random spread of the results.

All these errors are negligible for the titration of solutions which are stronger than decinormal, but they have an appreciable effect on the accuracy at lower concentrations.

We will suppose in this discussion that the titration reaction is quantitative; naturally, if it is not this may also limit the sensitivity.

Effect of the residual current

Potentiometry. Let us consider for example the titration of Fe^{2+} with Ce^{4+}. At the end point, when a mixture of equal amounts of Fe^{3+} and Ce^{3+} is present, the theoretical current–potential curve of the mixture is shown as the broken line in Fig. 278. The theoretical equilibrium potential which would be assumed by an electrode dipped in the solution $(i = 0)$ is E_1.

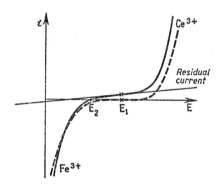

Fig. 278. The real equilibrium potential of a mixture of Fe^{3+} and Ce^{3+}.

In fact, the residual current must be added to the current given by the broken line, so the real curve representing the state of the solution at the end point is given by the full line in Fig. 278. When the current is zero, the potential of the electrode is $E_2 \neq E_1$, such that at this potential a current due to the reduction of Fe^{3+} exactly compensates for the residual current. E_2 is greater than or less than E_1 depending on the sign of the residual current.

The end point occurs at a potential E_2 which is slightly different from E_1. The point of inflection of the titration does not correspond exactly to the end point. The error introduced is greater if the residual current is larger near the end point (in particular, if the potential approaches that at which water is oxidized or reduced). This error becomes very important in the titration of dilute solutions.

This shows that those methods which are based on the differentiation of the potentiometric titration curve in order to increase the accuracy with which the end point is determined are only of limited value.

Amperometry. Similarly, if the potential is fixed at an arbitrary value E_1 corresponding to the limiting diffusion current of Fe^{2+}, the end point does not occur at $i = 0$ but at $i =$ the residual current at the potential E_1 (Fig. 279).

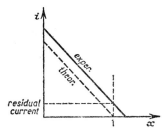

Fig. 279. Real amperometric titration curve.

The end point will occur exactly when the current is zero if the electrode potential is chosen as E_2, defined in Figs. 280 and 281.

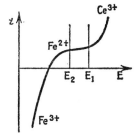

Fig. 280. Before the end point.
Amperometric titration:
$Fe^{2+} + Ce^{4+} \rightarrow Fe^{3+} + Ce^{3+}$.

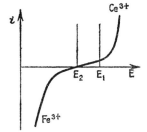

Fig. 281. At the end point.
Amperometric titration:
$Fe^{2+} + Ce^{4+} \rightarrow Fe^{3+} + Ce^{3+}$.

This error due to the existence of the residual current can be eliminated by a pre-determination of the end point, which may be done in several ways.

(*a*) The mixture which is present at the end point is made up specially, and the potential E_2 at which $i = 0$ is determined. Alternatively, with the same mixture the potential is set at E_1 and the current is determined (i_1). The titration can then be done potentiometrically at a constant current i_1, stopping at $E = E_1$; or it can be done amperometrically at potential E_1, stopping at $i = i_1$. This predetermination method is applicable to any system, whatever the value of R.

(*b*) A second solution is to fix the end point by a pre-titration: for the titration of Fe^{2+} with Ce^{4+}, for example, a mixture of Fe^{3+} and Ce^{3+} is prepared, and a little Ce^{4+} is added to give a suitable value of the current or the potential. The Fe^{2+} to be determined is then added, and the mixture is titrated with Ce^{4+} until the current or potential is exactly equal to the initial value. These titrations can also be done coulometrically [11-14].

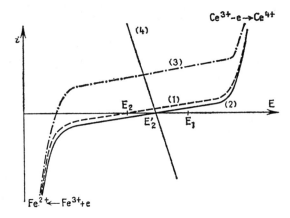

Fig. 282. Titration of traces of iron by Ce^{4+}.

Curve (1): current–potential curve for the original solution before the pre-titration.
Curve (2): the original solution after the pre-titration.
Curve (3): after the addition of traces of Fe^{2+}. The titration consists in bringing the current–potential curve back to that shown in curve (2), *i.e.* to $i = 0$ at $E = E'_2$. The straight line (4) represents the phenomena occurring during the titration.

Stability and reproducibility of the measurements

The instability of the measurements is mainly due to the variations in the diffusion conditions and also to changes in the surface of the electrode if solid electrodes are used. These variations are especially important when the rate of electron exchange is low (slow reactions); the residual current is thus rarely very reproducible. Voltage fluctuations can also have an effect.

These variations give rise to an error in the value of the concentration to be determined which is in principle independent of the method chosen (potentiometry or amperometry).

(a) In potentiometry, the variation dE/dC which is used during the titration is larger as the end point is approached; but the fluctuations in the measurements are also much greater near the end point. It is therefore best if possible to take the measurements a little before and a little after the end point ($C = 10^{-5}$). This is the method which must be used in classical potentiometry, $i = 0$, even if a pretitration is used. This is also what is done in constant-current potentiometry, by fixing the current at i_ε. But in any case, very dilute solutions cannot be titrated with accuracy, since the error in the concentration is of the order of 10^{-5} to 10^{-6}.

(b) In amperometry, the variation di/dC during the titration is constant in principle for the classical method (Fig. 206); but since the fluctuations are greater near the end point, measurements are not made there.

Fluctuations in the applied voltage V only cause a small variation in i as long as the potential E_A corresponds to the limiting diffusion current, while the variations of i will be maximum on that part of the curve near $i = 0$. It is therefore advisable to operate with a limiting diffusion current, and not with small ΔE (two indicator electrodes).

To summarize, neither method is likely to allow the titration of solutions which are more dilute than 10^{-3} to 10^{-4}. Any improvement is dependent on improving the stability of the diffusion, the reproducibility of the electrode surfaces, etc.

The sensitivity and accuracy of the measuring instruments do not usually limit the sensitivity of the titration.

Example. The titration of traces of iron, vanadium and manganese[11-13]

Let us take the example of the titration of Fe^{2+} with Ce^{4+} formed electrochemically from Ce^{3+} (coulometric titration, see Chapter X). Zero-current potentiometry in molar sulphuric acid should in theory give an end point at a potential of about 1.06 V (E_1). The real potential (E_2) is in fact slightly smaller (by a few tenths of a volt).

The influence of the residual current may be eliminated by a pre-titration. The applied voltage (see Fig. 263) is chosen so that the potential of the indicator electrode is within a few mV of a definite value E'_2, which should lie somewhere between 0.85 and 1.00 V, where the current in the circuit becomes zero (Fig. 264). The total resistance of the circuit is a few hundred ohms; the end point is determined by measuring the current. The initial solution is a sulphuric acid solution of Ce^{3+}, or better of a mixture of Ce^{3+} and Fe^{3+}. The solution is electrolyzed until $i = 0$ (pre-titration); the sample of Fe^{2+} is then added, and the solution is again electrolyzed until $i = 0$.

The measuring equipment does not limit the sensitivity: the indicator electrode has an area of 2 cm², and the galvanometer gives a deviation of 1 mm per 0.0005 μA. Under these conditions it is the stability and reproducibility of the current, especially of the residual current, which limit the sensitivity and accuracy. Other sources of error are voltage fluctuations and the electroactive impurities introduced together with the Fe^{2+}.

For such small quantities the current in the indicator circuit may not be negligible compared to the current in the coulometric circuit, thus causing the results to be low. In order to avoid this, the authors started the titration with a potentiometric arrangement, using a resistance of 100000 Ω which they removed just before the end point.

The titration of manganese as permanganate with Fe^{2+} is a back-titration which is carried out according to the same principles.

COOKE, REILLEY and FURMAN[13] have been able, using this method, to determine 10^{-8} g/ml of iron with an accuracy of 10^{-10} g/ml, and 5×10^{-10} g/ml of manganese to within 5%.

REFERENCES

Relationship between potentiometry and amperometry

[1] G. GOFFART, G. MICHEL and TH. PITANCE, *Anal. Chim. Acta*, 1 (1947) 393.
[2] G. DUYCKAERTS, *Anal. Chim. Acta*, 5 (1951) 233.
[3] R. GAUGUIN, G. CHARLOT and J. COURSIER, *Anal. Chim. Acta*, 7 (1952) 360.
[4] R. GAUGUIN, *Chim. anal.*, 36 (1954) 285.
[5] R. GAUGUIN and G. CHARLOT, *Anal. Chim. Acta*, 8 (1953) 65.
[6] J. E. DUBOIS and W. WALISH, *Compt. rend.*, 242 (1956) 1161, 1289.
[7] J. E. DUBOIS, in J. A. GAUTHIER (ed.), *Mises au point de Chimie analytique*, 5th series, Masson, Paris, 1957, p. 135.
[8] R. GAUGUIN, *Anal. Chim. Acta*, 18 (1958) 29.
[9] C. N. REILLEY, W. D. COOKE and N. H. FURMAN, *Anal. Chem.*, 23 (1951) 1223.
[10] G. DUYCKAERTS, *Anal. Chim. Acta*, 8 (1953) 57.

Limit of sensitivity of potentiometric and amperometric titrations

[11] W. D. COOKE, C. N. REILLEY and N. H. FURMAN, *Anal. Chem.*, 23 (1951) 1661.
[12] N. H. FURMAN, C. N. REILLEY and W. D. COOKE, *Anal. Chem.*, 23 (1951) 1665.
[13] W. D. COOKE, C. N. REILLEY and N. H. FURMAN, *Anal. Chem.*, 24 (1952) 205.
[14] L. MEITES, *Anal. Chem.*, 24 (1952) 1057.

Chapter X

COULOMETRY

Coulometry consists in the determination of the quantity of electricity involved in an electrochemical reaction.

Consider for example the electrochemical reaction Red — ne → Ox.

If we know the quantity of electricity, *i.e.* the total number of electrons exchanged, and n, *i.e.* the number of electrons exchanged per molecule of Red, we can calculate how much Red has been oxidized. This is a direct coulometric determination. Conversely, if we know how much Red is oxidized and how much electricity is involved, we can calculate n.

Electrolysis produces a substance A, which reacts chemically with the substance to be determined, B. The amount of electricity indicates how much A is involved. This is a coulometric titration, completely analogous to a volumetric titration.

The electrolysis in coulometry is usually carried out either at constant potential or at constant current. The various problems met with in this method are the same whether a determination is carried out by direct coulometry or by a coulometric titration, or n is determined:

1. To define the conditions of electrolysis so that only one electrochemical reaction is involved (100% current yield). A knowledge of the current–potential curves of all the substances present usually allows this problem to be solved.

2. To indicate the end of the electrochemical reaction in direct coulometry, or of the chemical reaction in a coulometric titration.

3. To determine the amount of electricity involved and to deduce from this the amount of the substance in question which has undergone the electrochemical reaction, using Faraday's equation: 1 Faraday or gram-electron, F = 96,500 coulombs.

I. DIRECT COULOMETRY

Controlled-potential coulometry

Principle

Let us suppose that the electrochemical reaction to be realized is the oxidation of a reducing agent

$$\text{Red} - ne \rightarrow \text{Ox} \tag{1}$$

If we know the current–potential curves at a given electrode for the reductant Red, the oxidant Ox and any other substances which may happen to be present in the solution, we can give the electrode potential such a value that only reaction (1) occurs (Fig. 283). All the current is used in this reaction. Under these conditions, the amount of the substance oxidized, expressed in gram-ions or gram-molecules, is $Q/n\text{F}$, where Q represents the amount of electricity involved.

We must (*a*) fix the electrode potential at a given value and keep it there (see

this Chapter, INSTRUMENTATION); (b) indicate the end of the electrochemical reaction;
(c) determine the amount of electricity involved.

End of the electrochemical reaction. The concentration c of the substance to be determined decreases continually during a direct coulometric determination, and the current tends to zero as c does (Fig. 283).

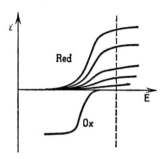

Fig. 283. The reaction
Red — $ne \rightarrow$ Ox.

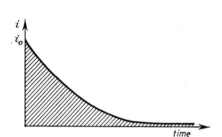

Fig. 284. The reaction Red — $ne \rightarrow$ Ox.

The current i decreases exponentially with respect to time (Fig. 284).

The amount of electricity involved during time dt, $i\mathrm{d}t = kc\mathrm{d}t$, corresponds to a
change in the amount of the electrolyzed substance present of $- V\mathrm{d}c$, where V is the
volume of the solution, and thus to a quantity of electricity $- V\mathrm{d}cnF$. It follows
that $- V\mathrm{d}cnF = kc\mathrm{d}t$, so $i = i_0\, 10^{-At}$, where i_0 is the initial value of the current.

$$k = \frac{nFD^{\alpha}S}{\delta} \quad (\text{p. 128})$$

so $$A = 0.43 \frac{D^{\alpha}S}{V\delta}$$

The potential is generally chosen so that the limiting diffusion current is obtained
(Fig. 283), *i.e.* so that the current is as large as possible.

In all cases, the end of the determination ($c = 0$, $i = 0$) is not reached, in theory,
until an infinite time has elapsed, and the amount of electricity involved in the determination is $q = \int_0^{\infty} i\mathrm{d}t$. In practice, however, the electrolysis may be stopped when a
sufficiently small current is reached. If for example the determination is stopped when
only one thousandth of the original concentration remains, thus giving a result which
is 0.1 % too small, the current will then be $i = i_0/1000$ if the current is the limiting
diffusion current.

Determination of the total amount of electricity. The quantity of electricity can be determined by measuring the current as a function of time, and obtaining the integral
$Q = \int_0^{\infty} i\mathrm{d}t$ by planimetry of the area between the current–time curve and the time
axis (Fig. 284). This area can also be calculated without continuing the electrolysis to
the end of the electrochemical reaction if the equation $i = i_0 10^{-At}$ holds [98]. The constant A can be determined by plotting the logarithm of the current against the time,
since $\log i = \log i_0 - At$.

Q is then given by the equation

$$Q = \int_0^\infty i_0 \, 10^{-At} \, dt = 0.43 \frac{i_0}{A}$$

The quantity of electricity can also be determined directly by placing a chemical coulometer, *i.e.* another electrolysis cell, in series in the circuit. The amount of electricity passing through the two cells is the same, and is determined by measuring how much of the substance in the coulometer has been electrolyzed. The current i varies in the maximum ratio 100 : 1 to 500 : 1 during the coulometry, and the electrochemical reaction occurring in the coulometer should be a known reaction with a 100% current yield over the range of currents involved. The determination of the number of gram-molecules produced or used up allows the quantity of electricity to be calculated: $Q = nFm$. The products of the reaction at the cathode or at the anode, or both, can be determined; but care must be taken that the substances produced at the anode do not react at the cathode or vice versa. This determination can be made gravimetrically, by measurement of a volume of gas, by colorimetry, polarography, volumetric analysis or constant-current coulometry. If volumetric analysis or coulometry is used, the end point can be determined by potentiometry, amperometry, colorimetry, conductimetry, etc. (see this Chapter, INSTRUMENTATION).

There are also electronic coulometers, integrating circuits which, mounted in series with the electrolysis cell, automatically measure the amount of electricity which passes (see this Chapter, INSTRUMENTATION).

Examples

This method can be used in a large number of cases which can be treated by means of the current–potential curves.

The deposition of metal. Consider the electrochemical reaction $Ag^+ + e \rightarrow Ag\downarrow$.

The current–potential curves during this reaction are shown in Fig. 285. The potential chosen must be greater than E_1 in order to avoid the simultaneous reduction of hydrogen ions, but at the same time fast enough to allow the Ag^+ ions to be reduced rapidly and completely. Let E_2 be such a potential [18] (Fig. 285).

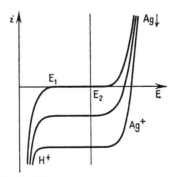

Fig. 285. The reaction $Ag^+ + e \rightarrow Ag\downarrow$.

The metal can also be deposited on a mercury cathode or on an amalgamated platinum electrode. This allows such ions as Pb^{2+}, Cd^{2+} and Zn^{2+} to be reduced;

under other conditions, these ions cannot be reduced without the evolution of hydrogen. It is possible to estimate Pb^{2+} in the presence of Cd^{2+} in this way[5, 155], by reduction at a potential E_1 as shown in Fig. 286.

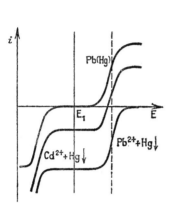

Fig. 286. The reaction
$Pb^{2+} + Hg\downarrow + 2e \rightarrow Pb(Hg)$.

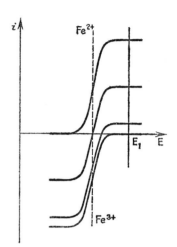

Fig. 287. The reaction
$Fe^{2+} - e \rightarrow Fe^{3+}$.

Oxidation and reduction of soluble systems. Consider for example the reaction $Fe^{2+} - e \rightarrow Fe^{3+}$, where Fe^{2+} ions are oxidized completely[97] at the potential E_1 shown in Fig. 287.

Now, consider the determination of Cr^{2+} in the presence of uranium; $Cr^{2+} - e \rightleftharpoons Cr^{3+}$ is a slow system. The current–potential curves for the systems Cr^{2+}/Cr^{3+} and U^{3+}/U^{4+} at a mercury electrode are shown in Fig. 288. At a potential of -0.15 V, the reactions $U^{3+} - e \rightarrow U^{4+}$ and $Cr^{2+} - e \rightarrow Cr^{3+}$ occur simultaneously. If, however, a pre-electrolysis is carried out at -0.55 V, then only the U^{3+} is oxidized. Experience shows that this reaction does not occur with a 100 % current yield, which means that it cannot be used for the estimation of uranium; but when all the U^{3+} has been removed from the solution, it is possible[176] to determine the Cr^{2+} by oxidizing it to Cr^{3+} with a 100 % yield at -0.15 V.

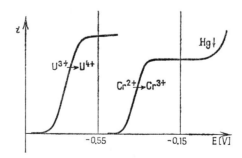

Fig. 288. The reactions $U^{3+} - e \rightarrow U^{4+}$ and $Cr^{2+} - e \rightarrow Cr^{3+}$ at a mercury electrode
(according to MEITES[176]).

The coulometry of non-electroactive substances. Complex redox systems

A non-electroactive substance can still be estimated coulometrically if a complex redox system may be found in which it takes part (cf. the paragraph on indicators, p. 56). Consider the substance B, which is not electroactive by itself, but which forms part of the redox system $AB + e \rightleftharpoons B + C$. The electrochemical reaction $B + C - e \rightarrow AB$ can be realized at a suitable potential E_1 by adding an excess of C, which may or may not be electroactive, to B. B thus limits the current. The current–potential curves during the electrochemical reaction are shown in Fig. 289.

We will give some examples of this kind of coulometry.

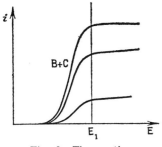

Fig. 289. The reaction
$B + C - e \rightarrow AB$.

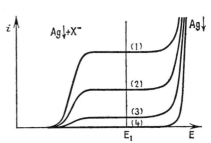

Fig. 290. The reaction
$Ag\downarrow + X^- - e \rightarrow AgX\downarrow$.

Determination of halides. In the presence of a halide X^-, a silver electrode can be oxidized according to the equation

$$Ag\downarrow + X^- - e \rightarrow AgX\downarrow$$

The current–potential curves during this reaction are shown in Fig. 290. The limiting diffusion current is proportional to the concentration of X^-. The X^- ions can be removed completely at a potential E_1.

Determination of EDTA (cf. p. 62 and 181). The reaction

$$Hg\downarrow + Y^{4-} - 2e \rightarrow HgY^{2-}$$

can be realized at a mercury electrode (Fig. 291). At the potential E_1, this reaction is limited by the diffusion of Y^{4-}, and the current becomes zero when the concentration of Y^{4-} in the solution is zero.

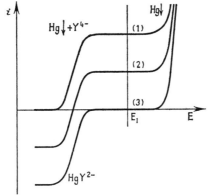

Fig. 291. The reaction $Hg\downarrow + Y^{4-} - 2e \rightarrow HgY^{2-}$.

This method may be used to follow a number of electrochemical reactions. Suppose that we wish to estimate M^{2+}. It cannot be titrated directly with EDTA ($M^{2+} + Y^{4-} \rightarrow MY^{2-}$) if M^{2+} is not electroactive; but an electroactive substance such as HgY^{2-} which does not react chemically with M^{2+} (HgY^{2-} more stable than MY^{2-}) can be added, and then the electrochemical reaction

$$M^{2+} + HgY^{2-} + 2e \rightarrow Hg\downarrow + MY^{2-}$$

can be realized. The current–potential curves during this reaction are shown in Fig. 292. An excess of HgY^{2-} is added to the solution of M^{2+} to be estimated. At the potential E_1, the current is limited by the diffusion of M^{2+}, and becomes zero at the end of the electrochemical reaction.

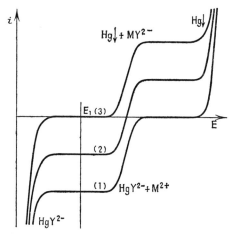

Fig. 292. The reaction $M^{2+} + HgY^{2-} + 2e \rightarrow Hg\downarrow + MY^{2-}$
(theoretical curves).

Back titrations

The substance to be estimated may undergo a chemical reaction with a known excess of an electroactive substance, and the excess can then be determined by direct coulometry, for example, the determination of EDTA. A known excess of an oxidizable or reducible ion which reacts with Y^{4-}, *e.g.* Fe^{3+}, is added to the solution. The chemical reaction

$$Y^{4-} + Fe^{3+} \rightarrow FeY^-$$

occurs. The electrochemical reaction $Fe^{3+} + e \rightarrow Fe^{2+}$ is then realized by direct coulometry at a potential E_1. Fe^{2+} does not react with FeY^-. The current–potential curves are given in Fig. 293.

Fe^{3+} may be added in a known amount either volumetrically or by coulometry.

This method can be used if the reaction (in this case $Y^{4-} + Fe^{3+} \rightarrow FeY^-$) is slow.

It is also sometimes possible to determine a non-electroactive substance by back titration with an electroactive substance. Consider the non-electroactive cation M^{2+} which is to be titrated with Y^{4-} according to the equation

$$M^{2+} + Y^{4-} \rightarrow MY^{2-}$$

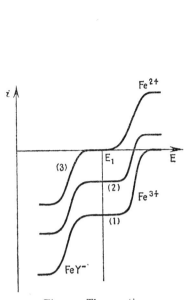

Fig. 293. The reaction
$Fe^{3+} + e \rightarrow Fe^{2+}$, back titration of
Y^{4-} with Fe^{3+}
(theorerical curves).

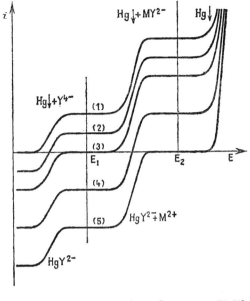

Fig. 294. The reaction $Hg\downarrow + Y^{4-} - 2e \rightarrow HgY^{2-}$
at the potential E_1, and the reaction
$Hg\downarrow + MY^{2-} - 2e \rightarrow HgY^{2-} + M^{2+}$
at the potential E_2 (theoretical curves).

A known excess of Y^{4-} can be added, and the excess of Y^{4-} determined in one of the ways described above, e.g. by oxidation at a mercury electrode

$$Hg\downarrow + Y^{4-} - 2e \rightarrow HgY^{2-} \tag{1}$$

The current–potential curves are given in Fig. 294, for the case where MY^{2-} is less stable than HgY^{2-}. At the potential E_1, the electrochemical reaction (1) occurs, and the current ceases when all the excess Y^{4-} has gone. The electrolysis may then be continued at the potential E_2. The electrochemical reaction

$$Hg\downarrow + MY^{2-} - 2e \rightarrow HgY^{2-} + M^{2+}$$

now occurs, and the current ceases again at the end of this reaction.

In these examples, the ideal curves are given. We have supposed that the chemical reactions are fast and sufficiently quantitative, and that the various complexes have widely different stability constants. In the examples involving EDTA we have represented this compound as Y^{4-}. It can in fact exist in various forms, e.g. HY^{3-} or H_2Y^{2-}. At a fixed pH, however, the treatment given above is still valid.

Characteristics of the method

Range of application. In the first place this method was limited to electroactive substances, especially to the reduction of cations to the metal at a mercury or platinum electrode. The examples we have given show that the method can be extended to the determination of a large number of non-electroactive substances.

Selectivity. It is often possible to realize the desired reaction, even in the presence of other substances, by a suitable choice of potential (see this Chapter, INSTRUMENTA-TION). There are also various ways of displacing the current–potential curves so as to increase the selectivity (see Chapters III and V).

Sensitivity. Whatever precautions are taken to increase the sensitivity, it is limited by the size and reproducibility of the residual current. In certain cases the sensitivity can be increased by depositing the substance to be determined as a metal or an amalgam and using coulometry during the anodic redissolution of the metal.

Accuracy. This depends on the accuracy with which the quantity of electricity necessary for complete oxidation or reduction of the substance can be measured. Now, $Q = Q_t - Q_r$, where Q_t is the amount of electricity measured during the electrolysis of the substance to be determined, and Q_r is the amount of electricity used up under the same conditions in the absence of the substance. For large values of Q, Q_r will be negligible compared to Q_t, and the accuracy then depends only on the method of measurement used. When Q_r is not negligible, the accuracy is mainly determined by the reproducibility of the value obtained for Q_r (see this Chapter, INSTRUMENTATION).

Chemical coulometers allow amounts of electricity greater than 10 coulomb to be determined to within $\pm$ 0.1 %. The accuracy of electronic integrators is dependent upon the particular design, but in general varies from $\pm$ 1 to 0.1 %. Planimetry of the surface enclosed by the current-potential curve and the time axis is the method to use for very small quantities (of the order of 10^{-5} coulomb). The accuracy is then from about $\pm$ 1 to about $\pm$ 5 % (see this Chapter, INSTRUMENTATION).

Constant-current direct coulometry

Principle. Constant-current coulometry may be used when the substance to be electrolyzed is present as a solid on the electrode (as metal, oxide or salt).

Consider for example the oxidation of a metal M

$$M\downarrow - ne \rightarrow M^{n+}$$

The current may be kept constant at a value I (Fig. 295). At the end of the reaction, when the last traces of metal have been oxidized, the current still being I, the electrons are now furnished by the oxidation of water, which involves a rapid change in the potential from E_1 to E_2 (Fig. 296).

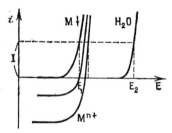

Fig. 295. The reaction
$M\downarrow - ne \rightarrow M^{n+}$.

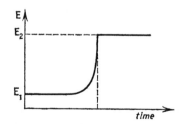

Fig. 296. The reaction
$M\downarrow - ne \rightarrow M^{n+}$
with a constant current I.

Similar phenomena are observed during the reduction of an oxide to the metal. The curves representing the reduction of an oxide to a lower oxide are shown in Fig. 297 and 298.

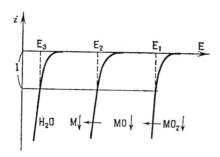

Fig. 297. The reactions
$MO_2\downarrow + H_2O + 2e \rightarrow MO\downarrow + 2\ OH^-$
and $MO\downarrow + H_2O + 2e \rightarrow M\downarrow + 2\ OH^-$
(ideal curves).

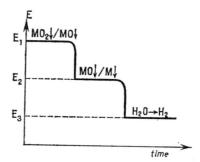

Fig. 298. The reactions
$MO_2\downarrow + H_2O + 2e \rightarrow MO\downarrow + 2\ OH^-$
and $MO\downarrow + H_2O + 2e \rightarrow M\downarrow + 2\ OH^-$
at constant current I (ideal curve).

This method is not applicable to substances which are in solution. Consider for example the oxidation of Fe^{2+}. As the reaction proceeds, the concentration of Fe^{2+} decreases and the limiting diffusion current decreases. A moment will come when the limiting current $i_{Fe^{2+}}$ becomes less than I, and from then on other substances (e.g. the solvent) will be oxidized with a current $I - i_{Fe^{2+}}$ (Fig. 299). This trouble can only be eliminated by imposing a very small current, say 1% or 0.1% of the original current, which will mean that the end point comes about 1% or 0.1% too early; but such an operation takes a very long time.

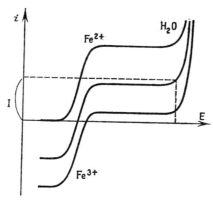

Fig. 299. The reactions $Fe^{2+} - e \rightarrow Fe^{3+}$ at constant current I.

Example of a back-titration. The determination of Fe^{3+}. A known quantity of copper can be deposited on e.g. a platinum electrode. In order to estimate an oxidant, e.g. Fe^{3+}, this substance can be reacted with the copper

$$Cu\downarrow + 2\ Fe^{3+} \rightarrow Cu^{2+} + 2\ Fe^{2+}$$

and the remaining copper determined by constant-current oxidation. The potential
changes from E_1 to E_2 at the end of the electrochemical reaction (Fig. 300).

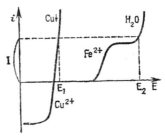

Fig. 300. The reaction $Cu\downarrow - 2e \rightarrow Cu^{2+}$; back-titration of Fe^{3+} with $Cu\downarrow$.

Characteristics of the method. This method can be used where metal coatings, oxide
layers, films, etc., are involved. It may be used whenever the substance to be determined can be deposited beforehand so as to adhere to a solid electrode (anodic redissolution coulometry). The sensitivity is high: 1 μA for 1 second corresponds to about
10^{-11} gram-equivalents, which is usually about 10^{-9} g. In fact, the accuracy is limited
by the residual current and by the fact that the last traces of metal do not disappear
uniformly from the surface of the electrode. The current can be fixed to within 1 %
by means of the simple circuit shown on p. 135, and to within 0.1 % by means of an
amperostat. The time can be measured accurately (0.1 %) by means of an electric or
mechanical chronometer placed in the circuit. Very short times can be measured (to
within 5 %) by recording the current–potential curves with an oscilloscope (see this
Chapter, INSTRUMENTATION). Like all constant-current coulometric methods, this
method allows very small quantities to be measured with good accuracy.

Direct coulometry with variable potential and current

When the last traces of metal disappear irregularly from the surface of the electrode
during an anodic redissolution, the potential jump occurs before the end point. Certain authors[22] have suggested that the redissolution should be carried out with a
variable current and potential. It is possible to determine 5×10^{-10} g of silver in this
way, by planimetry of the area under the current–time curve.

II. COULOMETRIC TITRATIONS

Principle. If a substance B is to be estimated, a reactant A is prepared by electrolysis, *e.g.* $C - e \rightarrow A$, and the chemical reaction

$$B + A \rightarrow AB$$

is realized. As we have said, the substance A must be prepared with a 100 % current
yield, the corresponding amount of electricity must be determined, and the end point
must be indicated. A variable current and potential, or a constant current or potential, may be used. Since however it is simplest to determine the amount of electricity
when the current is constant, a constant current is generally used.

Constant-current titrations

Determination of the quantity of electricity. Since the current is constant, it may be measured once and for all (see INSTRUMENTATION). The problem thus becomes simply one of measuring the time for which the current flows. Constant-current coulometric titrations are in many ways similar to volumetric titrations: the measurement of volume is replaced by one of time, and the homogeneity of the solution and its stability in time are equivalent to the constancy of the current. The aliquot of the solution to be determined is replaced by the exact knowledge of the current used. From a practical point of view, the manipulation of the switch in the circuit is similar to that of the tap of a burette.

Indication of the end point. The end point of the titration may be determined in the same way as in volumetric analysis: by chemical indicators, potentiometry, amperometry, spectrophotometry, etc.

The accuracy and sensitivity of these methods are known; the use of potentiometry is discussed on p. 186, amperometry on p. 218, the method of REILLEY, COOKE and FURMAN on p. 235. Absorption spectrophotometry is often very sensitive.

A number of conditions must be realized in a constant-current titration. The chemical reaction (it may be an acid–base reaction, or one of oxidation–reduction, complex-formation or precipitation) must be fast and quantitative. The redox systems used to produce the reactant may be fast or slow, as long as the current yield is 100 %. The knowledge of the current–potential curves and their deformations during the titration allows the conditions of electrolysis to be fixed. The current–potential curves have been studied in Chapters III and IV; we will give some examples here.

Coulometric titrations involving a chemical complex-formation, precipitation or acid–base reaction

We will consider the case where the reactant A is prepared by electrolysis: $C - e \rightarrow A$. This substance then reacts further with the substance to be determined

$$B + A \rightarrow AB$$

In other words, an excess of C is added to the solution of B, and C is then oxidized with a constant current. Examination of the current–potential curves (Fig. 301) shows that if the current is fixed at I, the two electrochemical reactions

$$B + C - e \rightarrow AB \tag{1}$$

$$C - e \rightarrow A \tag{2}$$

occur simultaneously, but A formed in reaction (2) diffuses through the solution and reacts with B according to the reaction $B + A \rightarrow AB$, so that the second reaction produces the same final result as the first, except that AB is formed at the electrode by reaction (1) and in the body of the solution by reaction (2). The nett result is the same as if the reaction $B + C - e \rightarrow AB$ were the only reaction.

Fig. 301 gives the current–potential curves during the titration (curves 1, 2) at the end point (curve 3) and after the end point (curve 4).

We will treat some examples here.

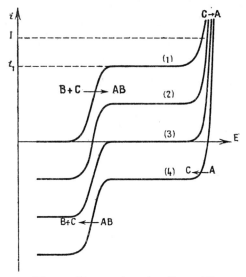

Fig. 301. The reactions $A + B \rightarrow AB$

and $\begin{cases} C - e \rightarrow A \\ B + C - e \rightarrow AB \end{cases}$

at constant current I.

Curves 1 and 2: before the end point. Curve 3: at the end point. Curve 4: after the end point.

Titration of an acid. Let us suppose that it is desired to estimate a strong acid. The current–potential curve is shown in Fig. 302. If the current is fixed at I, the two electrochemical reactions

$$2 H^+ + 2e \rightarrow H_2$$

and

$$2 H_2O + 2e \rightarrow 2 OH^- + H_2$$

occur, followed by

$$2 OH^- + 2 H^+ \rightarrow 2 H_2O$$

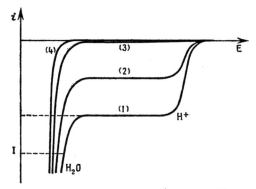

Fig. 302. The reactions $2 H^+ + 2e \rightarrow H_2$

and $\begin{cases} 2 H_2O + 2e \rightarrow H_2 + 2 OH^- \\ 2 OH^- + 2 H^+ \rightarrow 2 H_2O \end{cases}$

Both reactions give the same result, and all the current is used to reduce H^+. The displacement of the current potential curves as the reaction proceeds is shown in Fig. 302.

The results are similar if a weak acid is to be titrated

$$2 H_2O + 2e \rightarrow 2 OH^- + H_2$$

$$2 OH^- + 2 HA \rightarrow 2 A^- + 2 H_2O$$

and

$$2 HA + 2e \rightarrow 2 A^- + H_2$$

See the curves shown in Chapter III, Fig. 69 and following.

The end point may be determined by means of the colour change of an indicator, a pH-meter, constant-current potentiometry (platinum electrode), amperometry with one or two indicator electrodes, or spectrophotometry in conjunction with an indicator.

Precipitation reactions. Argentometry. The determination of halides. The Ag^+ required for the titration may be produced in known amounts by the oxidation of a silver electrode. Consider for example the titration of Cl^-. The current–potential curves during the titration are shown in Fig. 303.

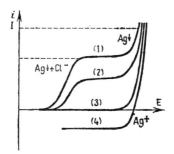

Fig. 303. The reactions $Ag + Cl^- - e \rightarrow AgCl\downarrow$
and $\begin{cases} Ag - e \rightarrow Ag^+ \\ Ag^+ + Cl^- \rightarrow AgCl\downarrow \end{cases}$

It will be seen that two equivalent electrochemical reactions can occur

$$Ag\downarrow + Cl^- - e \rightarrow AgCl\downarrow$$

and

$$Ag\downarrow - e \rightarrow Ag^+ \quad \text{followed by} \quad Ag^+ + Cl^- \rightarrow AgCl\downarrow$$

Electrolysis must be stopped when the concentration of Cl^- is zero. Various methods of indicating the end point (potentiometry, amperometry, etc.) may be used. The total quantity of electricity corresponds to the disappearance of one Cl^- ion per electron.

Complex-formation. Determination of EDTA. The reaction

$$Y^{4-} + Hg^{2+} \rightarrow HgY^{2-}$$

may be used. The necessary Hg^{2+} is prepared by oxidation of a mercury electrode. Two equivalent electrochemical reactions occur (Fig. 304):

    1. Direct oxidation of mercury

$$Hg\downarrow - 2e \rightarrow Hg^{2+}$$

followed by

$$Hg^{2+} + Y^{4-} \rightarrow HgY^{2-}$$

    2. Oxidation of mercury in the presence of EDTA

$$Hg\downarrow + Y^{4-} - 2e \rightarrow HgY^{2-}$$

Titrations with EDTA. Known amounts of Y^{4-} are produced by reduction of the mercuric complex [155]

$$HgY^{2-} + 2e \rightarrow Hg\downarrow + Y^{4-}$$

A number of cations which form complexes with EDTA can be determined in this way.

    1. M^{2+} gives a complex with Y^{4-} which is less stable than HgY^{2-}. The chemical reaction is $Y^{4-} + M^{2+} \rightarrow MY^{2-}$, so the overall reaction is

$$HgY^{2-} + M^{2+} + 2e \rightarrow Hg\downarrow + MY^{2-}$$

The current–potential curves during the titration are shown in Fig. 305. The first wave (i_1) corresponds to the formation of MY^{2-} near the electrode (overall reaction).

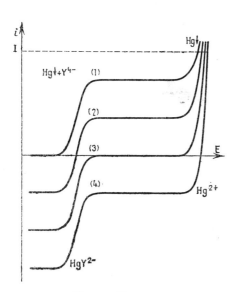

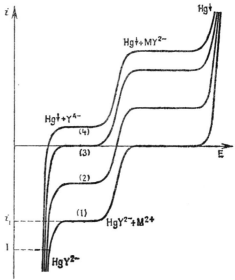

Fig. 304. The reactions
$$Hg\downarrow + Y^{4-} - 2e \rightarrow HgY^{2-}$$
$$\text{and} \begin{cases} Hg\downarrow - 2e \rightarrow Hg^{2+} \\ Hg^{2+} + Y^{4-} \rightarrow HgY^{2-} \end{cases}$$

Fig. 305. The reactions
$$HgY^{2-} + M^{2+} + 2e \rightarrow Hg\downarrow + MY^{2-}$$
$$\text{and} \begin{cases} HgY^{2-} + 2e \rightarrow Hg\downarrow + Y^{4-} \\ M^{2+} + Y^{4-} \rightarrow MY^{2-} \end{cases}$$

Curve 1: at the start. Curve 2: before the end point. Curve 3: at the end point. Curve 4: after the end point. (Theoretical curves).

The second wave $(I - i_1)$ corresponds to the reduction of HgY^{2-}, *i.e.* the production of Y^{4-}, which diffuses into the body of the solution and reacts there with M^{2+}. The end point can be indicated by potentiometry (p. 183), amperometry (p. 214), or by a chemical indicator.

2. M^{2+} gives a complex with Y^{4-} which is more stable than HgY^{2-}.

When an excess of HgY^{2-} is added to the M^{2+} to be determined, the chemical reaction

$$HgY^{2-} + M^{2+} \rightarrow Hg^{2+} + MY^{2-}$$

occurs. The only possible electrochemical reactions are

$$Hg^{2+} + 2e \rightarrow Hg\downarrow$$

and

$$HgY^{2-} + 2e \rightarrow Hg\downarrow + Y^{4-}$$

followed by

$$Y^{4-} + Hg^{2+} \rightarrow HgY^{2-}$$

i.e. the overall reaction

$$Hg^{2+} + 2e \rightarrow Hg\downarrow$$

These two mechanisms give the same result. The current–potential curves during the titration are shown in Fig. 306.

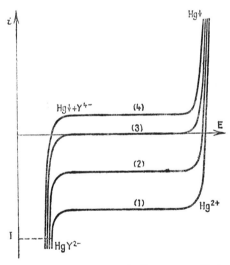

Fig. 306. The reactions $Hg^{2+} + 2e \rightarrow Hg\downarrow$

and $\begin{cases} HgY^{2-} + 2e \rightarrow Hg\downarrow + Y^{4-} \\ Y^{4-} + Hg^{2+} \rightarrow HgY^{2-} \end{cases}$

Back-titrations. A known excess of EDTA is added by reduction of HgY^{2-} to the solution of the non-electroactive cation M^{2+} which is to be determined. This is a useful method if the reaction $M^{2+} + Y^{4-} \rightarrow MY^{2-}$ is slow. The excess of EDTA can then be determined by the oxidation of mercury, as described above.

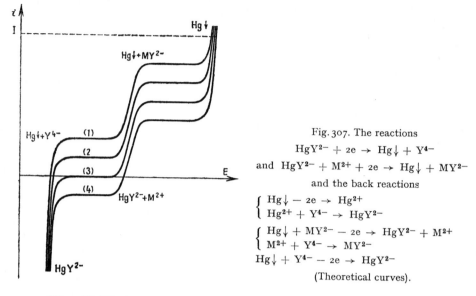

Fig. 307. The reactions

$$HgY^{2-} + 2e \rightarrow Hg\downarrow + Y^{4-}$$

and $HgY^{2-} + M^{2+} + 2e \rightarrow Hg\downarrow + MY^{2-}$

and the back reactions

$$\begin{cases} Hg\downarrow - 2e \rightarrow Hg^{2+} \\ Hg^{2+} + Y^{4-} \rightarrow HgY^{2-} \end{cases}$$

$$\begin{cases} Hg\downarrow + MY^{2-} - 2e \rightarrow HgY^{2-} + M^{2+} \\ M^{2+} + Y^{4-} \rightarrow MY^{2-} \end{cases}$$

$$Hg\downarrow + Y^{4-} - 2e \rightarrow HgY^{2-}$$

(Theoretical curves).

1. When HgY^{2-} is more stable than MY^{2-}, the current–potential curves are as shown in Fig. 307. There are three equivalent electrochemical reactions

$$Hg\downarrow + Y^{4-} - 2e \rightarrow HgY^{2-} \tag{1}$$

$$Hg\downarrow + MY^{2-} - 2e \rightarrow HgY^{2-} + M^{2+} \quad \text{followed by} \quad M^{2+} + Y^{4-} \rightarrow MY^{2-} \tag{2}$$

$$Hg\downarrow - 2e \rightarrow Hg^{2+} \quad \text{followed by} \quad Hg^{2+} + Y^{4-} \rightarrow HgY^{2-} \tag{3}$$

2. If HgY^{2-} is less stable than MY^{2-}, there are only two equivalent reactions (1) and (3) (Fig. 308).

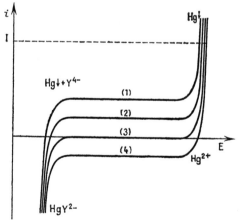

Fig. 308. The back reactions $\begin{cases} Hg\downarrow - 2e \rightarrow Hg^{2+} \\ Hg^{2+} + Y^{4-} \rightarrow HgY^{2-} \\ Hg + Y^{4-} - 2e \rightarrow HgY^{2-} \end{cases}$

Similar methods can be used for a large number of complexes: Al^{3+} and F^-, Hg^{2+} and CN^-, etc.

Coulometric titrations involving a redox reaction

The substance B is to be determined. The substance A is prepared by coulometry at potential E_1

$$C - e \rightarrow A$$

and the chemical redox reaction

$$B + A \rightarrow C + D$$

then occurs, the second redox system being

$$B - e \rightarrow D$$

at potential E_2. If the chemical reaction is to be possible, E_1 must be greater than E_2. The current–potential curves for this case have been discussed in Chapters III and IV, for fast and slow redox systems respectively. We will give some examples here.

The coulometric titration of Fe^{2+}. This involves the chemical reaction

$$Fe^{2+} + Ce^{4+} \rightarrow Fe^{3+} + Ce^{3+}$$

where the Ce^{4+} is produced by the electrochemical oxidation of Ce^{3+}. We thus have the two redox systems

$$Fe^{3+} + e \rightleftharpoons Fe^{2+}$$

$$Ce^{4+} + e \rightleftharpoons Ce^{3+}$$

which are fast at a suitable electrode. The ferrous iron is oxidized at the same time as the cerium (III), as is shown by curves 1 and 2 of Fig. 309. Under these condition, the fixed current, I, is composed of two parts, i_1 corresponding to the reaction $Fe^{2+} - e \rightarrow Fe^{3+}$ and $(I - i_1)$ corresponding to the reaction $Ce^{3+} - e \rightarrow Ce^{4+}$, which is followed by the chemical reaction $Fe^{2+} + Ce^{4+} \rightarrow Fe^{3+} + Ce^{3+}$.

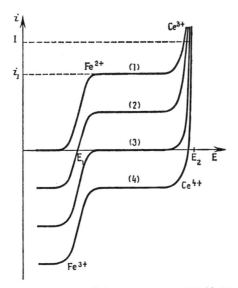

Fig. 309. The oxidation of Fe^{2+} in the presence of Ce^{3+} (ideal curves)

It is thus clear that the passage of one electron causes the disappearance of one Fe^{2+} ion, either directly (i_1) or by formation of Ce^{4+} $(I - i_1)$. This is why it is still said in this case that the Ce^{4+} is prepared with a 100 % current yield; it would be equally true to say that in the presence of Ce^{3+}, ferrous iron can be oxidized with a constant current with a 100 % current yield. The system Ce^{3+}/Ce^{4+} is then called the auxiliary system.

When the reactant is prepared out of contact with the solution to be titrated, the position of the current–potential curve of the substance to be titrated does not have any effect, and it is easy to get a 100 % current yield.

The titration of thiosulphate. Known quantities of iodine are prepared by oxidation of iodide which has been added to the solution of thiosulphate to be titrated, and the chemical reaction

$$I_3^- + 2\,S_2O_3^{2-} \rightarrow 3\,I^- + S_4O_6^{2-}$$

occurs. The first redox system $3\,I^- - 2e \rightleftharpoons I_3^-$ is fast (potential E_1), the second $2\,S_2O_3^{2-} - 2e \rightleftharpoons S_4O_6^{2-}$ is slow and $E_2 < E_1$.

The current–potential curves are shown in Fig. 310. If the current is fixed at I, the $S_2O_3^{2-}$ is oxidized with a 100 % current yield.

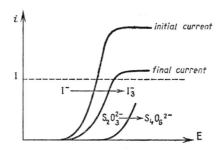

Fig. 310. The titration of thiosulphate (according to BADOZ-LAMBLING[18]).

Titrations involving bromination. Some substances can be titrated with bromine, either by oxidation, *e.g.*

$$H_2N-NH_2 + 2\,Br_2 \rightarrow N_2 + 4\,H^+ + 4\,Br^-$$

or by oxidation and bromination, *e.g.*

$$C_6H_5NH_2 + 3\,Br_2 \rightarrow C_6H_2Br_3NH_2 + 3\,Br^- + 3\,H^+$$

This method can be used with a large number of phenols, amines, oxine, ethylenic compounds, etc. The chemical reaction is often fast enough for a direct titration to be used, but it is sometimes necessary to add a known excess of bromine and determine the excess by back-titration. Both these methods can be used in coulometry, if the reductant to be determined belongs to a slow system, so that the bromide is oxidized electrochemically first (Fig. 311). In the case of the titration of aniline for example, the following reactions occur.

The electrochemical reaction

$$6 Br^- - 6e \rightarrow 3 Br_2$$

The chemical reaction

$$C_6H_5NH_2 + 3 Br_2 \rightarrow C_6H_2Br_3NH_2 + 3 Br^- + 3 H^+$$

The overall reaction

$$C_6H_5NH_2 + 3 Br^- - 6e \rightarrow C_6H_2Br_3NH_2 + 3 H^+$$

The end point can be indicated by various methods, usually amperometry or potentiometry.

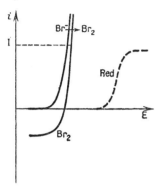

Fig. 311. The fixation of bromine by
organic compounds.

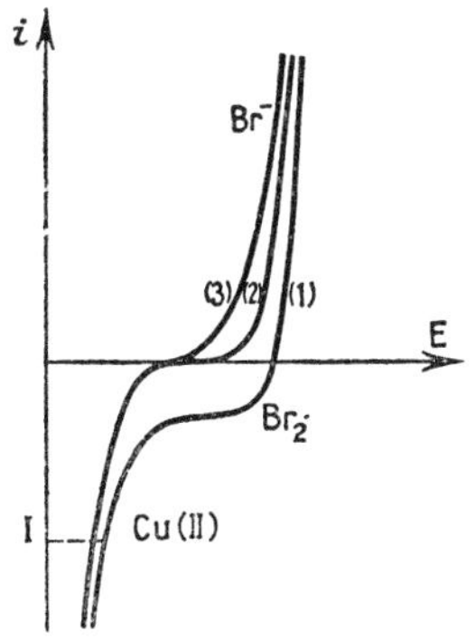

Fig. 312. The titration of bromine.

Back-titration of the excess of bromine. A known amount of bromine is formed by electrolysis for a given time. In order to determine the excess of bromine by electrochemical reduction at constant current, the solution must contain an oxidant which serves as the auxiliary system, like Ce^{3+} in the oxidation of Fe^{2+}. In this case a cupric salt is introduced into the solution before the titration. This does not interfere with the first stage of the determination (the oxidation of bromide). In the second part, we have the two equivalent reactions

$$Br_2 + 2e \rightarrow 2 Br^-$$

and

$$\begin{cases} 2 Cu(II) + 2e \rightarrow 2 Cu(I) \\ 2 Cu(I) + Br_2 \rightarrow 2 Cu(II) + 2 Br^- \end{cases}$$

The current–potential curves are shown in Fig. 312. The end point can be indicated by one of the usual methods.

Micro-coulometry. Coulometry has been used on volumes of solution as low as 0.01 ml. Since it is still possible to titrate millinormal solutions, this method can be used to determine 10^{-8} to 10^{-9} gram-ions.

Characteristics of the method

Range of application. Constant-current coulometry can be used in a large number of cases, in principle in most of the cases in which volumetric analysis can be used. It is even possible to use rather unstable substances such as U(V), Br_2, Cu(I), Ag(II) and Ti(III), which are difficult to use in volumetric analysis.

TABLE I

ELECTROLYTIC REACTIONS WITH 100% CURRENT YIELD

Reactions	References
$2 H_2O + 2e \rightarrow H_2 + 2 OH^-$ $2 H^+ + 2e \rightarrow H_2$	} 69, 74, 87, 88, 91, 104, 108, 110, 160.
$2 H_2O - 4e \rightarrow O_2 + 4 H^+$ $4 OH^- - 4e \rightarrow O_2 + 2 H_2O$	} 36, 71, 102, 120, 149, 168.
$Ag^+ - e \rightarrow Ag^{2+}$	85, 169.
$Ag\downarrow - e \rightarrow Ag^+$	18, 22, 103, 119.
$Ag\downarrow + X^- - e \rightarrow AgX\downarrow$	18, 29, 112, 113, 121, 135, 136, 181.
$Ag\downarrow + 2 CN^- - e \rightarrow Ag(CN)_2^-$	173.
$Ag\downarrow + RSH - e \rightarrow RSAg + H^+$	135.
$As(III) - 2e \rightarrow As(V)$	81.
$Bi^{3+} + (Hg)\downarrow - 3e \rightarrow Bi(Hg)$	27.
$2 Br^- - 2e \rightarrow Br_2$	{ 61, 63, 64, 70, 72, 73, 75, 76, 77, 78, 94, 105, 109, 116, 118, 139, 146, 151, 157, 158, 166, 170, 174.
$Br^- + H_2O - e \rightarrow BrO^- + 2 H^+$	139.
$Cd^{2+} + (Hg)\downarrow + 2e \rightarrow Cd(Hg)$	35, 129.
$CdY^{2-} + (Hg)\downarrow + 2e \rightarrow Cd(Hg) + Y^{4-}$	160.
$Cd(Hg) - 2e \rightarrow Cd^{2+} + (Hg)\downarrow$	23.
$Ce^{3+} - e \rightarrow Ce^{4+}$	{ 18, 68, 83, 89, 99, 106, 107, 122, 123, 124, 150, 163, 164.
$2 Cl^- - 2e \rightarrow Cl_2$	61, 78, 84, 93, 101, 152.
$Co^{2+} + 2e \rightarrow Co\downarrow$	128.
$Cr^{2+} - e \rightarrow Cr^{3+}$	172.
$Cr^{3+} - 3e \rightarrow Cr(VI)$	153.
$Cu^{2+} + e \rightarrow Cu(I)$	63, 79, 111, 178.
$Cu^{2+} + 2e \rightarrow Cu\downarrow$	140.
$CuX_2^- + e \rightarrow Cu\downarrow + 2 X^-$	65, 177.
$Cu^{2+} + (Hg)\downarrow + 2e \rightarrow Cu(Hg)$	35.
$Fe^{2+} - e \rightarrow Fe^{3+}$	96.
$Fe^{3+} + e \rightarrow Fe^{2+}$	{ 68, 80, 82, 90, 95, 97, 98, 125, 135, 143, 144, 162.
$Fe(CN)_6^{4-} - e \rightarrow Fe(CN)_6^{3-}$	126.
$Fe(CN)_6^{3-} + e \rightarrow Fe(CN)_6^{4-}$	114, 157.
$FeY^+ + e \rightarrow FeY^{2-}$	156.
$3 I^- - 2e \rightarrow I_3^-$	{ 18, 25, 36, 61, 72, 86, 100, 108, 115, 117, 133, 165, 167.
$Mn^{2+} - 5e \rightarrow Mn(VII)$	137.
$Hg\downarrow - 2e \rightarrow Hg^{2+}$ $2 Hg\downarrow - 2e \rightarrow Hg_2^{2+}$	} 175.
$2 Hg\downarrow + 2 X^- - 2e \rightarrow Hg_2X_2\downarrow$	138, 145, 154.
$Hg\downarrow + S^{2-} + 2e \rightarrow HgS\downarrow$	176.
$Hg\downarrow + 2 CN^- - 2e \rightarrow Hg(CN)_2$	173.
$HgY^{2-} + 2e \rightarrow Hg\downarrow + Y^{4-}$	155.
$Ni^{2+} + 2e \rightarrow Ni\downarrow$	128.
$Pb^{2+} + (Hg)\downarrow + 2e \rightarrow Pb(Hg)$	35.
$Pb(Hg) - 2e \rightarrow Pb^{2+} + (Hg)\downarrow$	34.
$2 SO_3^{2-} + 4 H^+ + 2e \rightarrow S_2O_4^{2-} + 2 H_2O$	182.
$Tl^+ - 2e \rightarrow Tl^{3+}$ $Tl^{3+} + 3 OH^- - 2e \rightarrow Tl(OH)_3\downarrow$	} 148.
$Ti(IV) + e \rightarrow Ti(III)$	93, 127, 130, 132, 141, 142, 171.
$U(VI) + e \rightarrow U(V)$	147.
$U(VI) + 2e \rightarrow U(IV)$	134, 161, 179.
$V(IV) - e \rightarrow V(V)$	92.
$Zn^{2+} + (Hg)\downarrow + 2e \rightarrow Zn(Hg)$	129.
$Zn(Hg) - 2e \rightarrow Zn^{2+} + (Hg)\downarrow$	23.
$Cl_3CCO_2^- + H_2O + 2e \rightarrow Cl_2CHCO_2^- + Cl^- + OH^-$	131.
Homocystine $\rightarrow$ Homocysteine	31.

Accuracy and sensitivity. The determination of the amount of electricity can be very accurate (the time can be meassured to better than 0.1 % and the current to within 0.1 %). The method can also be very sensitive: 1 μA for 1000 sec = 10^{-9} gram-equivalents. It is difficult to manipulate such small quantities in volumetric analysis. The sensitivity is limited, however, by the residual current. This can be corrected for, but the method then loses its simplicity. The method used to indicate the end point usually limits the accuracy and the sensitivity. The most sensitive methods are spectrophotometry, amperometry, and in particular the method of REILLEY, COOKE and FURMAN (see p. 235).

III. INSTRUMENTATION

Controlled-potential coulometry

The potential of the electrode (anode or cathode) must be kept constant at a value determined beforehand, and the amount of electricity consumed during the electrolysis must be measured. The cell used must be such that a 100 % current yield can be obtained during the electrolysis, which must not last too long (30 minutes at the most).

We have already discussed the principles of fixing the potential for small currents in Chapter VI, p. 133.

Simplified circuit. A voltage V is applied across the cell, and its value is controlled by a rheostat (Fig. 313). We then have the relationship

$$V = E_s - E_{aux} + |i| R_1$$

where E_s is the (stabilized) potential of the electrode at which the electrochemical reaction in question occurs, E_{aux} is the potential of the auxiliary electrode, R_1 is the internal resistance of the cell and i is the current. E_s must be kept constant while i varies during the electrolysis (i varies in the ratio 500 : 1 to 100 : 1).

The first solution is to keep V constant (accumulators or a stabilized power supply) and to use as auxiliary electrode a comparison electrode whose potential varies little with the current. If only small currents are used, as in the determination of small amounts of a substance, the ohmic drop across the cell is negligible (see this Chapter, *Cells*, p. 262). Under these conditions, $E_s - E_{aux} \approx V$; the potential of the

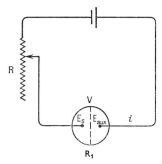

Fig. 313. Fixing the potential.
Simplified circuit.

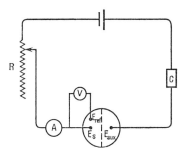

Fig. 314. C, coulometer; A, ammeter; and V, voltmeter.

stabilized electrode is constant. This method can only be used in a limited number of cases.

In general the variations of the ohmic drop iR_1 must be compensated by varying the applied voltage V so that the potential of the stabilized electrode remains constant with respect to that of a reference electrode which does not take any current, E_{ref}. Figure 314 shows the principles of a circuit for constant-potential electrolysis. A source of d.c. voltage (accumulators, galvanic cell, etc.) feeds the cell via a rheostat R; a millivoltmeter V allows the potential difference between the stabilized electrode and a reference electrode, $E_s - E_{ref}$, to be measured. An ammeter or galvanometer to measure the current and a coulometer to measure the amount of electricity are placed in series with the cell. The rheostat is adjusted manually so that the reading of the millivoltmeter remains constant during the electrolysis; the potential of the stabilized electrode is thus also kept constant.

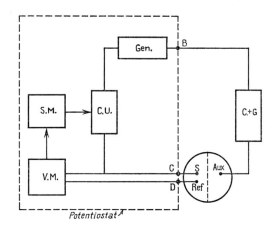

Fig. 315. Gen., current source; C.U., control unit; S.M., servomechanism; V.M., measure of $E_s - E_{ref}$; C. + G., coulometer and galvanometer; B, C and D, terminals of potentiostat; S, stabilized electrode; Aux, auxiliary electrode; Ref, reference electrode.

Potentiostats. As we have seen on p. 134, a potentiostat is an instrument which keeps the potential automatically constant. It consists in principle of a control unit operating on a d.c. generator (galvanic cell, accumulators, etc.) which is connected across the cell. The potential $E_s - E_{ref}$ is measured by a compensation method. The measuring unit actuates a servomechanism, which operates the current control unit. The various types of instruments differ mainly in the nature of the control unit (rheostat, grid voltage of a valve, transformer, magnetic amplifier, etc.) and of the servomechanism. The potentiostat appears to the user as a power supply with two terminals for the electrodes of the electrolysis cell, B and C, and a reference terminal D. It is possible to apply and measure a known and adjustable voltage between one of the electrolysis terminals and the reference terminal. The other instruments (coulometer, galvanometer) in series with the cell should be placed between the auxiliary electrode and its terminal B in order to ensure real constancy of the potential of the stabilized electrode S (Fig 315).

Characteristics of a potentiostat. Output. The output which the potentiostat is capable of supplying must be greater than that consumed in the circuit, $i\{E_s - E_{aux} + i(R_1 + R_2)\}$, where R_1 is the internal resistance of the cell and R_2 is the resistance of the rest of the circuit. The potentiostat cannot function above a certain current. The manufacturers therefore provide a table showing the maximum currents which may be used with various output voltages. Certain types of potentiostats have also a lower current limit below which they do not work.

Response time. The potential of the stabilized electrode must naturally be returned to E_s as quickly as possible if it deviates from this value during the electrolysis; particularly at the start of the reaction, the potential must reach E_s without any delay. This is a source of error with some instruments.

Dead range. The potentiostat does not function until there is a certain difference ΔE between the electrode potential and the desired potential. When selectively oxidizing or reducing substances whose current–potential curves lie near each other, an instrument with a small value of ΔE must be used. For most coulometric purposes, 5–10 mV is small enough.

Potentiostats can also be used for separations or for preparations at a controlled potential (see Chapter XI), or for kinetic studies. The potentiostat which gives the best performance under the conditions in question should then be chosen; for the simultaneous titrations of several substances, ΔE should be small, for separative and preparative procedures i should in general be large, and for kinetic studies the response time should be short. LINGANE [183] has described a large number of types of potentiostats and some French models are given by CHARLOT et al [184].

Determination of the amount of electricity. Coulometers

Coulometers measure the amount of electricity $Q = \int i\,dt$ used during the electrolysis.

1. *By recording the current as a function of time.* The amount of electricity can then be very simply determined by planimetry of the area under the current–time curve. The theoretical curve is shown as the full line in Fig. 316. In practice the measuring instrument has a certain inertia, so the observed curve has the form shown by the

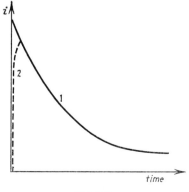

Fig. 316.

broken line near the beginning. The measured amount of electricity also includes that due to the residual current. These errors can be eliminated in two ways:

a. Choose an initial potential at which the electrolysis current is low, and then vary it to give a large current. The current–time curve thus produced has the form of curve 1 of Fig. 317. In the absence of the substance to be determined, the same operation gives 2 of Fig. 317, thus allowing the residual electricity to be determined. This method is the simplest to use when the maximum current is high, *i.e.* when large amounts have to be estimated, and the accuracy is good ($\pm$ 1 % to 0.1 %); but when the residual current is appreciable compared to the total current, the accuracy is low since the residual current is not very reproducible.

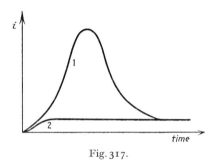

Fig. 317.

b. In order to improve the reproducibility of the residual current the supporting electrolyte can be electrolyzed at the chosen potential until the residual current is constant before adding the substance to be determined in a small volume. The current–time curve is shown in Fig. 318. Under these conditions the residual current is reproducible. This is the best method for the determination of traces.

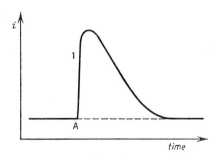

Fig. 318.

A galvanometer with a short response time and a spot follower (or a galvanometer-type d.c. amplifier coupled to a chart recorder) may be used to record the current–time curve. The galvanometer and the spot follower must be calibrated, and the paper speed must be known. A potentiometric recorder may also be used to record the voltage drop across a resistance in series with the cell; it is still necessary to calibrate the apparatus with respect to current and time.

2. *Chemical coulometers*. An electrolysis cell in series with the cell in which the determination is carried out has the same current flowing through it as the latter, so the amount of electricity used in each cell is the same. The reaction at the anode or cathode (or both) of this cell must occur with 100 % current yield throughout the electrolysis. The electrolysis product in question is then determined, which allows the amount of electricity to be calculated. There are different types of coulometer, depending on the method of analysis used (gravimetry, gasometry, volumetry, coulometry, polarography, colorimetry etc.).

'Coulometric' coulometer[111]. The chosen reaction is for instance the reduction of Cu^{2+}, which can easily be made to occur in 100 % yield by using a concentrated solution, and stirring well to give stationary diffusion conditions. The metallic copper deposited on the platinum electrode can be estimated by anodic redissolution with a constant current of known value i. The end point of this reaction is indicated by a sharp change in the electrode potential as the last trace of copper disappears from the electrode. The amount of electricity to be determined is then $i \cdot t$ (where t is the time taken by the redissolution).

Gravimetric coulometer[214, 216, 217]. The loss of weight of a silver electrode due to anodic dissolution, $Ag\downarrow - e \rightarrow Ag^+$, may be used to determine the amount of electricity. Conversely, the increase in the weight of the electrode due to the reduction of Ag^+ under conditions such that the current yield is 100 % may also be used.

Volumetric coulometer. If the reaction chosen is the anodic dissolution of silver, the Ag^+ formed may also be determined by titration, *e.g.* with a standard chloride solution. The end point may be indicated by an indicator, or by potentiometry or amperometry. The production of OH^- ions by the electrochemical reaction $2 H_2O + 2e \rightarrow H_2\uparrow + 2 OH^-$ may also be used, and the solution then titrated with a standard acid solution. The end point may be indicated by measuring the pH, or by the use of indicators[29, 225]. The oxidation of V(IV) to V(V) can easily be made to give a 100 % current yield, and the solution may then be titrated with standard ferrous iron, detecting the end point with a redox indicator, or by potentiometry or amperometry.

Colorimetric coulometer. The electrochemical reaction may be for example $2 I^- - 2e \rightarrow I_2$, and the iodine formed is estimated by colorimetry[213]. Or the reaction may be $Ag\downarrow - e \rightarrow Ag^+$, and the Ag^+ can then be estimated colorimetrically as silver dithizonate. These coulometers can be used to determine small quantities of electricity.

Gasometric coulometer. The electrolysis of water produces the reaction $2 H_2O - 4e \rightarrow O_2\uparrow + 4 H^+$ at the anode and $4 H_2O + 4e \rightarrow 2 H_2\uparrow + 4 OH^-$ at the cathode. If the anodic and cathodic compartments are not separated, the solution remains neutral, and the volume of gas evolved is a measure of the quantity of electricity. This coulometer has been developed by LINGANE[27]; the lower limit of accuracy is 10 coulombs. LINGANE has also suggested that the oxidation of water should be replaced by that of hydrazine, $NH_2NH_2 - 4e \rightarrow N_2\uparrow + 4 H^+$; the solution still remains neutral, and the accuracy is better for small amounts. The range of application of this instrument is from 5 to 20 coulombs[226].

    The accuracy of the chemical coulometers depends on that of the method of analysis used, and is about $\pm$ 0.2 % for normal volumetric analysis and constant-current coulometry, $\pm$ 1 % for colorimetry, $\pm$ 1–2 % for polarography and $\pm$ 0.1 % for gasometry or gravimetry of large amounts.

The sensitivity of these coulometers is limited on the one hand by that of the method of analysis, and on the other by the fact that the coulometer also has a residual current, *i.e.* that a certain fraction of the current passing through the cell is not used to produce the substance which is later estimated. This residual quantity of electricity, which causes the chemical coulometers to give low results, may more or less compensate for the residual amount of electricity for the other cell. Since however the residual currents are neither equal in the two cells, nor very reproducible, the error due to the residual current is difficult to estimate in any other way than by experiment. The sensitivity of the chemical coulometer may be increased by placing a d.c. current amplifier (with a gain of *e.g.* 1000) in series in the electrolysis circuit, and putting the coulometer at the output of the amplifier. As little as 0.01 coulomb can be determined in this way, at the expense of some loss of precision.

3. *Integrating coulometers.* These are instruments which record the amount of electricity passing through the circuit. They are mounted in series with the electrolysis cell and consist of a rotor whose speed of rotation is proportional to the electrolysis current. A revolution counter mounted on the rotor may then be calibrated directly in coulombs. A tachometer generator may be used[222]. Here the rate of rotation is proportional to the applied voltage, which is derived, after amplification, from the voltage drop produced across a resistance by the electrolysis current. It has recently been suggested[237, 240] that motors with permanent magnets, whose rate of rotation is also proportional to the applied voltage, should be used. In all these instruments it is assumed that there is a linear relationship between the electrolysis current and the numbers indicated by the revolution counter, and their accuracy clearly depends on the accuracy with which this linear relation is known. Moreover, the amplifier noise always causes a slow rotation of the rotor, which makes the reading too large. For a given quantity of electricity, this error increases with the duration of the electrolysis. The amplifier noise also limits the sensitivity. LINGANE[240] states that an instrument using a permanent-magnet motor gave an accuracy of $\pm$ 0.3 %, when the initial current was between 2.4 and 0.12 A, after correcting the reading. MEITES[222] was able to measure accurately quantities of electricity with a tachometer generator, but only when large currents were used.

Electronic instruments combining the potentiostat and the coulometer have also been proposed recently.

The electrolysis cells

These cells are different from those used for plotting the current–potential curves, for amperometry or for potentiometry, since they must provide for the electrolysis of larger amounts of substances, and must take much larger currents. They must fulfill two main conditions: 1) they must allow a 100 % current yield to be obtained, and 2) they must allow an electrolysis to be carried out in less than 30 minutes.

100 % current yield. A knowledge of the current–potential curves aids the chemist in choosing the solutions and the nature of the electrodes. The substances introduced initially into the cell are not the only ones which can interfere so as to reduce the yield: in general, the oxidation products from the anode are capable of being reduced at the cathode and vice versa. It is therefore necessary to use bridges which prevent the diffusion of the electroactive substances but which allow current to pass by the migration of the ions of the indifferent electrolyte. These bridges consist of a porous membrane (sintered glass, cellophane, resin, etc.) or gels containing the indifferent electrolyte (agar-agar, silica gel, etc.) (see p. 139). This considerably increases the internal resistance of the cell (from about 100 to about 2000 ohms). When the current is large, this entails large energy losses (Ri^2), so that the potentiostat cannot stabilize the potential properly. This inconvenience can be avoided in certain special cases, e.g. reduction of cations to the metal: the reduction product adheres to the cathode and stands no chance of diffusing across to the anode. Unless special precautions are taken, however, the products of the oxidation at the anode will be reduced with the cations. LINGANE has suggested that the oxidation of hydrazine, $NH_2NH_2 - 4e \rightarrow N_2\uparrow + 4\,H^+$, or that of hydroxylamine, $2\,NH_2OH - 2e \rightarrow N_2\uparrow + 2\,H_2O + 2H^+$, should be used as the reaction at the anode. The nitrogen produced is not reducible, and the use of a mercury cathode prevents H^+ from being reduced. This method is of special use in separations at constant potential, when large currents are used (see Chapter XI).

A 100 % current yield as predicted by the current–potential curves can only be obtained under steady-state conditions, which are generally obtained by stirring the solution with mechanical or magnetic stirrers. This is to be preferred to rotating the electrode which gives rise to the problem of the electrical contact with the rotating electrode, and often entails appreciable and variable ohmic drop, which make it difficult to get good stabilization of the potential.

Duration of the electrolysis. We have seen that at constant potential the current decreases with the time according to the equation $i = i_0\,10^{-At}$, where A is equal to $0.43\,D^aS/V\delta$; S is the surface area of the electrode, V the volume of the solution, δ the thickness of the diffusion layer, D the diffusion constant and a is a constant between 0 and 1 (see p. 238). The electrolysis is considered to be completed when the final value of the current i_f is equal to 10^{-2} or 10^{-3} times the original current i_0. The time needed to reach this value of i_f is shorter as the constant A is larger. It is therefore advisable to have electrodes with a large surface area, and a small volume of solution, while vigorous stirring gives a smaller value of δ. The various cells proposed up till now have been designed on these principles.

Junctionless cells. It has been proposed that the stabilized electrode should be a hollow cylinder of platinum gauze. The auxiliary electrode may be a platinum wire wound round a block of plastic material, used as a stirrer. The volume of the solution is thus reduced to a minimum. If a mercury electrode is used, it should consist of a large pool, and the depth of the solution should be as small as possible, while the anode often consists of a platinum disc. The reference electrode is usually a calomel electrode (see p. 149) which is connected to the solution by a bridge whose end is as close as possible to the stabilized electrode.

Cells with junctions. The various types of junctions have been examined on p. 139. A double porous membrane enclosing a solution of an indifferent electrolyte is often used.

Constant-current titrations

The problem is here to obtain a constant current and a 100% current yield. It is also necessary to determine the quantity of electricity, *i.e.* to measure the current and the time accurately.

Measuring the time. This is done with a mechanical chronometer or an electric or electronic clock working from the mains. In the latter case the fluctuations of the mains frequency must be taken into account. It is always best if the switch in the electrolysis circuit also starts and stops the clock. Under these conditions an accuracy of better than 0.1% is obtained even for very short times.

Obtaining a constant current (see p. 133). The most simple means of obtaining a constant current is to use a battery giving about 100 V in series with a resistance of about one megohm. It is possible to obtain a current of anything up to 10^{-3} A which is constant to within $\pm 1\%$. For higher currents the battery may be replaced by a voltage-stabilized power supply; or, more simply, an amperostat, which gives a current constant to within 0.1%, may be used (p. 135).

Measuring the current. A calibrated galvanometer in series with the cell allows the current to be determined with an accuracy of better than 0.5%, but the most accurate method is still to determine the voltage drop across a calibrated resistance by a null-point method. This may easily be done in the laboratory with a null-point pH-meter-potentiometer which can determine a voltage of 1 V to within 0.001 V, and a series of standard resistances. Certain firms have developed instruments which give stable currents which are known to within 0.1% in the range from 30 μA to 20 mA. These instruments, which are called constant-current coulometers, consist basically of an amperostat to which is added a chronometer whose operation is synchronized with the duration of the electrolysis.

100% current yield. A knowledge of the current–potential curves is an aid in choosing the right electrochemical reaction. These curves are only properly defined under steady-state conditions, so it is necessary to stir the solution well and uniformly (see Chapter VI). As in constant-potential coulometry, it is also necessary to prevent the products from the anode from reacting at the cathode and vice versa, which imposes certain conditions on the design of the cell.

Unlike constant-potential coulometry, however, it is not necessary that the ratio of electrode surface to volume of solution should be as large as possible. The surface area of the electrode need only be large enough to ensure that the limiting diffusion current is larger than the imposed current under the given conditions.

Integration of the amount of electricity[97]. It is also possible to carry out coulometric titrations by a slightly different method. The imposed current is taken from a non-stabilized source; it is not then possible to determine the amount of electricity by a simple determination of the current and the time, since the current is not strictly constant. An integrating coulometer is therefore used, as for constant-potential coulometry (see p. 239). Since, however, the current is not far from constant, it is much easier to obtain reproducible values of the amount of electricity by integration. It is still necessary, of course, to calibrate the integrator in coulombs.

REFERENCES

Books

1 J. J. LINGANE, *Electroanalytical Chemistry*, Interscience, New York, 2nd ed., 1958.
2 P. DELAHAY, *New Instrumental Methods in Electrochemistry*, Interscience, New York, 1954.
3 G. CHARLOT and D. BÉZIER, *Les méthodes électrochimiques d'analyse*, Masson, Paris, 1954.
4 G. W. C. MILNER, *The Principles and Applications of Polarography and Other Electroanalytical Processes*, Longmans, London, 1957.

Reviews

5 N. H. FURMAN, *Anal. Chem.*, 22 (1950) 33.
6 N. H. FURMAN, *Anal. Chem.*, 23 (1951) 21.
7 W. D. COOKE and N. H. FURMAN, *Anal. Chem.*, 22 (1950) 896.
8 S. E. Q. ASHLEY, *Anal. Chem.*, 24 (1952) 92.
9 P. S. TUTUNDZIC, *Anal. Chim. Acta*, 8 (1953) 168.
10 N. H. FURMAN, *Anal. Chem.*, 26 (1954) 84.
11 D. D. DE FORD, *Anal. Chem.*, 26 (1954) 135.
12 D. D. DE FORD, *Anal. Chem.*, 28 (1956) 662.
13 E. H. SWIFT, *Anal. Chem.*, 28 (1956) 1804.
14 F. CUTA, *Anal. Chim. Acta*, 18 (1958) 45.
15 D. D. DE FORD and R. C. BOWERS, *Anal. Chem.*, 30 (1958) 613.
16 W. D. COOKE, in W. G. BERL (ed.), *Physical Methods in Chemical Analysis*, Academic Press, New York, 1956, Vol. III, p. 98.

Theory based on current–potential curves

17 R. GAUGUIN and G. CHARLOT, *Anal. Chim. Acta*, 7 (1952) 408.
18 J. BADOZ-LAMBLING, *Anal. Chim. Acta*, 7 (1952) 585.
19 T. L. MARPLE and L. B. ROGERS, *Anal. Chim. Acta*, 11 (1954) 574.
20 W. M. MacNEVIN and B. B. BAKER, *Anal. Chem.*, 24 (1951) 941.
21 W. M. MacNEVIN, B. B. BAKER and R. D. McIVER, *Anal. Chem.*, 25 (1953) 274.
22 S. S. LORD, R. C. O'NEILL and L. B. ROGERS, *Anal. Chem.*, 24 (1952) 209.
23 K. W. GARDINER and L. B. ROGERS, *Anal. Chem.*, 25 (1953) 1393.

The coulomb as a standard

24 P. S. TUTUNDZIC, *Anal. Chim. Acta*, 8 (1953) 182.
25 P. S. TUTUNDZIC and S. MLADENOVIC, *Anal. Chim. Acta*, 8 (1953) 184.
26 P. S. TUTUNDZIC, *Anal. Chim. Acta*, 18 (1958) 60.

Constant-potential coulometry

27 J. J. LINGANE, *J. Am. Chem. Soc.*, 67 (1945) 1916.
28 J. J. LINGANE, *Anal. Chim. Acta*, 2 (1948) 584.
29 J. J. LINGANE and L. A. SMALL, *Anal. Chem.*, 21 (1949) 1119.
30 F. I. TRISHIN, *Zhur. Anal. Khim.*, 3 (1948) 21, 29.
31 M. J. ALLEN and H. G. STEINMAN, *J. Am. Chem. Soc.*, 74 (1952) 3932.
32 B. ALFONSI, *Anal. Chim. Acta*, 19 (1958) 276.

Micro-coulometry

33 J. J. LINGANE, *Electroanalytical Chemistry*, Interscience, New York, 1958, 2nd ed., p. 460.
34 T. L. MARPLE and L. B. ROGERS, *Anal. Chim. Acta*, 11 (1954) 574.
35 M. MASUI and H. SAYO, *J. Pharm. Soc. Japan*, 75 (1955) 1515.
36 R. A. SCHREIBER and W. D. COOKE, *Anal. Chem.*, 27 (1955) 1475.

Anodic stripping

37 C. ZBINDEN, *Bull. soc. chim. biol.*, 13 (1931) 35.
38 W. E. CAMPBELL and U. B. THOMAS, *Trans. Electrochem. Soc.*, 76 (1939) 303.
39 M. S. ZAKHAREVSKIJ, *Khim. Referat. Zhur.*, 2 (1939) 84.

Amalgams

40 A. HICKLING and J. A. MAXWELL, *Trans. Faraday Soc.*, 51 (1955) 44.
41 J. T. PORTER and W. D. COOKE, *J. Am. Chem. Soc.*, 77 (1955) 1481.
42 A. HICKLING, J. A. MAXWELL and J. V. SHENNAN, *Anal. Chim. Acta*, 14 (1956) 287.
43 M. M. NICHOLSON, *J. Am. Chem. Soc.*, 79 (1957) 7.

Corrosion

44 U. R. EVANS and L. C. BANNISTER, *Proc. Roy. Soc. (London)*, A 125 (1929) 370.
45 U. R. EVANS and H. A. MILEY, *J. Chem. Soc.*, (1937) 1295.
46 H. A. MILEY, *J. Am. Chem. Soc.*, 59 (1937) 2626.

[47] L. E. Price and G. J. Thomas, *Trans. Electrochem. Soc.*, 76 (1939) 329.
[48] A. L. Dighton and H. A. Miley, *Trans. Electrochem. Soc.*, 81 (1942) 321.
[49] H. T. Francis, *Trans. Electrochem. Soc.*, 93 (1948) 79.

Platings
[50] G. G. Grower, *Proc. Am. Soc. Testing Materials*, 17 (1917) 129.
[51] C. T. Kunze and A. R. Willey, *J. Electrochem. Soc.*, 99 (1952) 354.

Films on tin and tin-platings
[52] A. Brenner, *J. Electrochem. Soc.*, 103 (1956) 652.
[53] S. C. Britton and K. Bright, *Metallurgia*, 56 (1957) 163.
[54] R. P. Frankenthal, T. J. Butler and R. T. Davis Jr, *Anal. Chem.*, 30 (1958) 441.

Oxide films
[55] H. J. Engell, *Z. Elektrochem.*, 60 (1956) 905.
[56] W. Katz, *Stahl u. Eisen*, 76 (1956) 1672.
[57] F. W. Salt and J. G. N. Thomas, *Nature*, 178 (1956) 434.
[58] P. Berge, *Compt. rend.*, 245 (1957) 1249.
[59] A. R. Willey and D. F. Kelsey, *Anal. Chem.*, 30 (1958) 1804.

Coulometric titrations with externally generated reactant
[60] D. D. De Ford, J. N. Pitts Jr, and C. J. Johns, *Anal. Chem.*, 23 (1951) 938, 941.
[61] J. N. Pitts Jr, D. D. De Ford, J. W. Martin and E. A. Schmall, *Anal. Chem.*, 26 (1954) 628.
[62] N. Bett, W. Nock and G. Morris, *Analyst*, 79 (1954) 607.

Back-titrations
[63] R. P. Buck and E. H. Swift, *Anal. Chem.*, 24 (1952) 499.
[64] P. S. Farrington, D. J. Meier and E. H. Swift, *Anal. Chem.*, 25 (1953) 591.
[65] J. M. Dunham and P. S. Farrington, *Anal. Chem.*, 28 (1956) 1510.

Spectrophotometric coulometry
—, *As*(III) *with* Ce^{4+}
[66] N. H. Furman and A. J. Fenton Jr., *Anal. Chem.*, 28 (1956) 515.
—, Fe^{2+} *with* Ce^{4+}
[67] R. Gauguin, *Chim. anal.*, 36 (1954) 92.

Amperometric coulometry
[68] W. D. Cooke, C. N. Reilley and N. H. Furman, *Anal. Chem.*, 23 (1951) 1662.

Reactions with 100 % current yield
[69] L. Szebelledy and Z. Somogyi, *Z. anal. Chem.*, 112 (1938) 323, 332.
[70] L. Szebelledy and Z. Somogyi, *Z. anal. Chem.*, 112 (1938) 385, 391, 400.
[71] L. Szebelledy and Z. Somogyi, *Z. anal. Chem.*, 112 (1938) 395.
[72] A. Hickling, *Trans. Faraday Soc.*, 38 (1942) 27.
[73] J. W. Sease, C. Niemann and E. H. Swift, *Anal. Chem.*, 19 (1947) 197.
[74] J. Epstein, H. A. Sober and S. D. Silver, *Anal. Chem.*, 19 (1947) 675.
[75] R. J. Myers and E. H. Swift, *J. Am. Chem. Soc.*, 70 (1948) 1047.
[76] P. A. Shaffer Jr, A. Briglio Jr. and J. A. Brockman Jr., *Anal. Chem.*, 20, (1948) 1008.
[77] R. A. Brown and E. H. Swift, *J. Am. Chem. Soc.*, 71 (1949) 2717.
[78] W. S. Wooster, P. S. Farrington and E. H. Swift, *Anal. Chem.*, 21 (1949) 1457.
[79] D. J. Meier, R. J. Myers abd E. H. Swift, *J. Am. Chem. Soc.*, 71 (1949) 2340.
[80] W. Oelsen and P. Göbbels, *Stahl u. Eisen*, 69 (1949) 33.
[81] W. M. MacNevin and G. L. Martin, *J. Am. Chem. Soc.*, 71 (1949) 204.
[82] W. N. Carson Jr., *Anal. Chem.*, 22 (1950) 1565.
[83] W. D. Cooke and N. H. Furman, *Anal. Chem.*, 22 (1950) 896.
[84] P. S. Farrington and E. H. Swift, *Anal. Chem.*, 28 (1950) 889.
[85] D. J. Meier and E. H. Swift, *J. Am. Chem. Soc.*, 72 (1950) 5331.
[86] W. J. Ramsay, P. S. Farrington and E. H. Swift, *Anal. Chem.*, 22 (1950) 332.
[87] W. N. Carson Jr. and R. Ko, *Anal. Chem.*, 23 (1951) 1019.
[88] D. D. De Ford, J. N. Pitts Jr. and C. J. Johns, *Anal. Chem.*, 23 (1951) 938.
[89] N. H. Furman, W. D. Cooke and C. N. Reilley, *Anal. Chem.*, 23 (1951) 945.
[90] N. H. Furman, C. N. Reilley and W. D. Cooke, *Anal. Chem.*, 23 (1951) 1665.
[91] W. Oelsen, G. Graue and H. Haase, *Angew. Chem.*, 63 (1951) 557.
[92] V. S. Syrokomskii and T. I. Nazareva, *Zhur. Anal. Khim.*, 6 (1951) 15.
[93] P. Arthur and J. F. Donahue, *Anal. Chem.*, 24 (1952) 1612.
[94] R. P. Buck, P. S. Farrington and E. H. Swift, *Anal. Chem.*, 24 (1952) 1195.

95 W. D. COOKE, C. N. REILLEY and N. H. FURMAN, *Anal. Chem.*, 24 (1952) 205.
96 W. M. MACNEVIN and B. B. BAKER, *Anal. Chem.*, 24 (1952) 986.
97 L. MEITES, *Anal. Chem.*, 24 (1952) 1057.
98 W. OELSEN, H. HAASE and G. GRAUE, *Angew. Chem.*, 64 (1952) 76.
99 W. S. WOOSTER, P. S. FARRINGTON and E. H. SWIFT, *Anal. Chem.*, 24 (1952) 1195.
100 R. E. PRESS and R. A. MURRAY, *J. South African Chem. Inst.*, 5 (1952) 45.
101 F. CUTA and Z. KUCERA, *Chem. listy*, 47 (1953) 1166.
102 J. P. PHILLIPS, *Chemist Analyst*, 42 (1953) 101.
103 M. NAKANISHI and M. KOBAYASHI, *Bull. Chem. Soc. Japan*, 26 (1953) 394.
104 J. BADOZ-LAMBLING, *Anal. Chim. Acta*, 9 (1953) 455.
105 W. N. CARSON JR., *Anal. Chem.*, 25 (1953) 466.
106 N. H. FURMAN, C. E. BRICKER and R. V. DILTS, *Anal. Chem.*, 25 (1953) 482.
107 N. H. FURMAN and R. N. ADAMS, *Anal. Chem.*, 25 (1953) 1564.
108 E. N. WISE, P. W. GILLES and C. A. REYNOLDS JR., *Anal. Chem.*, 25 (1953) 1344.
109 R. N. ADAMS, *Anal. Chem.*, 26 (1954) 1933.
110 J. BADOZ-LAMBLING, *Chim. anal.*, 36 (1954) 291.
111 V. B. EHLERS and J. W. SEASE, *Anal. Chem.*, 26 (1954) 513.
112 R. L. KOWALKOWSKI, J. H. KENNEDY and P. S. FARRINGTON, *Anal. Chem.*, 26 (1954) 626.
113 J. J. LINGANE, *Anal. Chem.*, 26 (1954) 622.
114 J. J. LINGANE and A. M. HARTLEY, *Anal. Chim. Acta*, 11 (1954) 475.
115 K. ROWLEY and E. H. SWIFT, *Anal. Chem.*, 26 (1954) 373.
116 C. N. VAN ZYL and R. A. MURRAY, *African Ind. Chemist.*, 8 (1954) 222, 243.
117 G. W. EVERETT and C. N. REILLEY, *Anal. Chem.*, 26 (1954) 1750.
118 F. KAWAMURA, K. MOMOKI and S. SUZUKI, *Bull. Fac. Eng. Yokohama Nat. Univ.* 3 (1954) 223.
119 F. A. LEISEY, *Anal. Chem.*, 26 (1954) 1607.
120 J. J. LINGANE, *Anal. Chim. Acta*, 11 (1954) 283.
121 J. A. RAMSAY, R. H. J. BROWN and P. C. CROGHAN, *J. Exptl. Biol.*, 32 (1955) 822.
122 T. TAKAHASHI, K. KIMOTO and H. SAKURAI, *Rept. Inst. Ind. Sci.*, *Univ. Tokyo*, 5 (1955) 121.
123 T. TAKAHASHI, K. KIMOTO and H. SAKURAI, *Proc. XVth Intern. Congr. Pure Appl. Chem.*, Lisbon 1956, (*Actas do Congresso*), Lisbon, 1957.
124 R. V. DILTS and N. H. FURMAN, *Anal. Chem.*, 27 (1955) 1275.
125 A. D. R. HARRISON, A. J. LINDSEY and R. PHILLIPS, *Anal. Chim. Acta*, 13 (1955) 459.
126 A. M. HARTLEY and J. J. LINGANE, *Anal. Chim. Acta*, 13 (1955) 183.
127 J. J. LINGANE and R. T. IWAMOTO, *Anal. Chim. Acta*, 13 (1955) 465.
128 J. J. LINGANE and J. A. PAGE, *Anal. Chim. Acta*, 13 (1955) 281.
129 W. M. MACNEVIN and R. D. MCIVER, *Anal. Chem.*, 27 (1955) 1994.
130 H. B. MALMSTADT and C. B. ROBERTS, *Anal. Chem.*, 27 (1955) 741.
131 T. MEITES and L. M. MEITES, *Anal. Chem.*, 27 (1955) 1531.
132 J. S. PARSONS and W. SEAMAN, *Anal. Chem.*, 27 (1955) 210.
133 K. ROWLEY and E. H. SWIFT, *Anal. Chem.*, 27 (1955) 818.
134 W. D. SCHULTS II, P. F. THOMASON and M. T. KELLEY, *Anal. Chem.*, 27 (1955) 1750.
135 W. D. SCHULTS II and P. F. THOMASON, *U. S. Atomic Energy Commission, Oak Ridge Natl. Lab.*, *Rept.* (1955) 1846.
136 P. S. TUTUNDZIC, I. DOROSLOVACKI and O. TATIC, *Anal. Chim. Acta*, 12 (1955) 481.
137 P. S. TUTUNDZIC and S. MLADENOVIC, *Anal. Chim. Acta*, 12 (1955) 382, 390.
138 E. PRZYBYLOWICZ, *Anal. Chem.*, 28 (1956) 799.
139 G. M. ARCAND and E. H. SWIFT, *Anal. Chem.*, 28 (1956) 440.
140 J. M. DUNHAM and P. S. FARRINGTON, *Anal. Chem.*, 28 (1956) 1510.
141 J. J. LINGANE and J. H. KENNEDY, *Anal. Chim. Acta*, 15 (1956) 465.
142 H. B. MALMSTADT and C. B. ROBERTS, *Anal. Chem.*, 28 (1956) 1408, 1412, 1884.
143 J. S. HETMAN, *Analyst*, 81 (1956) 543.
144 A. BRUNSTAD, *U. S. Atomic Energy Commission*, TID-div. (1956) 7516.
145 D. D. DE FORD and H. HORN, *Anal. Chem.*, 28 (1956) 797.
146 M. A. V. DEVANATHAN and Q. FERNANDO, *Trans. Faraday Soc.*, 52 (1956) 1332.
147 K. W. EDWARDS and D. M. H. KERN, *Anal. Chem.*, 28 (1956) 1876.
148 W. T. FOLEY and R. F. POTTIE, *Anal. Chem.*, 28 (1956) 1101.
149 W. FUCHS and O. VEISER, *Arch. Eisenhütt*, 27 (1956) 429.
150 N. H. FURMAN and A. J. FENTON, *Anal. Chem.*, 28 (1956) 515.
151 F. A. LEISEY and J. F. GRUTSCH, *Anal. Chem.*, 28 (1956) 1553.
152 A. LIBERTI and P. LAZZARI, *Ricerca sci.*, 26 (1956) 825.
153 D. MONNIER and P. ZWAHLEN, *Helv. Chim. Acta*, 39 (1956) 1865.
154 E. P. PRZYBYLOWICZ and L. B. ROGERS, *Anal. Chem.*, 28 (1956) 799.
155 C. N. REILLEY and W. W. PORTERFIELD, *Anal. Chem.*, 28 (1956) 443
156 R. W. SCHMID and C. N. REILLEY, *Anal. Chem.*, 28 (1956) 520.

[157] J. Coursier, J. Huré and C. Cornet, *Proc. XVth Intern. Congr. Pure Appl. Chem., Lisbon 1956,* (*Actas do Congresso*) Lisbon, 1957, p. 572.

[158] F. Cůta and Z. Kučera, *Proc. XVth Congr. Intern. Pure Chem., Lisbon 1956,* (*Actas do Congresso*) Lisbon, 1957, p. 597.

[159] B. Foresti and S. Musemuci, *Proc. XVth Intern. Congr. Pure Appl. Chem., Lisbon 1956,* (*Actas do Congresso*) Lisbon, 1957, p. 661.

[160] H. H. Stein, *Dissertation Abstr.,* 16 (1956) 2326.

[161] G. L. Booman, W. B. Holbrook and J. E. Rein, *Anal. Chem.,* 29 (1957) 219.

[162] W. N. Carson Jr., J. W. Vanderwater and H. S. Gile, *Anal. Chem.,* 29 (1957) 1417.

[163] A. J. Fenton Jr., and N. H. Furman, *Anal. Chem.,* 29 (1957) 221.

[164] J. J. Lingane, C. H. Langford and F. C. Anson, *Anal. Chim. Acta,* 16 (1957) 165.

[165] J. J. Lingane and A. J. Bard, *Anal. Chim. Acta,* 16 (1957) 271.

[166] J. W. Miller and D. D. De Ford, *Anal. Chem.,* 29 (1957) 475.

[167] M. A. V. Devanathan, Q. Fernando and P. Peries, *Anal. Chim. Acta,* 16 (1957) 292.

[168] J. A. Page and J. J. Lingane, *Anal. Chim. Acta,* 16 (1957) 175.

[169] D. G. Davis and J. J. Lingane, *Anal. Chim. Acta,* 18 (1958) 245.

[170] J. K. Lee and R. N. Adams, *Anal. Chem.,* 30 (1958) 240.

[171] J. J. Lingane and J. H. Kennedy, *Anal. Chim. Acta,* 15 (1956) 465; 18 (1958) 240.

[172] L. Meites, *Anal. Chim. Acta,* 18 (1958) 364.

[173] E. P. Przybylowicz and L. B. Rogers, *Anal. Chem.,* 30 (1958) 65.

[174] J. Badoz-Lambling and C. Dutruc-Rosset, *Anal. Chim. Acta,* 19 (1958) 43.

[175] E. Przybylowicz and L. B. Rogers, *Anal. Chim. Acta,* 18 (1958) 596.

[176] E. Przybylowicz and L. B. Rogers, *Anal. Chem.,* 30 (1958) 1064.

[177] J. J. Lingane, *Anal. Chim. Acta,* 19 (1958) 394.

[178] G. M. Arcand, *Anal. Chim. Acta,* 19 (1958) 267.

[179] L. G. Farrar, P. F. Thomason and M. T. Kelley, *Anal. Chem.,* 30 (1958) 1511.

[180] R. T. Iwamoto, *Anal. Chim. Acta,* 19 (1958) 273.

[181] O. E. Sundberg, H. C. Craig and J. S. Parsons, *Anal. Chem.,* 30 (1958) 1842.

[182] M. Munemori, *Talanta,* 1 (1958) 110.

Books on instrumentation

[183] J. J. Lingane, *Electroanalytical Chemistry,* Interscience, New York, 2nd ed., 1958, p. 296, 450.

[184] G. Charlot, J. Badoz-Lambling and B. Trémillon, *Les réactions électrochimiques,* Masson, Paris, 1959, p. 261.

Constant potential

—, potentiostats

[185] C. W. Caldwell, R. C. Parker and H. Diehl, *Ind. Eng. Chem., Anal. Ed.,* 16 (1944) 532.

[186] J. J. Lingane, *Anal. Chem.,* 17 (1945) 332.

[187] H. Diehl, *Electrochemical Analysis with Graded Cathode Potential Control,* G. F. Smith Chemical Co. Colombus, 1948.

[188] J. J. Lingane, *Anal. Chem.,* 21 (1949) 497.

[189] C. J. Penther and D. J. Pompeo, *Anal. Chem.,* 21 (1949) 178.

[190] J. J. Lingane and S. L. Jones, *Anal. Chem.,* 22 (1950) 1169, 1220.

[191] F. W. Chambers, *J. Sci. Instruments,* 27 (1950) 292.

[192] R. W. Lamphere and L. B. Rogers, *Anal. Chem.,* 22 (1950) 463.

[193] P. Wehner and J. C. Hindman, *J. Am. Chem. Soc.,* 72 (1950) 3911.

[194] M. J. Allen, *Anal. Chem.,* 22 (1950) 804.

[195] E. B. Thomas and R. J. Nook, *J. Chem. Educ.,* 27 (1950) 217.

[196] A. Coche, *J. Chim. phys.,* 48 (1951) 146.

[197] R. W. Lamphere, *Anal. Chem.,* 23 (1951) 258.

[198] M. L. Greenough, W. E. Williams Jr. and J. K. Taylor, *Rev. Sci. Instruments,* 22 (1951) 484.

[199] D. G. Foster, *J. Chem. Educ.,* 28 (1951) 626.

[200] A. L. Hodgkin, A. F. Huxley and B. Katz, *J. Physiology,* 116 (1952) 424.

[201] G. W. C. Milner and R. N. Whitten, *Analyst,* 77 (1952) 11.

[202] M. Ishibashi and T. Fujinaga, *Bull. Inst. Chem. Research, Kyoto Univ.,* 31 (1953) 254.

[203] G. Schouten and J. G. F. Doornekamp, *Applied Scientific Research,* B 3 (1953) 265.

[204] J. F. Palmer and A. I. Vogel, *Analyst,* 78 (1953) 428.

[205] F. Kaufman, E. Ossofsky and H. J. Cook, *Anal. Chem.,* 26 (1954) 516.

[206] J. Schoen and K. E. Staubach, *Regel Techn.,* 7 (1954) 157.

[207] W. Vielstich and H. Gerischer, *Z. phys. Chem.* (Frankfurt), 4 (1955) 10.

[208] J. Tacussel, *Thèse,* Lyon, 1956.

[209] G. L. Booman, *Anal. Chem.,* 29 (1957) 213.

[210] M. Breiter and F. G. Will, *Z. Elektrochem.,* 61 (1957) 1177.

[211] C. Aville, *Electron. Ind.* (1957).

—, *chemical coulometers*

[212] R. A. LEHFELDT, *Phil. Mag.*, 15 (1908) 614.
[213] E. W. WASHBURN and S. J. BATER, *J. Am. Chem. Soc.*, 34 (1912) 1341.
[214] T. W. RICHARDS, *J. Am. Chem. Soc.*, 37 (1915) 692.
[215] E. B. ROSA and G. W. VINAL, *Bull. Bur. Standards*, 13 (1916) 447, 479.
[216] L. SZEBELLEDY and Z. SOMOGYI, *Z. anal. Chem.*, 112 (1938) 313.
[217] A. WOGRINZ and G. ZENGSWETTER, *Österr. Chem. Ztg.*, 48 (1947) 1924.
[218] D. N. CRAIG and J. L. HOFFMAN, *Phys. Revs.*, 80 (1950) 487.
[219] V. S. SYROKOMSKII and T. I. NAZAREVA, *Zhur. Anal. Khim.*, 6 (1951) 15.
[220] T. DE VRIES and J. L. KROON, *J. Am. Chem. Soc.*, 75 (1953) 2484.
[221] V. B. EHLERS and J. W. SEASE, *Anal. Chem.*, 26 (1954) 513.
[222] L. MEITES, *Anal. Chem.*, 27 (1955) 1114.
[223] T. C. FRANKLIN and C. C. ROTH, *Anal. Chem.*, 27 (1955) 1197.
[224] E. SCHWARZ-BERKAMPF and R. REICHERT, *Mikrochim. Acta*, (1955) 1031.
[225] H. W. HOYER, *J. Phys. Chem.*, 60 (1956) 372.
[226] J. A. PAGE and J. J. LINGANE, *Anal. Chim. Acta*, 16 (1957) 175.

—, *integrating coulometers*

[227] G. L. FREEMAN and E. L. HOFFMAN, *Rev. Sci. Instr.*, 11 (1940) 283.
[228] E. JACOBSON, *Rev. Sci. Instr.*, 11 (1940) 415.
[229] C. J. CAMPBELL and R. A. MC LEAN, *Rev. Sci. Instr.*, 19 (1948) 808.
[230] R. J. WATTS, *Rev. Sci. Instr.*, 22 (1951) 356.
[231] D. J. MONTGOMERY, *Rev. Sci. Instr.*, 22 (1951) 840.
[232] S. BOGAN, L. MEITES, E. PETERS and J. M. STURTEVANT, *J. Am. Chem. Soc.*, 73 (1951) 1584.
[233] K. W. KRAMER and R. B. FISCHER, *Anal. Chem.*, 26 (1954) 415.
[234] J. S. PARSONS, W. SEAMAN and R. M. AMICK, *Anal. Chem.*, 27 (1955) 1754.
[235] W. FUCHS and O. VEISER, *Arch. Eisenhütt.*, 27 (1956) 429.
[236] N. H. FURMAN and A. J. FENTON JR., *Anal. Chem.*, 28 (1956) 515; 29 (1957) 1213.
[237] L. E. SMYTHE, *Analyst*, 82 (1957) 228.
[238] L. L. MERRITT, E. L. MARTIN JR. and R. D. BEDI, *Anal. Chem.*, 30 (1958) 487.
[239] L. G. FARRAR, P. F. THOMASON and M. T. KELLEY, *Anal. Chem.*, 30 (1958) 1511.
[240] J. J. LINGANE, *Anal. Chim. Acta*, 18 (1958) 349.

—, *cells*

[241] V. MAJER, *Mikrochemie*, 18 (1935) 74.
[242] J. J. LINGANE, C., G. SWAIN and M. FIELDS, *J. Am. Chem. Soc.*, 65 (1943) 1348.
[243] T. MEITES and L. MEITES, *Anal. Chem.*, 23 (1951) 1893.
[244] G. A. GILBERT and E. K. RIDEAL, *Trans. Faraday Soc.*, 47 (1951) 396.
[245] W. M. MACNEVIN and B. B. BAKER, *Anal. Chem.*, 24 (1952) 986.
[246] L. G. FARRAR, P. F. THOMASON and M. T. KELLEY, *Anal. Chem.*, 30 (1958) 1511.

Constant current

—, *amperostats*

[247] A. HICKLING, *Trans. Faraday Soc.*, 41 (1945) 333.
[248] W. N. CARSON JR., *Anal. Chem.*, 22 (1950) 1565.
[249] C. N. REILLEY, W. D. COOKE and N. H. FURMAN, *Anal. Chem.*, 23 (1951) 1030.
[250] J. J. LINGANE, *Anal. Chem.*, 26 (1954) 1021.
[251] G. E. GERHARDT, H. C. LAWRENCE and J. S. PARSONS, *Anal. Chem.*, 27 (1955) 1752.
[252] N. H. FURMAN, L. J. SAYEGH and R. N. ADAMS, *Anal. Chem.*, 27 (1955) 1423.
[253] L. GIERST, *Anal. Chim. Acta*, 15 (1956) 262.
[254] T. TAKAHASHI and E. NIKI, *Japan Analyst*, 7 (1958) 93.
[255] T. TAKAHASHI and H. SAKURAI, *Japan Analyst*, 7 (1958) 98.

—, *automatic constant-current coulometry*

[256] R. H. MÜLLER and J. J. LINGANE, *Anal. Chem.*, 20 (1948) 795.
[257] E. N. WISE, P. W. GILLES and C. A. REYNOLDS JR., *Anal. Chem.*, 25 (1953) 1344.
[258] G. E. GERHARDT, H. C. LAWRENCE and J. S. PARSONS, *Anal. Chem.*, 27 (1955) 1752.
[259] H. B. MALMSTADT and C. B. ROBERTS, *Anal. Chem.*, 27 (1955) 741; 28 (1956) 1408.
[260] H. L. RICHTER JR., *Anal. Chem.*, 27 (1955) 1526.
[261] R. W. STELZNER, D. J. FISHER and M. T. KELLEY, *U.S. Atomic Energy Commission, Oak Ridge Natl. Lab.*, (1955) 8.
[262] A. LIBERTI, F. LEPRI, L. CIAVATTA and G. P. CARTONI, *Ricerca sci.*, 27 (1957) 21.

—, *measuring the time*

[263] E. M. FRY and E. L. BALDESCHWIELER, *Ind. Eng. Chem., Anal. Ed.*, 12 (1940) 472.
[264] R. S. CRAIG, C. B. SATTERTHWAITE and L. E. WALLACE, *Anal. Chem.*, 20 (1948) 555.

—, *cells*, see also refs., 75, 89, 114, 127 and 182

[265] J. J. LINGANE and A. M. HARTLEY, *Anal. Chim. Acta*, 11 (1954) 283.

—, *applications*

[266] J. J. LINGANE, *Electroanalytical Chemistry*, Interscience, New York, 2nd ed., 1958, p. 536.

—, *integration*

[267] J. A. RAMSAY, R. H. J. BROWN and P. C. CROGHAN, *J. Exptl. Biol.*, 32 (1955) 822.
[268] O. E. SUNDBERG, H. C. CRAIG and J. S. PARSONS, *Anal. Chem.*, 30 (1958) 1842.

—, *equipment for external generation of the reactants*

[269] J. S. PARSONS and W. SEAMAN, *Anal. Chem.*, 27 (1955) 210.
[270] W. FUCHS and W. QUADT, *Z. anal. Chem.*, 147 (1955) 184.
[271] A. LIBERTI and P. LAZZARI, *Ricerca sci.*, 26 (1956) 825.

Chapter XI

OTHER APPLICATIONS OF THE
CURRENT–POTENTIAL CURVES

Many important applications of electrochemical reactions are known. It is not in-
tended to give a complete survey of these in this chapter, but to give by means of
some examples an idea of the many uses to which a knowledge of current–potential
curves may be put.

We will distinguish two types of applications:

The analysis of phenomena

1. The determination of the current–potential curves and their analysis allows
the electrode phenomena, *i.e.* electrochemical reactions, to be studied in the following
ways:

a) The determination of the number of electrons involved in the electrochemical
reaction (from the form of the wave, or by measuring the limiting diffusion current,
or by coulometry: see the equations involving n in Chapters II and IX) and, more
generally, the determination of all the reaction coefficients;

b) the determination of the standard potential of the redox system (measurement
of half-wave potentials and equilibrium potentials; see Chapters II and VI);

c) the determination of the kinetic characteristics of the redox system (calculation of the constants i_0, α and β from the form of the curve or from the half-wave
potentials; see Chapter II).

2. When the electrochemical reaction is known, the displacement of the current–
potential curves during, or owing to, a chemical reaction allows the latter to be studied. The usual method is to plot the curves of $E_{\frac{1}{2}}$ as a function of the concentration of
one of the substances involved in the chemical reaction (see Chapter III), or the curves
of the equilibrium potential as a function of this concentration (often titration
curves), or the curves of the limiting diffusion current as a function of the concentration (amperometric titration curves). The analysis of these curves allows the rate
constants, equilibrium constant, etc., of the reaction in question to be determined.

We will not treat this vast field, in which much research is being and has been
done, but will refer the reader to specialized works which deal with it or give biblio-
graphies on it.

The prediction and application of certain reactions

1. A knowledge of the current–potential curves allows a number of electrochemical reactions to be predicted:

a) the attack of metals, especially by acids and bases; corrosion and passivation;

b) reduction by metals and amalgams;

c) heterogeneous catalysis of redox reactions by metals or conducting oxides or
salts of metals.

2. Electrochemical reactions can be brought about or prevented in a number of ways: involving the nature and surface area of the electrodes, temperature, stirring (see Chapter V); or by chemical means: complexing, pH, etc. (see Chapters III and IV), solvent (see Chapter XIII). These factors allow the reactions to be controlled and employed in inorganic or organic preparations, separating mixtures, and in the control of manufacturing processes.

We will now give examples of such applications.

I. DISSOLUTION OF METALS

Principle

The rate of attack of a metal M

$$M\downarrow - ne \rightarrow M^{n+}$$

by an oxidant Ox (which may be H^+, H_2O, O_2, etc.) can in principle be predicted by means of the current–potential curves. Fig. 319 shows the oxidation curve of the metal M, acting as an anode. The reduction curve of the oxidant at an electrode of the metal M can only be observed if it is situated to the left of the anode curve (1 in Fig. 319). If it is placed like the curve 2, oxidation of M and reduction of Ox will occur simultaneously, and only the curve representing the overall reaction is observed. The reduction curve of Ox can then be deduced.

If an electrode of the metal M is dipped into a solution containing Ox, the equilibrium potential of the electrode will be E_1 if the reduction curve of Ox is curve 1, and E_2 if the reduction curve is curve 2. In the first case, the rate of oxidation of the metal and the rate of reduction of Ox at a potential E_1 are negligible. In the second case, the metal M is oxidized at an appreciable rate, corresponding to the current i_{an} at a potential E_2, while Ox is reduced at the surface of M at the same rate $(i_{cat} = - i_{an})$.

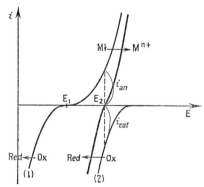

Fig. 319. Attack of a metal by an oxidant.

The possible redox reactions are

$$M\downarrow - ne \rightarrow M^{n+}$$
$$Ox + me \rightarrow Red$$

and the overall reaction

$$mM\downarrow + nOx \rightarrow mM^{n+} + nRed$$

occurs at the surface of the metal, where the rate of electron exchange is given by i_{an}.

It is thus possible to predict the attack of metals by an oxidant (or the reduction of an oxidant by a metal) by means of the current–potential curves. For example, the rate of dissolution of a metal in acid media, according to the reaction

$M\downarrow + nH^+ \rightarrow M^{n+} + \dfrac{n}{2} H_2$ can be predicted from a knowledge of the oxidation

curve of the metal and the reduction curve of H^+ at an electrode of the metal. The attack by water, dissolved oxygen, dissolved chlorine, etc., can be treated in a similar way.

This attack may be reduced or stimulated by all the usual means of displacing the current–potential curves, especially by complex-formation, precipitation, the influence of the pH and the presence of another metal.

Examples

We will give here some examples of the use of the current–potential curves in the prediction of the attack on metals by various reagents.

The attack on aluminium. It is known that aluminium is attacked very slowly by strong acids, not at all by weak acids or bases, and that it dissolves rapidly in strong bases.

Figure 320 shows the current–potential curves obtained with an aluminium wire of 99.98 % purity in various buffers under an atmosphere of nitrogen. The cathodic curves are due to the reduction of H^+ ions, either free or complexed in the form of the weak acid of the buffer; the anodic curves are due to the oxidation of the metal forming the electrode.

In very acid media

$$Al\downarrow - 3e \rightarrow Al^{3+}$$

while in less acid media

$$Al\downarrow + 3 H_2O - 3e \rightarrow Al(OH)_3\downarrow + 3 H^+$$

and in sufficiently alkaline media

$$Al\downarrow + 4 OH^- - 3e \rightarrow AlO_2^- + 2 H_2O$$

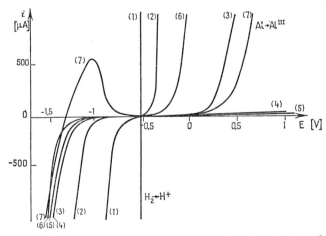

Fig. 320. Current–potential curves at an aluminium electrode, under an atmosphere of nitrogen. Solutions: (1) N HCl; (2) pH 1; (3) pH 3; (4) pH 5; (5) pH 7; (6) pH 9; (7) pH 11 (after DUMONTIER-GOUREAU and TRÉMILLON[4]).

It may be seen from these curves that the very slow attack of aluminium by acids is due to the fact that the reduction curve of H+ at an aluminium electrode is situated at very low potentials (very large hydrogen overvoltage), so that at the potential E_M at which $i = 0$ the rate of oxidation of aluminium (= rate of reduction of H+) is low.

The aluminium is not attacked at all in buffers of pH between 3 and 10, since it is rapidly covered by an impermeable film of alumina of low conductivity (*i.e.* is made passive). This is shown in the current–potential curves by the large voltage difference between the reduction curve and the oxidation curve.

The attack may be favoured by the presence of a substance which is reduced at higher potentials than H+ (*e.g.* dissolved oxygen, see Fig. 321) or of a substance which forms a complex with the Al^{3+} ion (*e.g.* F⁻), thus displacing the oxidation curve of the aluminium towards more negative potentials (Fig. 321).

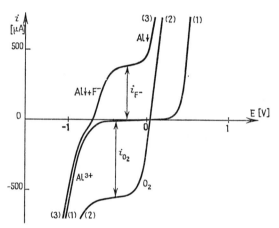

Fig. 321. Current–potential curves at an aluminium electrode in a buffer solution of pH 3. Curve 1: nitrogen atmosphere; curve 2: oxygen atmosphere, solution saturated with oxygen; curve 3: nitrogen atmosphere + 4 × 10⁻³ M F⁻ (after DUMONTIER-GOUREAU and TRÉMILLON[4]).

The attack may be catalyzed by the presence of another metal in electrical contact with the aluminium, at which the overvoltage of hydrogen is lower than for aluminium. For example, Fig. 322 shows the reduction curve of H+ at a platinum electrode. It may be seen that H+ ions are reduced more rapidly at a platinum electrode than at an aluminium one, so that if the two electrodes are short-circuited at pH < 3, the H+ ions are reduced at the platinum electrode, and the aluminium is oxidized, at appreciable rates.

This may be demonstrated by the following experiment: dip a strip of aluminium in a decinormal solution of sulphuric acid; the aluminium is hardly attacked. If now the strip is touched by a platinum wire which is also immersed in the solution, a reaction is produced immediately, as shown by the bubbles of hydrogen which form on the platinum wire. Platinum thus catalyzes the attack of metal by H+.

Dissolution of zinc. Zinc is attacked more rapidly in acid media than aluminium, although the standard potential of the Zn/Zn^{2+} system is higher than that of the Al/Al^{3+} system.

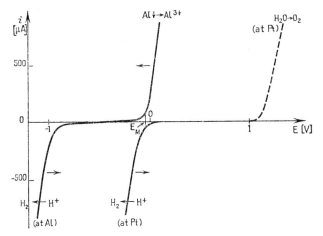

Fig. 322. Catalysis of the attack of aluminium by platinum. Buffer solution, pH 3, nitrogen atmosphere (after Dumontier-Goureau and Trémillon[4]).

It may be seen from Fig. 323, which shows the phenomena at a pH of about 3 to 4, that the rate of the reaction is limited by the diffusion of H^+ ions. We know (Chapter V) what factors affect the rate of diffusion: stirring and increasing the surface area of the metal, e.g. by using finely divided metal, increase the rate of reaction.

These phenomena have been verified experimentally.

Attack on copper by dissolved oxygen. Massive copper is only attacked very slowly by dissolved oxygen, as can be seen from an inspection of Fig. 324 (curve 1).

In the presence of ammonia, the oxidation curve of copper is displaced towards lower potentials, and attack by oxygen occurs

$$Cu\!\downarrow + \tfrac{1}{2}O_2 + 4\,NH_3 + H_2O \rightarrow Cu(NH_3)_4{}^{2+} + 2\,OH^-$$

The rate of reaction is limited by the rate of diffusion of oxygen. It may be shown that this is proportional to the surface area of the metal.

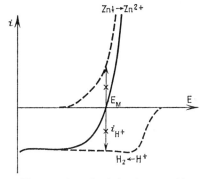

Fig. 323. Attack of zinc by an acid (theoretical curves).

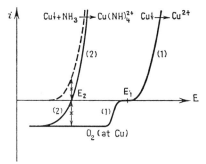

Fig. 324. Attack of copper by dissolved oxygen.
Curve 1: in acid medium. Curve 2: in ammoniacal buffer solution (theoretical curves).

Corrosion. Passivation. Inhibitors

The phenomenon of metallic corrosion does not differ in principle from that of the attack of metals described above; but the time scale is different, so that even very slow reactions have to be taken into account. The currents involved are of the order of magnitude of the residual current, and we have seen (Chapter VII) that it is very difficult to interpret the phenomena under these conditions. Finally, the phenomena must be studied on the microscopic scale: it is no longer sufficient to assume that the surface of the metal is homogeneous. All this means that the phenomenon of corrosion is very complex and difficult to study. Current–potential curves are of use in this study, however, and have been widely used.

It is well known that the phenomenon of passivity is due to the surface of the metal no longer being liable to corrosion. This is easily shown by the current–potential curves. The passivity of aluminium in neutral media is shown in Fig. 320. The oxidation of aluminium at these pHs leads to the formation of aluminium hydroxide, which is difficultly soluble, nonconducting and impermeable. The resistance of the circuit thus increases considerably and current does not pass until a much higher potential is reached.

Inhibitors are substances which displace the current–potential curves so as to reduce the rate of oxidation of the metal (see Chapter V).

These three phenomena are of great practical importance, and are dealt with in a large number of books and other publications. We will not discuss them further here.

Protection of metals by a 'reactive anode'

The attack of iron by H^+ ions or by water may be prevented by placing some zinc in contact with it. The zinc is then attacked instead. This may be used to protect a metal part of some equipment by allowing another metal in another, not so important, part of the apparatus to be attacked in its place.

It may be seen from Fig. 325 that if the iron is alone in water, it assumes the potential E_M and is attacked slowly. If it makes contact with a piece of zinc, the two metals attain a common potential E_M', at which iron is no longer attacked. The zinc is now attacked, and hydrogen is evolved at the surface of the iron. This is the reverse of the catalysis of the attack of aluminium by platinum, described on p.274.

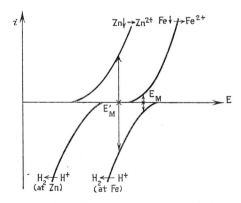

Fig. 325. Protection of iron by a reactive zinc anode (theoretical curves)

II. REDUCTION BY METALS AND AMALGAMS

Reduction by metals is a method of great importance in inorganic and organic preparations. It is also used sometimes in analytical chemistry.

The phenomena occurring here are the same as in the attack of metals, but the
problems of interest are different. In the previous section, we wanted to predict under
what conditions a metal would be oxidized, usually by air or oxygen. Here, on the
contrary, we want to know how a given substance can be reduced by a metal or an
amalgam. The same procedure can be used to solve both problems.

1. A study of the equilibrium potentials of the two redox systems shows whether
the reaction is possible.

2. The rate of reaction can be deduced from the current–potential curves.

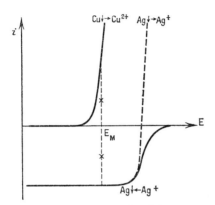

Fig. 326. The reduction of Ag+ by copper.

Reduction by metals

Let us take a simple example: the reduction of Ag^+ ions by metallic copper. The
current–potential curves corresponding to the reactions $Cu\downarrow - 2e \rightarrow Cu^{2+}$ and
$Ag^+ + e \rightarrow Ag\downarrow$ are shown in Fig. 326. They show that the rate of the reaction

$$2\ Ag^+ + Cu\downarrow\ \rightarrow\ 2\ Ag\downarrow + Cu^{2+}$$

is limited by the diffusion of the Ag^+ ions at the surface of the copper. We have seen
(Chapter V) the various factors which allow the rate of diffusion, and thus of reaction,
to be increased: stirring, increasing the surface area of the metal (using finely divided
metal). Naturally, the deposition of silver on the surface of the copper may slow down
the reaction.

The reduction of H^+, water or dissolved oxygen limits the possibilities of reduction of other substances. The reduction of substances whose reduction curve at an
electrode of the reducing metal is near that of H^+ ions is accompanied by the evolution of hydrogen. It is not possible to reduce an oxidant by a given metal if the reduction curve of the oxidant at an electrode of the metal is to the left of that of H^+ ions
(or of O_2).

We know that very reducing conditions are necessary to reduce H^+ at a mercury
electrode; it is thus possible to achieve vigorous reductions in the presence of mercury
or of amalgams.

The use of chemical means of shifting the current–potential curves (see Chapter III) can prevent or facilitate certain reductions.

This method thus differs very little from that of electrochemical reduction at constant potential (see below). It is less flexible, but often simpler to use.

Metals most commonly used as reducing agents

These are the alkali metals in non-aqueous solvents, used especially in organic chemistry, and in water

Mg	$(E_0 = -2.4$ V)	Al	$(E_0 = -1.7$ V)	Zn	$(E_0 = -0.76$ V)
Fe	$(E_0 = -0.4$ V)	Cd	$(E_0 = -0.4$ V)	Ni	$(E_0 = -0.25$ V)
Sn	$(E_0 = -0.14$ V)	Pb	$(E_0 = -0.13$ V)	Sb	$(E_0 = +0.10$ V)
Cu	$(E_0 = +0.3$ V)	Ag	$(E_0 = +0.8$ V)	Hg	$(E_0 = +0.8$ V)

Alloys can also be used.

The surface area of the metals may be increased by preparing them in a very finely divided state. For example, if an alloy of nickel and aluminium is allowed to react with caustic soda, the aluminium is oxidized and passes into solution, leaving the nickel in a finely divided state (Raney metal). But it must not be forgotten that the systems H_2O/H_2 and H^+/H_2 also become faster at finely divided metals (see Chapter V). Mercury, being liquid, has the advantage that it can be stirred vigorously with the solution, thus giving a large surface area.

Large-scale reductions can best be carried out in columns. This method is also sometimes used in analytical chemistry.

Chemical methods of reduction

We will give here a few examples of the most commonly used methods.

a) Reduction by silver in the presence of chloride. We have seen (Chapter III) that the oxidation of silver in the presence of chloride

$$Ag\downarrow + Cl^- - e \rightarrow AgCl\downarrow \qquad E_1 = 0.2 \text{ V}$$

occurs at less oxidizing potentials than the oxidation of $Ag\downarrow$ to Ag^+ ($E_0 = 0.8$ V). Silver is thus a strong reducing agent in the presence of chloride. For example, Fe^{3+} is reduced to Fe^{2+}, but Ti^{4+} is not reduced to Ti^{3+}.

Cyanide has the same effect

$$Ag\downarrow + 2 CN^- - e \rightarrow Ag(CN)_2^- \qquad E_1 = -0.4 \text{ V}$$

b) Reduction by mercury. Like silver, mercury can be made a stronger reducing agent by the addition of a large number of anions which give sparingly soluble compounds or complexes with Hg^{2+} or with Hg^{2+}, *e.g.*

$$2 Hg\downarrow + 2 Cl^- - 2e \rightarrow Hg_2Cl_2\downarrow \qquad E_1 = 0.3 \text{ V}$$
$$2 Hg\downarrow + 2 CN^- - 2e \rightarrow Hg_2(CN)_2\downarrow \qquad E_1 = -0.4 \text{ V}$$
$$Hg\downarrow + Y^{4-} - 2e \rightarrow HgY^{2-} \qquad E_1 = 0.25 \text{ V}$$

The current–potential curves of these systems are shown in Chapter III. In normal hydrochloric acid, for example, mercury can reduce Mo(VI) to Mo(III).

c) It is also possible to treat the oxidant so as to make it more easily reducible. *e.g.* by adding substances which form complexes with the reduction product.

The combination of all these methods can give rapid and specific results.

We will give an example showing how such methods can be used in practice: *The reduction of Ag^+ by mercury in the presence of EDTA at various pH* [42]. The equilibrium potentials of the systems $Ag\downarrow/Ag^+$ and $Hg\downarrow/Hg^{2+}$ are given by the equations

$$Ag\downarrow/Ag^+ \qquad E_1 = 0.80 \text{ V} + 0.058 \log |Ag^+|$$
$$Hg\downarrow/Hg^{2+} \qquad E_2 = 0.85 \text{ V} + 0.029 \log |Hg^{2+}|$$

In acid media, pH < 4, silver reduces Hg^{2+}. At pH above 4, mercuric oxide starts to precipitate, and the oxidation of mercury now occurs according to the reaction $Hg\downarrow + H_2O - 2e \rightarrow HgO\downarrow + 2 H^+$. The equilibrium potential of the $Hg\downarrow/Hg^{2+}$ system varies as -0.058 pH. As the pH increases, therefore, there arrives a value at which mercury begins to reduce Ag^+ ions (about pH 6). Ag_2O starts to precipitate at about pH 9 to 10. The effect of the pH alone therefore allows mercury to reduce Ag^+ at an appreciable rate, but only at pH 8 to 9.

In the presence of EDTA, the electrochemical reactions become

$$Ag\downarrow + Y^{4-} - \ e \rightarrow \ AgY^{3-}$$
$$Hg\downarrow + Y^{4-} - 2e \rightarrow \ HgY^{2-}$$

The corresponding equilibrium potentials, $E_1{}'$ and $E_2{}'$, now depend on the concentration of EDTA (Y^{4-}) and the dissociation constants of the complexes AgY^{3-} and HgY^{2+}, and also on the pH, since EDTA is a weak acid

$$Y^{4-} \ \ + H^+ \rightleftharpoons HY^{3-} \qquad pk_4 = 10.3$$
$$HY^{3-} \ + H^+ \rightleftharpoons H_2Y^{2-} \qquad pk_3 = \ \ 6.2$$
$$H_2Y^{2-} + H^+ \rightleftharpoons H_3Y^- \qquad pk_2 = \ \ 2.8$$
$$H_3Y^- \ \ + H^+ \rightleftharpoons H_4Y \qquad pk_1 = \ \ 2.0$$

The equilibrium potentials decrease as the concentration of free Y^{4-} increases, *i.e.* as the pH increases. They are shown in Fig. 327.

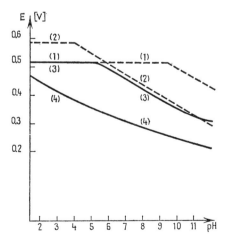

Fig. 327. Potential–pH diagram.
Curve 1: silver electrode, $10^{-3}M$ Ag^+. Curve 2: mercury electrode, $10^{-3}M$ Hg^{2+}.
Curve 3: silver electrode, $10^{-3}M$ Ag^+ + $10^{-2}M$ EDTA.
Curve 4: mercury electrode, $10^{-3}M$ Hg^{2+} + $10^{-2}M$ EDTA
(after SCRIBNER and REILLEY [42]).

The reduction of Ag⁺ by mercury is known to be quantitative when the difference $E_1' - E_2'$ exceeds about 200 mV, *i.e.* about pH 5 to 6 under present conditions. In practice, the pH is fixed at this value by means of a hexamethylenetetramine buffer, $(CH_2)_6N_4/H(CH_2)_6N_4^+$, which does not form complexes with Ag⁺ or Hg²⁺ in the presence of an excess of EDTA.

Reduction by amalgams

The use of amalgams has the following advantages:

The reduction curves of H⁺ and H_2O are shifted to very low potentials in the presence of mercury, so that very vigorous reductions are possible, *e.g.* with sodium amalgam.

The use of various amalgams allows various well-determined reduction conditions to be obtained. The equilibrium potentials of the systems

$$M\downarrow - ne \rightleftharpoons M^{n+} \qquad E = E_0 + \frac{0.058}{n} \log |M^{n+}| \qquad (1)$$

and

$$M(Hg) - ne \rightleftharpoons M^{n+} + Hg\downarrow \qquad E = E_1 + \frac{0.058}{n} \log \frac{|M^{n+}|}{|M(Hg)|} \qquad (2)$$

usually only differ by tens of millivolts when the amalgam is concentrated.

The rate of diffusion of the metal through the amalgam may limit the rate of reduction, just like diffusion through the solution. If liquid amalgams are used, vigorous stirring can aid the diffusion as well as increasing the surface area of the electrode.

This method is very similar to that of electrochemical reduction at a mercury cathode. It is used widely in organic chemistry, especially with sodium amalgam, and also in analytical chemistry. The amalgams most used are those of very reducing metals: sodium ($E_0 = -2.7$ V), zinc ($E_0 = -0.8$ V), cadmium ($E_0 = -0.4$ V),

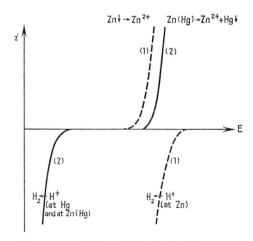

Fig. 328. Oxidation of zinc and reduction of H⁺ with:
(1) a zinc electrode; (2) an electrode of dilute zinc amalgam.

lead ($E_0 = -0.1$ V), bismuth ($E_0 = +0.3$ V), which belong to fast or fairly fast systems. Some metals cannot be used in this way because they do not form amalgams (iron, nickel) or belong to slow systems (manganese, chromium).

These phenomena can be predicted with the aid of the current–potential curves. The reduction curves of several oxidants, e.g. H^+ and H_2O, are practically the same at an electrode of dilute amalgam as at an electrode of pure mercury (Fig. 328). The reduction curves at a mercury electrode thus allow the reduction by amalgams to be predicted[65]. The values of the half-wave potentials obtained by polarography with a dropping mercury electrode may be used in this connection.

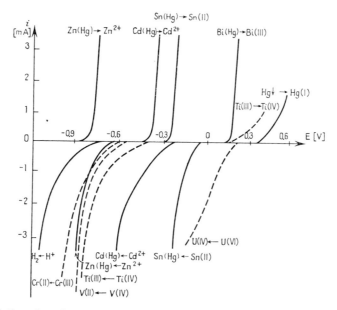

Fig. 329. Oxidation of amalgams and reduction of some oxidants at a mercury electrode in N HCl (after COURSIER[65]).

Fig. 329 shows the oxidation curves for several amalgams (concentration about 1 %) and the reduction curves of some oxidants at a mercury electrode (5×10^{-3} N solutions in a hydrochloric acid medium). Since the half-wave potentials of Fe(III) and V(V) are greater than the oxidation potential of mercury, the full current–potential curves cannot be traced at a mercury electrode though the limiting diffusion currents for the reductions can be measured at lower voltages.

It is clear from this that both Fe(III) and V(V) are reducible by all four amalgams shown in the figure.

On the other hand, zinc amalgam is necessary for the reduction of Cr(III), Ti(IV) and V(IV). It follows from the position of the reduction curve of H^+ ions that reductions by zinc amalgam are always accompanied by the evolution of hydrogen. The most vigorous reductions are achieved by alkali metal amalgams, but these also reduce H^+ ions at a considerable rate.

TABLE I

REDUCTIONS BY LIQUID AMALGAMS

Amalgam of	Zinc	Cadmium	Lead	Tin	Bismuth
E_0' (in N HCl)	$-$ 0.8 V	$-$ 0.4 V	$-$ 0.2 V	$-$ 0.2 V	0.0 V
Reduction reactions	Fe(III)$\rightarrow$ Fe(II)	Fe(III)$\rightarrow$ Fe(II)	Fe(III)$\rightarrow$ Fe(II)	Fe(III)$\rightarrow$ Fe(II)	Fe(III)$\rightarrow$ Fe(II)
	Ti(IV)$\rightarrow$ Ti(III)	Ti(IV)$\rightarrow$ Ti(III)			
	W(VI)$\rightarrow$ W(III)	W(VI)$\rightarrow$ W(III)	W(VI)$\rightarrow$ W(III)	W(VI)$\rightarrow$ W(V)	
	V(V)$\rightarrow$ V(II)	V(V)$\rightarrow$ V(IV)	V(V)$\rightarrow$ V(IV)	V(V)$\rightarrow$ V(IV)	V(V)$\rightarrow$ V(IV)
	U(VI)$\rightarrow$ U(IV)	U(VI)$\rightarrow$ U(IV)	U(VI)$\rightarrow$ U(IV)	U(VI)$\rightarrow$ U(IV)	
	U(VI)$\rightarrow$ U(III)				
	Sn(II)$\rightarrow$ Sn(Hg)	Sn(II)$\rightarrow$ Sn(Hg)			
	Cu(II)$\rightarrow$ Cu(Hg)	Cu(II)$\rightarrow$ Cu(Hg)	Cu(II)$\rightarrow$ Cu	Cu(II)$\rightarrow$ Cu	Cu(II)$\rightarrow$ Cu
	As(V)$\rightarrow$ As $\downarrow$	As(V)$\rightarrow$ As $\downarrow$	As(V)$\rightarrow$ As $\downarrow$		
			As(V)$\rightarrow$ As(III)	As(V)$\rightarrow$ As(III)	As(V)$\rightarrow$ As(III)
	Cr(VI)$\rightarrow$ Cr(III)	Cr(VI)$\rightarrow$ Cr(III)	Cr(VI)$\rightarrow$ Cr(III)	Cr(VI)$\rightarrow$ Cr(III)	Cr(VI)$\rightarrow$ Cr(III)
	Cr(VI)$\rightarrow$ Cr(II)				

after COURSIER [65]

As with the reduction by metals, various chemical means are available for facilitating or preventing reduction, and for making it more specific. For example, the presence of EDTA and the simultaneous effect of the pH modify the action of amalgams considerably, and extend the field of application in organic and inorganic chemistry.

Table I shows the reductions which may be carried out by liquid amalgams of zinc, cadmium, lead, tin and bismuth in N HCl. The table below shows the reductions which can be performed with solid zinc amalgam in sulphuric acid media, in a Jones reductor.

TABLE II

REDUCTION BY SOLID ZINC AMALGAM

(Jones Reductor)

In dilute H_2SO_4		
Fe(III) $\rightarrow$ Fe(II)	Cr(VI) $\rightarrow$ Cr(II)	Sb(V) $\rightarrow$ Sb$\downarrow$
Mo(VI) $\rightarrow$ Mo(III)	Cr(III) $\rightarrow$ Cr(II)	Sb(III) $\rightarrow$ Sb$\downarrow$
U(VI) $\rightarrow$ U(IV)	Cu(II) $\rightarrow$ Cu$\downarrow$	Au(III) $\rightarrow$ Au$\downarrow$
U(VI) $\rightarrow$ U(III)	Ni(II) $\rightarrow$ Ni$\downarrow$	Pt(IV) $\rightarrow$ Pt$\downarrow$
Ti(IV) $\rightarrow$ Ti(III)	As(V) $\rightarrow$ As$\downarrow$	V(V) $\rightarrow$ V(II)
Pu(VI) $\rightarrow$ Pu(III)	As(III) $\rightarrow$ As$\downarrow$	NO_3^- $\rightarrow$ NH_3OH^+

III. ELECTROCHEMICAL CATALYSIS OF REDOX REACTIONS

Redox reactions can be effected by chemical or electrochemical means. In the first case, the reductant of system 1

$$Ox_1 + e \rightleftharpoons Red_1 \qquad E_1$$

gives up electrons directly to the oxidant of system 2

$$Ox_2 + e \rightleftharpoons Red_2 \qquad E_2 > E_1$$

In the second case, the reductant 1 gives up its electrons to a conductor, which in its turn gives them to the oxidant 2.

A knowledge of the value of the difference $E_2 - E_1$ allows us to predict whether the reaction

$$Red_1 + Ox_2 \rightleftharpoons Red_2 + Ox_1$$

is possible, but gives no information about its rate.

A determination of the current–potential curves allows the rate of the reaction to be predicted. In general, two cases are possible, depending upon the relative positions of the oxidation and reduction curves:

1. The oxidation curve of Red_1 and the reduction curve of Ox_2 have the relative positions shown in Fig. 331. An isolated electrode dipped into a solution containing Ox_2 and Red_1 will take up a mixed potential E_M corresponding to a zero net current; Red_1 will be oxidized at a rate measured by i, and Ox_2 will be reduced at an equal rate measured by $-i$.

2. The curves have the relative positions shown in Fig. 330. An isolated electrode dipped into a solution containing Ox_2 and Red_1 will now assume an ill-defined mixed potential E_M, at which the rates of the electrochemical reactions are negligible.

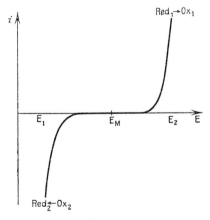

Fig. 330.

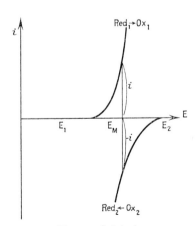

Fig. 331. Catalysis.

If the chemical reaction between Red_1 and Ox_2 is slow, and if it is possible to find a conducting substance such that the current–potential curves of Red_1 and Ox_2 at an electrode of this substance are situated as shown in Fig. 331, then the presence of this substance catalyzes the redox reaction, i.e. the reaction occurs by electrochemical means at the surface of the catalyst much more rapidly than by chemical means.

We have seen that an important method of increasing the rate of electrochemical reactions is to increase the surface area of the electrode (see Chapter V). Electrochemical catalysis is therefore almost always produced by finely divided metals or conducting compounds. Finely divided platinum, Raney nickel, etc., are used to catalyze a large number of redox reactions in this way.

We will give some examples of this type of catalysis.

Examples

Oxidation of titanium (III) by iodine in the presence of graphite[65]. A solution containing Ti^{3+} is violet, and a solution of I_3^- is brown. If the two solutions are mixed, the colour of the mixture does not change with time, which indicates that the oxidation of Ti(III) by iodine, which should occur according to the redox potentials of the systems, does not occur at an observable rate.

The current–potential curves of these substances at a graphite electrode are shown in Fig. 334. It will be seen that an isolated graphite rod will assume a potential E_M at which the rates of reduction of I_3^- and of oxidation of Ti(III) are quite large. If the graphite rod is replaced by powdered graphite, the reaction becomes even faster.

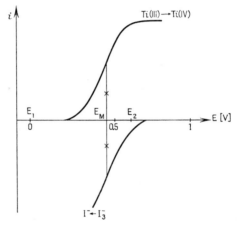

Fig. 332. Oxidation of Ti(III) by iodine in the presence of graphite (after COURSIER [65]).

Reductions by hypophosphite[65]. The system

$$H_3PO_2 + H_2O \rightleftharpoons H_3PO_3 + 2 H^+ + 2e$$

has a theoretical redox potential of -0.5 V at pH $= 0$. It would be expected from this value of the potential that hypophosphorous acid and the hypophosphites should be very strong reducing agents, capable of reducing water with the evolution of hydrogen. Experiment shows that this is not so: the reaction is slow.

It might be thought that it should be possible to realize reductions with hypophosphites in the presence of finely divided metals, in the light of what we have seen above; and it is found that nickel, palladium, silver, mercury, platinum, etc., do indeed have this effect. It may be remarked that all these metals are not very oxidizable; this is necessary so that they do not disappear by oxidation during the reaction.

Thus, whatever the pH, the addition of a little palladium powder to a solution of hypophosphite gives rise to the reduction of water and the evolution of hydrogen. In neutral solution, hypophosphite can reduce palladous ions chemically to palladium metal at normal temperatures. Once some palladium metal is formed, hydrogen is evolved as in the previous case.

Raney nickel gives identical results.

In neutral media (pH 6–8), methylene blue is decolorized in the presence of palladium, copper powder or graphite. This reduction cannot be attributed to hydrogen, since the last two substances do not reduce water.

It is known that mercuric salts are reduced very slowly to calomel by hypophosphite. This reduction is catalyzed by Ag^+ ions. It seems therefore that the hypophosphite can reduce silver ions chemically to finely divided silver, which presents a very large active surface at which $H_2PO_2^-$ and Hg^{2+} ions are electroactive and can react with each other. This reaction is not specific to metallic silver: platinum black or palladium give identical results.

Many other reactions involving metals can be explained in a similar way[65].

Catalysis of the reduction of hydrogen by finely divided metals. The equilibrium potential of the systems

$$H_2 - 2e \rightleftharpoons 2 H^+ \quad \text{and} \quad H_2 + 2 OH^- - 2e \rightleftharpoons 2 H_2O$$

is $E_{eq} = -0.058$ pH. Hydrogen is thus, in principle, a strong reducing agent; but in practice it reacts slowly, often infinitely slowly, with most oxidants. For example, MnO_4^- (1.6 V) and Ce^{4+} (1.4 V) ions are not reduced by hydrogen.

The current–potential curves for the oxidation of hydrogen show that at most electrodes it is only oxidized under very oxidizing conditions, often after water (*i.e.* it is not electroactive) (Fig. 333).

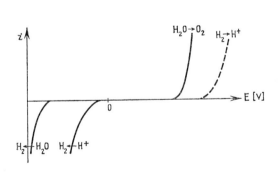

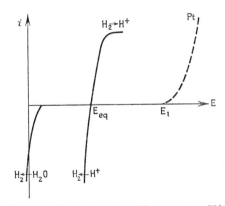

Fig. 333. The slow system $H_2 - 2e \rightleftharpoons 2 H^+$.   Fig. 334. The fast system $H_2 - 2e \rightleftharpoons 2 H^+$ (after COURTOT-COUPEZ[75]).

But in the presence of finely divided metals, such as platinized platinum, the curves correspond to a fast system (Fig. 334). All the oxidants whose curves lie to the right of E_{eq} at these electrodes can be reduced by hydrogen.

The current–potential curves of the oxidant in question must also be situated to the left of E_1, *i.e.* the oxidant must not be too strong, or the platinum (or other metal catalyst) will be oxidized. For example, Raney nickel is oxidized by H^+ ions (Fig. 335). This problem can sometimes be solved by changing the solvent. The curve of the system H_2/H^+ in a protolytic solvent having the properties of a weaker acid than water may be displaced so as to give an overall picture like that of Fig. 334 (see Chapter XIII).

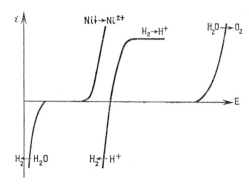

Fig. 335. Reductions by H_2 in the presence of Raney nickel, in acid media (theoretical curves).

Many examples of reduction by hydrogen in the presence of finely divided metals are known, *e.g.* $Ni(NH_3)_m^{2+}$ in the presence of finely divided Ni, Cu^{2+} under the same conditions. Many catalytic hydrogenations used in organic chemistry may be explained or predicted in this way[75].

We have mentioned above that the attack of metals is catalyzed by placing other metals in contact with them (see p. 274). Other examples of catalysis are contained implicitly in the current–potential curves which have been discussed in this book. For example, permanganate oxidizes water in the presence of platinum.

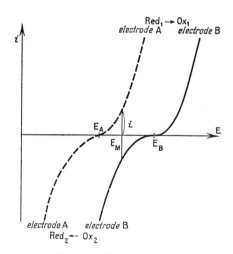

Fig. 336. Mixed catalysts.

Mixed catalysts. Let us consider the current–potential curves of Red_1 and Ox_2 at two different electrodes (Fig. 336). Neither electrode A nor electrode B alone can catalyze the reaction

$$Ox_2 + Red_1 \rightleftharpoons Ox_1 + Red_2$$

but if the two electrodes are dipped into the solution so that they make contact with each other, the reaction is catalyzed with a velocity corresponding to the current i.

IV. ELECTROLYTIC SEPARATIONS

Electrolytic separations are usually carried out by the deposition of a metal, an oxide or a salt on the surface of the electrode, and are often used in the consecutive determination of several substances.

This is a very important field of electrochemical analysis. We will only recall the principle of these methods here, and refer to more specialized works for descriptions of the methods in practice.

For a long time, analysis by this method was carried out by weighing the compound deposited on the electrode; this is called electrogravimetric analysis, and is still one of the most important methods. It is also possible, however, to effect the determination by other methods, *e.g.* coulometry involving the redissolution of the deposit, or volumetric or colorimetric analysis of the dissolved deposit. In these last cases it is not necessary that the deposit has a definite composition. The principles and practical application of this method are not very different from those of coulometry (Chapter X), except that here a 100 % current yield is not necessary, since the current is not measured. The main thing that is sought for here is specificity. Electrolysis should be carried out at constant potential, which allows the electrochemical reaction to be accurately defined. When possible, however, a constant current is used, since it is quicker. It does not matter if substances other than the one to be separated are electrolyzed at the same time, as long as they do not give deposits on the electrode, but only soluble or gaseous products. It is thus possible to electrolyze hydrogen ions or water during the deposition of a metal in the presence of non-electroactive substances. This is in fact an advantage, since the rate of deposition of the metal is increased, owing to the enhancement of the migration current (see Chapter I, p. 00).

Fixing the conditions for electrolysis

When dealing with fast systems (Ag, Zn, Hg, etc.), the electrolysis can be approximately predicted by consideration of the equilibrium potentials of the systems. But in general, a knowledge of the current–potential curves determined with the equipment to be used for the electrolysis allows the most favourable conditions to be accurately chosen: stirring, temperature, nature and surface area of the electrodes, potential difference between the electrodes, the current and the length of the electrolysis.

In the simplest cases, it is hardly necessary to control the conditions of electrolysis, and a nearly constant current is often used. For instance, when depositing copper from a solution which contains no other reducible metallic cations, a fairly large current may be used, so that hydrogen is evolved at the cathode.

But where two metallic cations have to be separated, *e.g.* Ag^+ and Cu^{2+}, it is necessary to work at constant potential. A platinum electrode is used, and the potential is fixed at 0.4–0.5 V, at which the diffusion current of Ag^+ is limiting, while Cu^{2+} is not reduced. The principles of this method are usually the same as for coulometry at constant potential (see Chapter X).

Instrumentation

The problem of the stabilization of the potential at a constant value is the same as in coulometry at a constant potential, and may be solved by manual adjustment or by means of a servomechanism (see INSTRUMENTATION, Chapter VI). The electrolysis cells also have to satisfy the same conditions as coulometric cells (see Chapter X).

The solution may be stirred with a magnetic stirrer. When carrying out a series of determinations on the same sample, much time is saved by increasing the stirring by rotating the electrodes, or by making them vibrate[94]. It is then possible to deposit 200 mg of metal in 10–15 minutes.

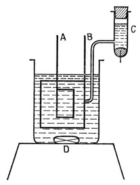

Fig. 337. Electrolytic separation at a constant potential.
A, B = electrodes. C = reference electrode. D = magnetic stirrer (after LINGANE[92]).

Stabilizing the potential by means of an auxiliary system

It is sometimes possible to stabilise the potential of the electrode at which deposition occurs at the desired value without making use of controlled current sources. A substance is added to the solution which when electrolyzed does not interfere with the deposition, gives products which do not interfere (soluble or gaseous), and prevents the electrolysis of substances which might cause trouble. We will give some examples:

1. If it is desired to determine lead by depositing it at the anode as PbO_2, care must be taken that no lead is deposited as the metal at the cathode. It is thus necessary to control the potential of the cathode. An excess of copper salt may be added to the solution for this purpose: even with a large current, the potential of the cathode is fixed by the reduction of Cu^{2+}, and the deposition of Pb is excluded.

2. Ag^+ may be reduced to the metal, which is deposited at the cathode, in the presence of Cu^{2+} if the potential of this electrode is controlled. This may be done by adding a ferric salt to the solution. Even when the current is large, Ag^+ is reduced first, and then Fe^{3+}, and Cu^{2+} is not reduced; the Fe^{2+} thus formed is reoxidized at the anode. This implies that the presence of Fe^{3+} is undesirable if copper has to be

deposited from the solution, since it is reduced first and its concentration does not decrease, as the Fe^{2+} formed is reoxidized.

3. When operating in the presence of chloride ion, which is often the case, the platinum anode may be oxidized as follows

$$Pt\downarrow + 6\,Cl^- - 4e \rightarrow PtCl_6{}^{2-}$$

This may be prevented by adding to the solution a substance which is oxidized more easily than the platinum, and which does not interfere or give troublesome oxidation products, e.g. hydroxylamine[95]

$$NH_2OH - e \rightarrow \tfrac{1}{2}N_2 + H_2O + H^+$$

4. When depositing cobalt

$$Co^{2+} + 2e \rightarrow Co\downarrow$$

a little cobalt (III) oxide may be deposited at the anode

$$2\,Co^{2+} + 3\,H_2O - 2e \rightarrow Co_2O_3 \cdot aq\downarrow + 6\,H^+$$

This reaction may be prevented by adding a stronger reductant than Co^{2+} to the solution, to limit the anode potential or to reduce chemically any Co_2O_3 formed.

Hydrazine[95] may be used for this purpose

$$NH_2NH_2 - 4e \rightarrow N_2 + 4\,H^+$$

Electrolysis at a mercury cathode

This method is mainly used to remove large amounts of undesirable substances from solution, so that smaller amounts of another substance may be determined. For example, 4 g of cadmium may be separated from 0.3 g of zinc[92].

It is also used, though less frequently, to deposit elements which must be estimated. These may then be recovered by distillation of the mercury, or redissolved by electrochemical oxidation, which may be at a constant potential.

The large overvoltage of hydrogen at a mercury electrode allows vigorous reductions to be carried out without much hydrogen being evolved. The deposition of some metals is aided by amalgam formation. Such separations are rapid: 1 g of copper or iron can be deposited in about one hour, using standard equipment with a current of 4 A.

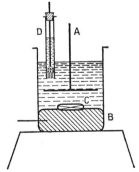

Fig. 338. Constant-potential electrolysis at a mercury cathode.
A = platinum disc, B = mercury electrode, C = magnetic stirrer, D = reference electrode
(see LINGANE[92]).

References p. 304–307

The following elements may be deposited in this way from 0.1 N H_2SO_4, without controlling the potential: Fe, Cu, Ni, Co, Zn, Ge, Ag, Cd, In, Sn, Cr, Mo, Pb, Bi, Se, Te, Os, Tl, Hg, Au, Pt, Ir, Rh, Pd. Mn is deposited with difficulty, and Ru, As and Sb are not deposited quantitatively. Al, B, Be, Ta, Nb, W, the rare earths, Ti, Zr, Th, U, V, and Pu remain in solution. Certain elements are reduced to a lower oxidation state, *e.g.* Ti(IV) → Ti(III), U(VI) → U(III).

The selectivity is increased if the potential is controlled. This may be investigated with the aid of polarographic curves obtained at a dropping mercury electrode. When two elements have half-wave potentials which differ by at least 250 to 300 mV, they may be separated quantitatively at a potential corresponding to the limiting diffusion current of the more easily reduced substance. It is *e.g.* possible to deposit cadmium while leaving Zn²⁺ in solution if the right potential is used.

Chemical methods used to effect a separation

Various chemical methods of improving the separation are available: pH, complex formation, etc. Everything which has been said on this subject for the reduction by metals and amalgams holds here.

An example is the separation of Cu, Bi, Pb and Sn with controlled potential[93]. Hydrazine forms a complex with Cu²⁺, or reduces it chemically to Cu⁺, according to the operating conditions. Fig. 339 shows the variation of the deposition potentials of

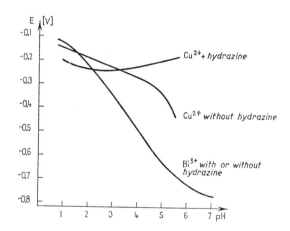

Fig. 339. Deposition potentials of Cu and Bi as a function of the pH in tartrate medium (after LINGANE and JONES[93]).

Bi and Cu in a tartrate medium as a function of the pH, all the other conditions being constant. It will be seen that pH 5–6 and the presence of hydrazine are the most favourable conditions for the separation. Cu is deposited at this pH and the appropriate potential; then Bi and Pb are deposited at pH 4- 5, and finally the solution is made very acid so as to decompose the tartrate complex of Sn(IV), and Sn is deposited.

Electrolytic refining

Electrolytic refining of metals uses an anode of the impure metal and a cathode of the pure metal in a solution of a very pure salt of the metal. The reaction

$$M\downarrow - ne \rightarrow M^{n+}$$

takes place at the anode, and

$$M^{n+} + ne \rightarrow M\downarrow$$

at the cathode. The net result is the transport of the metal from one electrode to the other. If the system $M\downarrow/M^{n+}$ is a fast one, the electrolysis may be carried out rapidly even with a low potential difference.

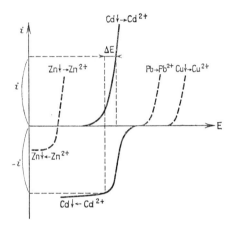

Fig. 340. The electrolytic refining of cadmium.

It can be shown that the impurities are eliminated in this way. The metals which are more difficult to oxidize than the metal to be refined are not oxidized at the anode, but form a sludge at the bottom of the electrolysis cell. This is the case with Cu and Pb during the refining of cadmium (Fig. 340). The metals which are more easily oxidized pass in solution, but they are not reduced at the cathode. This is the case with zinc in the above example (Fig. 340). Such substances concentrate slowly in the solution. The metal which is deposited at the cathode is thus very pure.

Separation of traces

The separation of very small amounts of substances cannot easily be predicted by means of the current-potential curves. The electrolysis must be continued for a very long time. It is in general advisable to use a cathode with a very small surface area, e.g. a wire. It is known that traces of copper can be separated in this way as the metal from lead which is deposited as PbO_2 at the cathode.

When the amounts deposited are so small that the electrodes are not covered completely, the conditions are very different. These phenomena have been studied [98], [99].

Internal electrolysis

The name of 'internal electrolysis' has been given to the special case where the two electrodes are short-circuited and an oxidation reaction is produced at one of the electrodes, and a reduction reaction at the other (galvanic cell).

If, for example, a platinum electrode and a zinc electrode are connected electrically and dipped into a solution containing Cu^{2+}, the current–potential curves are as shown in Fig. 341. It may be seen from these that the two electrodes take up a potential E_M, at which the copper is deposited on the platinum, while the zinc is attacked. If zinc were used alone, it would become covered with copper, and the reaction would stop. The copper is in this way removed from the solution by deposition on the platinum. The same method may be used to deposit traces of antimony, cobalt and bismuth.

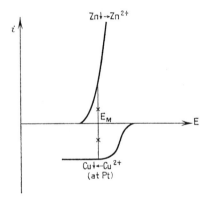

Fig. 341. Deposition of copper by internal electrolysis.

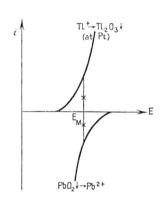

Fig. 342. Deposition of Tl_2O_3 by internal electrolysis (after LIPTSCHINSKY [109]).

Further example. A platinum electrode and a PbO_2 electrode are dipped into a solution of Tl^+. The current–potential curves are shown in Fig. 342. At the potential E_M, thallium is deposited on the platinum as Tl_2O_3, while lead oxide is redissolved [109].

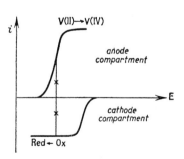

Fig. 343. Internal electrolysis with separate compartments.

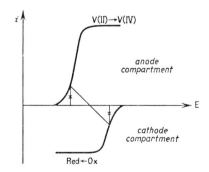

Fig. 344. Internal electrolysis with separate compartments and a high circuit resistance.

One of the electrodes may be an amalgam. It is then possible to remove a disturbing substance from the solution and replace it by another element coming from the amalgam

$$M_1{}^{n+} + M_2(Hg) \rightarrow M_1(Hg) + M_2{}^{n+}$$

(see reduction by amalgams, p. 280).

It is further possible to use separate anode and cathode compartments, and to have an anode of an inert metal (*e.g.* platinum) in a solution of a suitable reducing agent (V(II), Cr(II), or of sodium amalgam in a solution of caustic soda [108]. The reaction at the anode is then the oxidation of V(II), Cr(II) or Na(Hg) (see Fig. 343).

In this case the resistance of the circuit may be high, so the current is low and the separation takes longer (Fig. 344, see Chapter IX for the theory).

Characteristics of the method

This is a relatively old method, and for this very reason, its considerable possibilities have not yet been used to the full.

It can be very fast, especially with fast stirring: 200 mg of copper may for example be deposited in 3 to 4 minutes.

Very slight traces of some elements can be separated in this way.

With the modern automatic methods of controlling the potential, this method requires less personal attention than other methods of separation.

Example of an industrial application

The use of amalgams for the semi-industrial preparation of very pure metals from low-grade ores

Dry metallurgy cannot be used to obtain very pure metals from low-grade ores.

Electrolytic preparation and purification of zinc. The ore is first attacked by chlorine at high temperature, then dissolved in water to give practically neutral solutions of impure zinc chloride, which are electrolyzed.

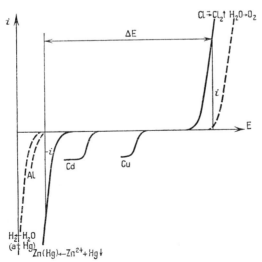

Fig. 345. The deposition of zinc amalgam starting from a concentrated solution of impure zinc chloride.

The purification is carried out by the method of electrolytic refining (see p. 291). The impure zinc (containing cadmium, nickel, cobalt, copper, silver, etc.) is first deposited by electrolysis of the impure chloride. A mercury electrode is used to avoid the simultaneous reduction of water and evolution of hydrogen, which would give rise to a lower current yield. Chlorine is evolved at the anode, and used to attack another sample of the ore. The current–potential curves are shown in Fig. 345.

The zinc amalgam is then reoxidized, using a very pure solution of zinc chloride and a pure zinc cathode. The metal thus deposited is very pure. The current–potential curves are shown in Fig. 346.

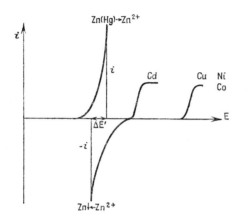

Fig. 346. The electrolytic refining of zinc starting from the amalgam.

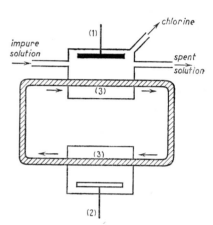

Fig. 347. Continuous purification of zinc. (1) Graphite (2) Zinc (3) Zinc amalgam.

The two stages of purification can be combined into one continuous process in the following way. The impure solution of zinc chloride is electrolyzed in one cell with a graphite anode and a mercury cathode, the solution being passed continuously through the cell. A pure solution of zinc chloride is electrolyzed in a second cell with a pure zinc cathode and zinc amalgam obtained from the first cell as anode (Fig. 347). The amalgam circulates continuously between the two cells, acting as the cathode in the first and the anode in the second. The electrolysis voltage $\Delta E + \Delta E'$ is applied between the graphite electrode of the first cell and the zinc electrode of the second. This total voltage is divided between the two cells, so that in the first (ΔE) zinc is deposited in the mercury, giving a current $-i$, while in the second ($\Delta E'$) the amalgam is reoxidized with the current $+i$, and the zinc deposited at the cathode with the current $-i$.

A steady state is thus produced, with the net result that zinc passes from the original impure solution to the zinc electrode, giving a metal of very high purity (99.999 %). The impurities slowly concentrate in the mercury. The circulating amalgam contains 2.2 % zinc before entering the first cell, and 2.6 % before entering the second.

Electrolytic preparation and separation of zinc and lead. An ore containing zinc and lead is treated with chlorine, so that $ZnCl_2$ and $PbCl_2$ are formed. The chlorides are then dissolved.

The solution of Zn^{2+} and Pb^{2+} thus obtained is shaken with zinc amalgam. The current–potential curves (Fig. 348) show that Pb^{2+} is reduced and passes into the mercury as amalgam, together with all the other impurities which are reducible by zinc amalgam, while an equivalent amount of Zn^{2+} goes into solution. The pure solution of Zn^{2+} obtained is led to an electrolysis cell where the zinc is deposited.

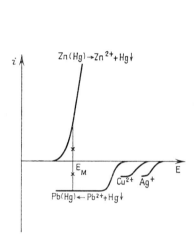

Fig. 348. Reduction of Pb^{2+} by zinc amalgam.

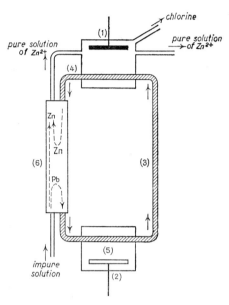

Fig. 349. Continuous purification of zinc and lead. (1) Graphite (2) Lead (3) Lead amalgam. (4) Lead-zinc amalgam (5) Solution of lead perchlorate (6) Counter-current column containing amalgam and solution.

The impure lead amalgam is led to another (sealed) electrolysis cell containing a solution of pure lead perchlorate (which is very soluble and completely ionized) and a pure lead cathode. Only the lead amalgam is reoxidized, giving a very pure metal (refining).

This operation is also carried out as a continuous process. The reduction of the Pb^{2+} in the initial solution by zinc amalgam is realized in a counter-current column (Fig. 349). The zinc reoxidized in this operation is regenerated in the mercury by an electrolysis of the pure zinc solution in which only a part of the zinc is deposited, the rest remaining in solution until it reaches a second electrolysis cell, where it is all deposited on a pure zinc cathode. The lead amalgam circulates continuously between the reduction column, the cell containing lead perchlorate (where part of the lead is reoxidized) and the zinc chloride cell (where, according to the principle of the purification, the lead and the other impurities are not reoxidized). The amalgam contains 1.2 % lead before entering the column and 1.6 % on leaving the column. The impurities are gradually concentrated in the amalgam.

References p. 304–307

Electrolytic preparation and separation of zinc, lead and tin. Pb^{2+} and Sn^{2+} have very similar electrochemical properties; the standard potentials of the systems $Pb\downarrow/Pb^{2+}$ and $Sn\downarrow/Sn^{2+}$ are -0.13 V and -0.14 V respectively. It is not possible to separate them in hydrochloric acid solution. In alkaline media, however, the complex ions ZnO_2^{2-}, PbO_2^{2-} and $HSnO_2^-$ exist; these ions have different stabilities. Reduction at a mercury electrode proceeds according to the reactions

$$ZnO_2^{2-} + 2\ H_2O + (Hg) + 2e \rightarrow Zn(Hg) + 4\ OH^-$$
$$PbO_2^{2-} + 2\ H_2O + (Hg) + 2e \rightarrow Pb(Hg) + 4\ OH^-$$
$$SnO_2H^- + \quad H_2O + (Hg) + 2e \rightarrow Sn(Hg) + 3\ OH^-$$

The current–potential curves are shown in Fig. 350.

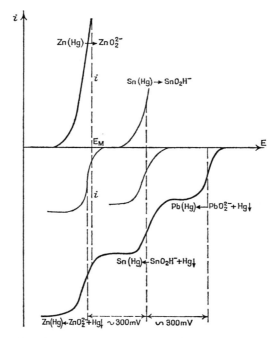

Fig. 350. Reduction of plumbite and stannite by zinc amalgam (theoretical curves).

Plumbite and stannite are reducible by zinc amalgam. At first, only plumbite is reduced, with a current $-i$. If any tin amalgam is formed, this also reduces the plumbite. When all the Pb^{2+} has been reduced, the Sn^{2+} can be reduced in its turn. A solution of pure zincate is then left.

This operation has also been realized in a countercurrent column, with very fine droplets of zinc amalgam falling through the ascending solution of zincate, plumbite and stannite. Since the effective surface is large, the reduction is rapid. At the top of the column, where the zinc amalgam is in excess, all the Sn^{2+} is reduced, so a solution of pure zincate leaved the top of the column. About the middle of the column, therefore, tin amalgam descends in countercurrent with a solution of zincate, plumbite and stannite, which is reduced, giving pure lead amalgam which leaves the bottom of the column. By suitable adjustment of the flow, it is possible to obtain lead amalgam at the bottom, tin amalgam in the middle and a pure solution of zincate at the top (Fig. 351).

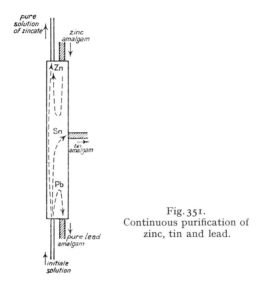

Fig. 351.
Continuous purification of
zinc, tin and lead.

The lead and tin amalgams are used to prepare the pure metals by electrolysis (see p. 294). The resulting mercury, which is poor in tin and lead, is converted into zinc amalgam by partial electrolysis of the pure zincate solution (see p. 294) and recycled to the top of the column. The pure zinc is obtained by complete electrolysis of the zincate solution

$$ZnO_2{}^{2-} + 2\,H_2O + 2e \rightarrow Zn\downarrow + 4\,OH^-$$

This electrolysis also provides OH⁻ ions which are used to make alkaline the solution obtained by treatment of the ore.

V. ELECTROLYTIC PREPARATIONS

It is not possible to give a complete treatment of the important subject of the electrochemical preparation of compounds here. Whole books have been written on this subject. We will only recall here the means which we have at our disposal to tackle these problems: a knowledge of the current–potential curves determined in the same cell which is to be used for the electrolysis gives an indication of the conditions under which the electrochemical reaction will occur.

The reactions can then be carried out at a suitable potential, controlled automatically by a potentiostat, or at constant current with the aid of a suitable device (see Chapter VI).

We can use the following factors which have already been discussed to displace the current–potential curves so as to make it possible to carry out the desired reaction: the nature and surface area of the electrodes, the addition of an auxiliary system, the choice of solvent, the temperature, and a combination of chemical means such as pH and complex-formation. It is often possible by suitable choice of conditions to carry out an electrochemical reaction which is specific and which also has 100 % current yield.

In Chapter X, COULOMETRY, we have seen some examples of preparation of substances with 100 % yield. When it is only a matter of carrying out consecutive preparations, it is not necessary to obtain a 100 % current yield in the reaction.

Most of the conditions and methods used have already been described in Chapter X, COULOMETRY, and Chapter VI, INSTRUMENTATION.

The advantage of electrochemical preparations over chemical ones is that the potential at which the reaction takes place can be fixed very accurately.

Large-scale electrolytic preparations raise a number of important and often intractable problems, which we will not discuss in detail here.

The ohmic drops iR are often far from small when large currents are used and the anode and cathode compartments are separated by diaphragms. The temperature of the cell therefore increases during the reaction, and it is often necessary to cool it.

The potential variations in the solution between the electrodes depend on the shape of the electrodes. The stirring is usually not enough to make the solution really homogeneous, especially near the electrodes, because of the high concentrations and current densities used. The transport phenomena are much more complicated than in the simple scheme which we have adopted here.

Oxidation reactions

Here electrolytic methods find their main use in the more vigorous oxidation reactions: Ce(III) to Ce(IV), Co(II) to Co(III), Cr(III) to Cr(VI), Cl⁻ to Cl_2, SO_4^{2-} to $S_2O_8^{2-}$, OH⁻ to H_2O_2, etc.

All these reactions occur at potentials near those at which water is oxidized, and the nature of the electrode is therefore obviously of great importance. The most vigorous oxidations must be realized at electrodes at which water is most difficultly oxidizable. An electrode covered with PbO_2 is one of the best for carrying out the most difficult oxidations.

Reduction reactions

As with the oxidation reactions, very vigorous reduction reactions may be realized at the surface of electrodes at which water is most difficultly reducible. A mercury electrode is the best for this purpose. Many organic compounds in particular can be prepared in this way. The current–potential curve may be determined, *e.g.* at a dropping mercury electrode. If necessary, the number of electrons involved may be determined by one of the available methods. This knowledge enables the reaction itself to be carried out properly.

Examples

We will give a few characteristic examples. Many more may be found in the literature.

Formation of Ag(II) and Ag(III) by oxidation of Ag(I) in alkaline solution at a gold electrode[119]. Ag(II) and Ag(III) are very strong oxidizing agents, which are unstable because they oxidize water (or rather HO⁻ ions in alkaline solution) fairly slowly. They may be prepared in very alkaline solution. The electrochemical method is the most convenient.

The oxidation curves of Ag_2O are shown in Fig. 352. Two successive waves are seen, the first due to the oxidation of Ag(I) to Ag(II)

$$2 Ag_3O_2^- + 4 OH^- - 6e \rightarrow 3 Ag_2O_2\downarrow + 2 H_2O$$

and the second due to the oxidation of Ag(II) to Ag(III)

$$Ag_2O_2\downarrow + 2 OH^- - 2e \rightarrow Ag_2O_3\downarrow + H_2O$$

The oxidation of Cu(II) to Cu(III) is similar.

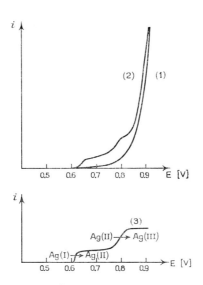

Fig. 352. The oxidation of $2.3 \times 10^{-4} M$ Ag_2O in $13.4 N$ KOH at a rotating gold electrode (3100 r.p.m.).
Curve 1: oxidation of the $13.4 N$ OH^- ions alone.
Curve 2: oxidation of Ag(I) in the $13.4 N$ OH^-.
Curve 3: theoretical oxidation curve of Ag(I) deduced from curves 1 and 2 (after PLESKOV[119]).

The preparation of dichromate by oxidation of Cr (III) at a PbO_2 electrode[120]. Cr (VI) is also a strong oxidant in acid solution. Very strong oxidizing agents (*e.g.* bismuthate, persulphate) are needed to oxidize Cr(III) chemically. Moreover, the chemical oxidation is fairly slow, and water is also oxidized to a certain extent at the same time.

It is possible to oxidize Cr(III) to Cr(VI) electrochemically at a number of electrodes, but water is generally oxidized simultaneously. The table given below shows the current yield for the oxidation of Cr(III) to Cr(VI) at various electrodes with a current density of 10 mA/cm² (0.2 M Cr(III) in 0.5 N H_2SO_4).

Electrode	Current yield (after GROSS and HICKLING [120])
Bright platinum	1 %
Platinized platinum	53 %
Lead dioxide	100 %

The use of a PbO_2 electrode, at which water is most difficult to oxidize, enables the dichromate to be prepared with the maximum yield (Fig. 353).

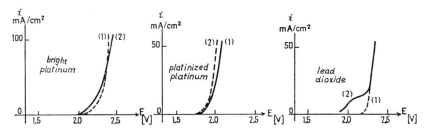

Fig. 353. Oxidation of Cr(III) in sulphuric acid solution at various electrodes. Curves 1: 0.5 N H_2SO_4 alone; curves 2: 0.5 N H_2SO_4 + 0.2 M Cr(III) (after GROSS and HICKLING [120]).

A lead electrode, which becomes covered with PbO_2 by oxidation, is used in practice. Hydrogen ions are reduced at the cathode, with the evolution of hydrogen.

Preparation of sodium hypochlorite by the electrolysis of a solution of sodium chloride [121]. Fig. 354 shows the current–potential curves for the systems $Cl^-/Cl_2/Cl(I)$ at a graphite electrode.

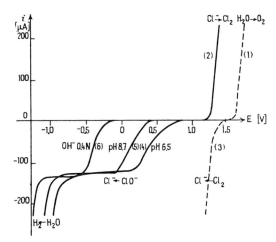

Fig. 354. The systems $Cl^-/Cl_2/ClO^-$ at a vibrating graphite electrode. Solutions: curve 1: N $HClO_4$; curve 2: M Cl^- + N $HClO_4$; curve 3: saturated Cl_2 + N $HClO_4$; curves 4, 5, 6: 4 × 10^{-3} M ClO^- + pH buffer (after MARONI *et al.* [121]).

We will give a brief account of the main reactions which occur during the electrolysis of a neutral solution of an alkaline chloride. At the anode, Cl^- is oxidized to chlorine

$$2\,Cl^- - 2e \rightarrow Cl_2$$

which disproportionates in neutral solution according to the equation

$$Cl_2 + H_2O \rightleftharpoons HClO + H^+ + Cl^- \tag{1}$$

The solution near the electrode rapidly becomes acid, so the Cl_2 no longer disproportionates, but diffuses through the solution. Water is reduced at the cathode

$$2 H_2O + 2e \rightarrow H_2\!\downarrow + 2 OH^-$$

The solution near the cathode soon becomes alkaline, and the OH^- ions formed also diffuse through the solution. The reaction

$$Cl_2 + OH^- \rightarrow ClO^- + Cl^-$$

then takes place in the body of the solution. A pH gradient is thus set up, the solution being acid near the anode and alkaline near the cathode.

The overall reaction is

$$Cl^- + H_2O \rightarrow ClO^- + H_2\!\uparrow$$

But hypochlorite can also be reduced at the cathode

$$ClO^- + H_2O + 2e \rightarrow Cl^- + 2 OH^-$$

This reaction must be prevented as far as possible, which may be done by depositing a thin film of chromic oxide on the electrode by adding 0.1% of dichromate to the solution. This film does not prevent water from being oxidized (no appreciable voltage drop), but it is impermeable to ClO^- ions, so these cannot diffuse to the electrode and be reduced there (see p. 121). The dichromate can be replaced by a calcium salt: lime is then deposited on the electrode, and has the same effect as the chromic oxide.

The final concentration is nevertheless limited by electrochemical and chemical side reactions: loss of chlorine at the anode, leading to loss of ClO^- and H^+; possibility of the oxidation of water (evolution of oxygen); possibility of the oxidation of HClO to chlorate in very concentrated solution; and finally, disproportionation of hypochlorite

$$3 ClO^- \rightarrow 2 Cl + ClO_3^-$$

which occurs more rapidly in concentrated hot solution.

The reduction of 9-(o-iodophenyl)acridine at a mercury electrode[122]. 9-(o-iodophenyl)acridine can be reduced electrochemically in a two-step process. Fig. 355 shows the current-potential curves obtained at a dropping mercury electrode. The two waves correspond to the two successive reactions

The intermediate, 9-(*o*-iophenyl)dihydroacridine, may be prepared with a current yield of 100% at a mercury electrode if the electrode potential is fixed between -1.11 V and -1.14 V.

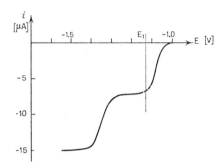

Fig. 355. Reduction of 9-(*o*-iodophenyl)acridine at a dropping mercury electrode, in 0.1 *N* KOH/90% ethanol (after LINGANE *et al.*[122]).

Reduction of 8-chlorotheophylline in alkaline solution[123]. The current–potential curves for the reduction at a mercury electrode shows that this reaction proceeds in several stages (3 steps). Different reduction products are obtained according to the potential: from -0.3 V to -0.5 V, reduction to theophylline; at -1.20 V, reduction to 6-hydroxydeoxytheophylline; at -1.50 V, reduction of the 'carbonyl' radical.

Theophylline may be obtained in 90% yield if the potential is kept between -0.3 V and -0.5 V.

Preparation of phenylhydrazine, by reduction of diazonium chloride[123]. The current–potential curve for the reduction of diazonium chloride in chloride solution (0.1 *N* HCl or KCl) at a dropping mercury electrode shows two waves with half-wave potentials of 0.00 V and -0.70 V.

The first wave corresponds to the reaction

$$[Ar - N \equiv N]Cl + e \rightarrow Ar - N \equiv N + Cl^-$$

and the second wave, which is three times as high, to the reaction

$$Ar - N \equiv N + 3 H^+ + 3e \rightarrow Ar - NH - NH_2$$

The potential must correspond to the limiting portion of the second step if the highest yield of phenylhydrazine is to be obtained. The authors used an auxiliary system, the reduction of hydrogen ions, to stabilize the potential between -1.4 V and -1.5 V in a solution containing 0.5 *N* HCl and 2 *M* KCl.

Even though the potential is controlled, this does not prevent secondary chemical reactions, which reduce the yield considerably. The phenylhydrazine reacts mainly with the starting product

$$Ar - NH - NH_2 + [Ar - N \equiv N]Cl \rightarrow Ar - N\underset{N}{\overset{N}{\langle \|}} + ArNH_3^+ + Cl^-$$

Under optimum conditions, the authors obtained a 70% yield with respect to phenylhydrazine by this method; 48% of the current was used up by the reduction of hydrogen ions.

Anodic halogenation of organic compounds. A solution of a halide is oxidized at a platinum or graphite electrode. The halogen formed reacts with an organic compound. This method may be used at constant current.

For example, iodoform can be prepared by the oxidation of an alkaline solution of ethanol and iodine. The overall electrochemical reaction is

$$C_2H_5OH + 3 I^- + 7 OH^- + 10 e \rightarrow CHI_3 + CO_2 + 6 H_2O$$

The rate of the reaction is limited by the diffusion of the substance present in the lowest concentration, in this case ethanol. But with a higher current, the consecutive reactions

$$10 I^- + 10 e \rightarrow 5 I_2$$

$$C_2H_5OH + 5 I_2 + 7 OH^- \rightarrow CHI_3 + CO_2 + 7 I^- + 6 H_2O$$

can occur. The two mechanisms are equivalent. The current yield is in theory 100%. The principle of this method is the same as that of constant-current coulometry (see p. 246).

The same results may be obtained by chemical halogenation, by adding the halogen to a solution of the organic compound; but this generally produces halide ions at the same time, which must be recovered and reoxidized. It is better to carry out both operations *in situ* by this electrochemical method. It is then only necessary to add enough halide to react with all the compound to be halogenated.

Here are some examples of the many electrochemical halogenations:

chlorinations: preparation of chloral from ethanol, of chloroform from ethanol or acetone; chlorination of hydrocarbons (ethylene, benzene, toluene), of aromatic amines, of quinones;

brominations: preparation of bromoform from acetone, of eosine from fluorescein, bromination of aniline and of indigo;

iodinations: preparation of iodoform from ethanol or acetone, iodination of phenolphthalein and of 8-hydroxyquinoline;

fluorinations: preparation of fluoroform and carbon tetrafluoride from acetone, fluorination of organic acids, etc.

Many other substitution reactions can be carried out by this method.

VI. ELECTROGRAPHY

Electrography makes use of the anodic attack of a metal or a conducting mineral. The ions produced are identified by means of appropriate reagents. This method is mainly used for qualitative analysis, but semi-quantitative results can also be obtained under well defined conditions.

The anode consists of the substance under investigation, and the cathode of a block of aluminium. The solution (KCl, NH_4Cl, $NaNO_3$, etc.) impregnates a filter paper which is placed between the two electrodes (see Fig. 356). Current is passed for a few seconds, and the electrogram is then developed.

The method is very fast, very sensitive, and nondestructive.

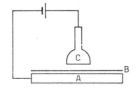

Fig. 356. Electrography.
A = anode of substance under
    investigation,
B = filter paper impregnated
    with electrolyte solution,
C = cathode.

REFERENCES

The analysis of phenomena

[1] G. CHARLOT and R. GAUGUIN, *Les méthodes d'analyse des réactions en solution*, Masson, Paris, 1951.
[2] I. M. KOLTHOFF and J. J. LINGANE, *Polarography*, Interscience, New York, 1952.
[3] P. DELAHAY, *New Instrumental Methods in Electrochemistry*, Interscience, New York, 1954.

Dissolution of metals

—, *aluminium*

[4] N. DUMONTIER-GOUREAU and B. TRÉMILLON, *Bull. soc. chim.*, (1959) 132.

—, *zinc*

[5] U. R. EVANS and D. E. DAVIES, *J. Chem. Soc.*, (1951) 2607.

—, *copper*

[6] J. HALPERN, *J. Electrochem. Soc.*, 100 (1953) 421.

—, *dissolution of various metals by iodine*

[7] L. L. BIRCUMSHAW and A. C. RIDDIFORD, *J. Chem. Soc.*, (1951) 598, 1490.
[8] A. C. RIDDIFORD and L. L. BIRCUMSHAW, *J. Chem. Soc.*, (1952) 698, 701.

Corrosion, Passivation, Inhibitors

[9] U. R. EVANS, *Metallic Corrosion, Passivity and Protection*, Longmans Green, London, 1948.
[10] P. DELAHAY, *J. Electrochem. Soc.*, 97 (1950) 198.
[11] U. R. EVANS, *Précis de Corrosion*, Dunod, Paris, 1952 (translation).
[12] G. V. AKIMOV, *Théorie et méthodes d' essai de la corrosion des métaux*, Dunod, Paris, 1957 (translation).
[13] U. F. FRANCK, *Korrosion*, 9 (1958) 504.

Protection of metals by a 'reactive anode'

[14] M. POURBAIX, *Rev. Ecole Polytech. Univ. Libre (Bruxelles)*, 30 (1950) 157.
[15] J. VAN MUYLDER, C. VANLEUGENHAGUE and M. POURBAIX, *Centre belge de corrosion (Cebelcor) Rept.* 65, 1958.

Reduction by metals and amalgams

—, *aluminium*

[16] L. DEUTSCH, *Ann. Chim. Anal.*, 18 (1936) 10.
[17] E. R. RIEGEL and R. D. SCHWARTZ, *Anal. Chem.*, 24 (1952) 1803; 26 (1954) 410.
[18] L. ERDEY, I. BUZAS and E. BODOR, *Acta Chim. Acad. Sci. Hung.*, 7 (1955) 287.
[19] R. A. G. DE CARVALHO, *Anal. Chim. Acta*, 14 (1956) 28.

—, *antimony*

[20] M. L. MALAPRADE, *Bull. soc. chim.*, (1951) 739.
[21] C. YOSHIMURA, *J. Chem. Soc. Japan*, 76 (1955) 409.

—, *silver (in the presence of chloride)*

[22] G. H. WALDEN JR., L. P. HAMMETT and S. M. EDMONDS, *J. Am. Chem. Soc.*, 56 (1934) 350.
[23] C. YOSHIMURA, *J. Chem. Soc. Japan*, 73 (1952) 362.
[24] G. F. SMITH and F. W. CAGLE, *Anal. Chem.*, 20 (1948) 183.
[25] C. C. MILLER and R. A. CHALMERS, *Analyst*, 77 (1952) 2.

—, *bismuth*

[26] E. V. ANKUDIMOVA, *Otdel. Khim. Nauk*, 5 (1954) 197.

—, *cadmium*

[27] M. CENTNERSZWER and W. HELLER, *Z. phys. Chem.*, A 161 (1932) 113.
[28] C. V. KING and M. M. BURGER, *Trans. Electrochem. Soc.*, 65 (1934) 403.
[29] A. CLAASSEN and J. VISSER, *Rec. trav. chim.*, 60 (1941) 213.
[30] L. MAZOR and L. ERDEY, *Acta Chim. Acad. Sci. Hung.*, 2 (1952) 331.
[31] M. G. FOUAD and J. F. HERRINGSHAW, *J. Chem. Soc.*, (1954) 1207.
[32] W. D. TREADWELL and R. NIERIKER, *Helv. Chim. Acta*, 24 (1941) 1067, 1098.

—, *copper*

[33] J. O. PERCIVAL, *Ind. Eng. Chem., Anal. Ed.*, 13 (1941) 71.
[34] C. YOSHIMURA, *J. Chem. Soc. Japan*, 73 (1952) 702.
[35] R. GLICKSMAN, H. MOUQUIN and C. V. KING, *J. Electrochem. Soc.*, 100 (1953) 580.

—, *copper* + *CN* + *tartrate*

[36] A. Bryson and S. Lenzer-Lowy, *Analyst*, 79 (1954) 636.

—, *tin*

[37] C. Yoshimura, *J. Chem. Soc. Japan*, 74 (1953) 116.

—, *iron*

[38] C. Yoshimura, *J. Chem. Soc. Japan*, 74 (1953) 544.
[39] W. A. Dupraw, *Anal. Chem.*, 26 (1954) 1642.

—, *mercury*

[40] L. W. McKay, *Ind. Eng. Chem., Anal. Ed.*, 5 (1933) 1.
[41] E. R. Caley and L. B. Rogers, *J. Am. Chem. Soc.*, 68 (1946) 2202.
[42] W. G. Scribner and C. N. Reilley, *Anal. Chem.*, 30 (1958) 1452.

—, *mercury* + *CN⁻ and* + *SCN⁻*

[43] F. Burriel-Marti, F. Lucena-Conde and S. Bolle-Taccheo, *Anal. Chim. Acta*, 9 (1953) 293.

—, *nickel*

[44] A. Robertshaw and G. C. Brookfield, *Analyst*, 69 (1944) 340.
[45] A. C. Simon, P. S. Miller, J. C. Edwards and F. B. Clardy, *Anal. Chem.*, 18 (1946) 496.

—, *lead*

[46] B. L. Clarke, L. A. Wooten and J. D. Struthers, *Ind. Eng. Chem., Anal. Ed.*, 9 (1937) 349.
[47] W. D. Cooke, J. F. Hazel and W. M. McNabb, *Anal. Chem.*, 22 (1950) 654.
[48] C. W. Sill and H. E. Peterson, *Anal. Chem.*, 24 (1952) 1175.
[49] J. S. Fritz, M. O. Fulda, S. L. Maagerum and E. I. Lane, *Anal. Chim. Acta*, 10 (1954) 513.
[50] G. Norwitz and M. Codel, *Anal. Chim. Acta*, 11 (1954) 33.

—, *zinc* (see also references 27, 28, 31 and 35)

[51] G. F. Smith and J. Rich, *J. Chem. Educ.*, 7 (1930) 2948.
[52] G. Norwitz, *Metallurgia*, 43 (1951) 154.
[53] E. Gagliardo and W. Pilz, *Monatsh. Chem.*, 82 (1951) 1012.

Finely divided metals and Raney metals

—, *copper*

[54] J. Piccard, *Helv. Chim. Acta*, 5 (1932) 147.

—, *nickel*

[55] J. Bougault, E. Cattelain and P. Chabrier, *Bull. soc. chim.*, 5 (1938) 1699.
[56] J. Bougault, E. Cattelain and P. Chabrier, *Bull. soc. chim.*, 6 (1939) 34.
[57] J. Bougault, E. Cattelain and P. Chabrier, *Bull. soc. chim.*, 7 (1940) 781.
[58] J. Aubry, *Bull. soc. chim.*, 5 (1938) 1333.
[59] R. Paul, *Bull. soc. chim.*, 7 (1940) 296.

—, *cobalt*

[60] J. Aubry, *Bull. soc. chim.*, 9 (1942) 882.

—, *review*

[61] W. I. Stephen, *Ind. Chemist*, 28 (1952) 13, 55, 107.

Reduction by amalgams

[62] E. Brennecke, *Neuere Massanalytische Methoden*, Enke, Stuttgart, 1951.
[63] I. M. Kolthoff and R. Belcher, *Volumetric Analysis*, Vol. III, Interscience, New York, 1957.

—, *review*

[64] W. I. Stephen, *Ind. Chemist*, 29 (1953) 31, 128, 169.

—, *prediction by means of current–potential curves*

[65] J. Coursier, *Thesis*, Masson, Paris, 1954.

—, *use of amalgams in titrations* (see *reference 42*)

—, *bismuth amalgam*

[66] C. Yoshimura, *J. Chem. Soc. Japan*, 75 (1954) 603.

—, *cadmium amalgam*

[67] S. Ishimaru and K. Saito, *J. Chem. Soc. Japan*, 72 (1951) 305.

—, *tin amalgam*

[68] I. TANANAEV and E. DAVITASCHVILI, *Z. anal. Chem.*, 107 (1936) 175.

—, *lead amalgam*

[69] T. KIBA, *J, Chem. Soc. Japan*, 59 (1938) 54.
[70] F. VLASAK, *Coll. Czechoslov. Chem. Communs.*, 10 (1938) 278.
[71] M. L. HOLT and A. G. GRAY, *Ind. Eng. Chem., Anal. Ed.*, 12 (1940) 144.

—, *zinc amalgam, solid* (see also references 31 and 37)

[72] H. W. STONE and D. N. HUME, *Ind. Eng. Chem., Anal. Ed.*, 11 (1939) 598.

—, *zinc amalgam, liquid*

[73] T. NITTAR, *J. Chem. Soc. Japan*, 73 (1952) 885.

—, *equipment and methods* (*see also references 43 and 72*)

[74] G. F. SMITH and L. T. KURTZ, *Ind. Eng. Chem., Anal. Ed.*, 14 (1942) 854.

Electrochemical catalysis of redox reactions (see also reference 65)

[75] J. COURTOT-COUPEZ, *Thesis*, Masson, Paris, 1960.

Electrolytic separations

[76] A. LASSIEUR, *Electroanalyse rapide*, Presses Universitaires, Paris, 1927.
[77] W. BÖTTGER, *Elektroanalyse*, in: *Physikalische Methoden der analytischen Chemie*, Vol. II, Akademische Verlagsgesellschaft, Leipzig, 1936.
[78] H. J. S. SAND, *Electrochemistry and Electrochemical Analysis*, Vol. II, Blackie, London, 1940.
[79] S. GLASSTONE, *The Fundamentals of Electrochemistry and Electrodeposition*, American Electroplaters' Society, Springfield, 1943.
[80] A. SCHLEICHER, *Elektroanalytische Schnellmethoden*, Enke, Stuttgart, 1947.
[81] H. DIEHL, *Electrochemical Analysis with Graded Cathode Potential Control*, G. F. Smith Chemical Co., Columbus, 1948.
[82] I. M. KOLTHOFF and J. J. LINGANE, *Polarography*, Interscience, New York, 1952, p. 386.
[83] J. J. LINGANE, *Electroanalytical Chemistry*, Interscience, New York, 2nd Ed., 1958.

—, *reviews*

[84] S. E. Q. ASHLEY, *Anal. Chem.*, 21 (1949) 70.
[85] S. E. Q. ASHLEY, *Anal. Chem.*, 22 (1950) 1379.
[86] S. E. Q. ASHLEY, *Anal. Chem.*, 24 (1952) 91.
[87] D. D. DE FORD, *Anal. Chem.*, 26 (1954) 135.
[88] D. D. DE FORD, *Anal. Chem.*, 28 (1956) 660.

—, *applications*

[89] J. J. LINGANE, *Ind. Eng. Chem., Anal. Ed.*, 17 (1945) 640.
[90] J. J. LINGANE, *Ind. Eng. Chem., Anal. Ed.*, 16 (1944) 147.
[91] S. E. WIBERLEY and L. G. BASSETT, *Anal. Chem.*, 21 (1949) 609.
[92] J. J. LINGANE, *Anal. Chim. Acta*, 2 (1948) 584.
[93] J. J. LINGANE and S. L. JONES, *Anal. Chem.*, 23 (1951) 1798.
[94] G. FACSKO, *Proc. XVth Intern. Congr. Pure Applied Chem., Lisbon, 1956 (Actas do Congresso)*, Lisbon, 1957, p. 639.
[95] J. J. LINGANE and S. L. JONES, *Anal. Chem.*, 23 (1951) 1804.

—, *microelectrolysis*

[96] R. B. HAHN, *Anal. Chem.*, 25 (1953) 1749.
[97] A. J. LINDSEY, *Analyst*, 73 (1948) 67.

—, *ultramicroelectrolysis*

[98] L. B. BOGERS, *Anal. Chem.*, 22 (1950) 1386.
[99] M. HAÏSSINSKY, *Electrochimie des substances radioactives et des solutions extrêmement diluées*, Hermann, Paris, 1946.

—, *mercury cathode* (see also reference 83)

[100] F. T. RABBITS, *Anal. Chem.*, 20 (1948) 181.
[101] J. CORIOU, J. GUÉRON, H. HÉRING and P. LÉVÊQUE, *J. Chim. phys.*, 48 (1951) 55.
[102] H. BOZON and S. BOZON, *Bull. soc. chim.*, 18 (1951) 917.

—, *mercury cathode, reviews*

[103] W. BÖTTGER, *Elektroanalyse*, in: *Physikalische Methoden der analytische Chemie*, Vol. II, Akademische Verlagsgesellschaft, Leipzig, 1936, p. 142.
[104] J. A. MAXWELL and R. P. GRAHAM, *Chem. Revs.*, 46 (1950) 4171.

—, *internal electrolysis* (see also references 83 and 86)

[105] A. SCHLEICHER, *Z. anal. Chem.*, 26 (1944) 412.
[106] A. SCHLEICHER and T. TODOROFF, *Z. Elektrochem.*, 50 (1944) 2.
[107] A. SCHLEICHER and O. SCHLÖSSER, *Z. anal. Chem.*, 130 (1949) 1.
[108] S. ISHIMARU and S. MIZOGUCHI, *J. Chem. Soc. Japan*, 73 (1952) 267.
[109] A. LIPSCHINSKY, *Zhur. Anal. Khim.*, 12 (1957) 83.

Use of amalgams for the semi-industrial preparation of very pure metals from low-grade ores

[110] H. HOHN, *Research*, 3 (1950) 16, 407.

Electrolytic preparations

[111] S. GLASSTONE and A. HICKLING, *Electrolytic Oxidation and Reduction*, Chapman Hall, London, 1935.
[112] S. GLASSTONE, *An Introduction to Electrochemistry*, Van Nostrand, New York, 1942.
[113] F. FICHTER, *Organische Elektrochemie*, Steinkopf, Dresden, 1942.
[114] R. AUDUBERT, *Electrolyse*, Presses Universitaires, Paris, 1953.
[115] V. GAERTNER, *Electrochimie pratique*, Gauthiers-Villars, Paris, 1955 (translation).
[116] E. C POTTER, *Electrochemistry*, Cleaver-Hume, London, 1956.
[117] S. WANN JR., *Electrolytic reactions*, in: A. WEISSBERGER (ed.), *Techniques of Organic Chemistry*, Vol. II, Interscience, New York, 1956.
[118] M. J. ALLEN, *Organic Electrode Processes*, Chapman Hall, London, 1958.
[119] Y. V. PLESKOV, *Dokl. Akad. Nauk S.S.S.R.*, 117 (1957) 645.
[120] R. F. J. GROSS and A. HICKLING, *J. Chem. Soc.*, (1937) 325.
[121] J. C. MARONI, E. AUTHIER-CABIBEL and B. TRÉMILLON, *Bull. soc. chim.*, (1959) 127.
[122] J. J. LINGANE, C. G. SWAIN and M. FIELDS, *J. Am. Chem. Soc.*, 65 (1943) 1348.
[123] N. URABE and K. YASHIKACHI, *J. Electrochem. Soc. Japan*, 22 (1954) 525.
[124] P. RUETSCHI and G. TRÜMPLER, *Helv. Chim. Acta*, 36 (1953) 1649.

—, *electrography*

[125] H. W. HERMANCE and H. V. WADLOW, *Electrography and Electrospots*, in: W. G. BERL (ed.), *Physical Methods in Chemical Analysis*, Vol. II, Academic Press, New York, 1951.

—, *reviews*

[126] P. R. MONK, *Analyst*, 78 (1953) 148.
[127] R. A. IRKOVSKY, *Zavodskaya Lab.*, 22 (1956) 898.
     S. E. Q. ASHLEY, *Anal. Chem.*, 24 (1952) 93.

Chapter XII

RECENT ELECTROCHEMICAL METHODS

So far, we have always supposed that the steady state has been reached, *i.e.* that the current–potential curves obtained are independent of time (at least for the period of time needed to carry out the measurements). This is by far the most important case, as most practical examples satisfy this condition.

We include all phenomena which change with time under the name of the non-steady state, the most important class of these being those which precede the establishment of the steady state. These phenomena have also been made use of in physico-chemical studies and analysis.

At constant concentration, these phenomena can be described by a function of three variables: current, potential and time. In practice, two methods may be used:

a) Control the electrode potential and measure the variation of the electrolysis current with time. The potential is said to be controlled when it is constant or when it varies in a known way with time. Methods using these current–time curves at a known potential are known as *"chronoamperometry"*; but it is possible to use any other characteristic curve which describes the phenomena at the known potential.

b) Control the electrolysis current and measure the electrode potential as a func tion of time. The current may be constant, or vary in a known fashion with time. Methods using the potential–time curves at a known current are classed under the heading of *"chronopotentiometry"*, but any other curve which is characteristic of the phenomena at a known current may also be used.

One approach which has received considerable attention is to vary the independent variable (current or electrode potential) periodically with time with a fairly high frequency. The response, which is also periodic, is characteristic of the electrochemical phenomena at the electrodes.

All the methods which make use of a cathode-ray oscilloscope as the measuring instrument can be grouped under the heading *oscillographic polarography*. The measurement is often chronoamperometric or chronopotentiometric (the current–time curve or potential–time curve being shown on the screen of the oscilloscope), but any other suitable curve may be used.

Another method is *a.c. polarography*, in which the measuring electrode is given a constant potential, which is modulated by an alternating voltage of small amplitude.

An alternating state is thus superimposed on the steady state due to the constant applied voltage, not disturbing the latter to any appreciable extent since its amplitude is small (although the alternating state can have a considerable effect on the steady state in certain cases, as has been shown by FOURNIER [111, 112].

The alternating component of the electrolysis current is measured. The magnitude of this quantity varies with the mean potential applied to the electrode, giving a curve characteristic of the electrochemical phenomena.

Other methods also exist, *e.g.* measuring the characteristics of an electrolysis cell under the influence of an alternating voltage of low amplitude (5 millivolts) with the aid of an electronic measuring bridge (see RANDLES[106], GRAHAME[109] and RANDLES AND SOMERTON[115]).

Fixed electrodes, and no stirring, are used for the study of slowly varying phenomena. This is not so for rapidly (periodically) varying phenomena.

A remark must be made here concerning the dropping mercury electrode, which is so often used. We have seen (Chapter VI) that at constant potential the electrolysis current obtained with this electrode varies periodically with the time (with a period equal to the drop time). If the electrode potential or the electrolysis current also varies periodically, we have two periodic phenomena superimposed on each other. In general, this would entail a synchronization problem; but the normal drop time of a dropping mercury electrode is much greater than the period of the electric variable. If the measurement is made for a sufficiently short time and at intervals equal to the drop time, the dropping mercury electrode then acts like an electrode of constant surface area.

Another important factor when varying the electrode potential periodically is the capacitive residual current. As we have seen in Chapter V, the electrode-solution interface is equivalent to a resistance in parallel with a capacitance, so the current will have an alternating component due to the capacitance of the electrical double layer. This component becomes large when the frequency with which the potential varies is large. The large size of the residual current therefore limits the sensitivity of these methods, unless it is possible to eliminate this effect.

We will now briefly examine the principles of these methods. Further theoretical and practical details may be obtained from the specialized books and other publications cited throughout this chapter.

I. CHRONOAMPEROMETRY

Chronoamperometry at constant potential

The electrode potential is kept constant at such a value that the electrochemical reaction in question occurs at a measurable rate (current). The solution is not stirred, and the electrode is fixed. As in the methods mentioned previously, the migration of the electrolyzed species is prevented by addition of an excess of an indifferent electrolyte.

Principle

Let us suppose that the electrochemical reaction is infinitely fast. We have seen that as soon as the electrolysis circuit is closed the concentrations at the surface of the electrode adjust themselves to values determined by the imposed potential E. In the absence of convection, the concentration of the electrolyzed substance throughout the solution is determined by diffusion, and the distribution varies with time as shown in Fig. 357. The transport by diffusion thus gradually decreases, so the current decreases from a very large initial value, to zero for semi-infinite linear or cylindrical diffusion or to a very small value for spherical diffusion (Fig. 358) as $t \to \infty$.

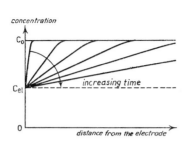

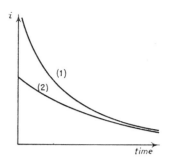

Fig. 357. Diffusion towards the electrode at constant potential
(after DELAHAY[1]).

Fig. 358. Current–time curves at constant potential.
Curve 1: instantaneous electrochemical reaction.
Curve 2: slow electrochemical reaction
(after DELAHAY[1]).

If the electrochemical reaction is slow, the current decreases from a lower initial value which depends on the speed of the reaction (Fig. 358).

In practice, it is not possible to prevent all convection, so the current will tend to a very small finite value.

Applications. The current–time curves have been used for studying electrochemical reactions, but rarely for analytical purposes.

Linear chronoamperometry (chronoamperometry with linearly varying potential)

The electrode potential may in principle be made to vary in any desired fashion with time; but in practice only simple and easily realizable functions have been used.

The simplest method is to let the potential vary linearly with time, $E = E_i + vt$, with the initial potential E_i chosen so that the electrochemical reaction in question occurs at a negligible rate, and with v as the rate of change of the potential $\left(= \dfrac{dE}{dt} \right)$.

Since the potential varies linearly with the time, the current-time curves obtained in this way are analogous to the current–potential curves.

We will only consider here the case where the potential sweep occurs once at a low rate (single-sweep method). The case of multiple (periodic) rapid sweeps is discussed below (multi-sweep method).

Principle

In the common recording instruments of this type, the electrode potential is varied linearly at a rate of between 0.1 and 2 volts per minute. If the steady state at the electrode is attained very rapidly, the system is always more or less in the steady state as the potential changes. The recorded curve therefore has practically the same shape as the current–potential curves we have considered so far. This is the case in practice with a dropping mercury electrode.

If on the other hand the steady state does not have time to establish itself, the recorded curve shows a maximum (or a minimum), as shown in Fig. 359. This may be explained qualitatively as follows. Consider an oxidation reaction: as the applied potential increases, the rate of the electrochemical reaction increases rapidly, giving the ascending portion of the curve. At the same time, the concentration of the electro-

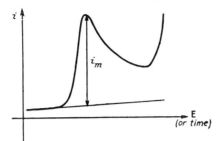

Fig. 359. Oxidation reaction.

lyzed substance at the surface of the electrode decreases as a result of the electrolysis, giving rise to diffusion. After a certain time (*i.e.* above a given potential) the decrease of the rate of transport of the electrolyzed substance becomes larger than the increase of the rate of the electrochemical reaction due to the increase in the potential. The current–potential curve (current–time curve) thus passes through a maximum and then decreases until the potential is large enough for another substance (and finally the solvent) to be electrolyzed. The phenomena are similar for a reduction reaction, except that then the current passes through a minimum (Fig. 360).

The form of the curves can be interpreted theoretically. Calculation shows that to a first approximation the maximum current is given by

$$i_m = kSn^{\frac{3}{2}}D_0^{\frac{1}{2}}v^{\frac{1}{2}}C_s \tag{1}$$

where S = surface area of electrode in cm²; n = number of electrons; D_0 = diffusion constant in cm²/sec; v = rate of potential change in V/sec; C_s = concentration in moles per litre; k = proportionality constant.

The maximum current i_m is thus proportional to the concentration, and increases with the rate of potential change (the voltage sweep rate) (see Fig. 361). The potential at which the maximum occurs is independent of the concentration, and is

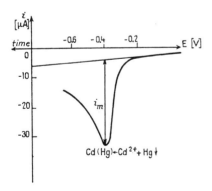

Fig. 360. Reduction of 10^{-4} *M* Cd²⁺ in 10^{-2} *M* KNO₃. Mercury electrode (2.86 cm²). Rate of potential change = 0.2 V/min. (after Streuli and Cooke[15]).

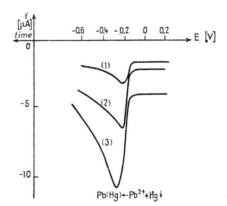

Fig. 361. Reduction of 10^{-5} *M* Pb²⁺ in 10^{-2} *M* KNO₃. Mercury electrode (1 cm²). Voltage sweep rates: curve 1: 0.1 V/min; curve 2: 0.4 V/min; curve 3: 1.2 V/min (after Streuli and Cooke[15]).

related to the standard potential. It is thus characteristic of the electrochemical reaction.

Equation (1) indicates that the sensitivity can be considerably increased by increasing the voltage sweep rate. In fact, it may be shown that the capacitive residual current at a given potential is proportional to the sweep rate v, while i_m is only proportional to $v^{\frac{1}{2}}$, so the capacitive current limits the sensitivity of the method.

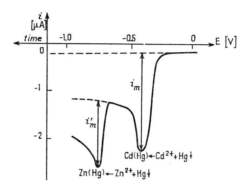

Fig. 362. Reduction of 10^{-4} M Cd^{2+} + 10^{-4} M Zn^{2+} in 0.1 M KCl. Hanging mercury drop electrode. Voltage sweep rate about 1 V/min (after Ross, De Mars and Shain [19]).

When several substances are electrolyzed simultaneously (Fig. 362), the interpretation of the curves is more complicated. The above results are still true for the first maximum, but not for the others. In particular, the heights of the maxima are no longer proportional to the concentrations.

A comparison method may however be used to determine the concentrations: two electrolysis cells are used, each operating under the same conditions. One contains the unknown solution, and the other a known solution; both solutions contain the same indifferent electrolyte. The difference between the electrolysis currents of the two cells is measured at each value of the potential (differential method, see page 000). If the unknown solution contains the substances 1, 2, 3, etc., numbered in the order

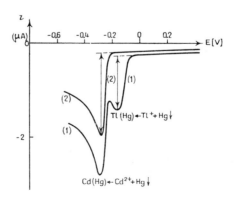

Fig. 363. Reduction of 10^{-4} M Tl$^+$ and 10^{-4} M Cd^{2+} in 0.1 M KCl, in acetic buffer of pH 5.4, at a hanging mercury drop electrode. Voltage sweep rate = 1.7 V/min. Curve 1: direct curve. Curve 2: differential curve, compensated for thallium (after Martin and Shain [20]).

of their ease of reduction, the concentration of 1 is determined from the curve obtained with only the indifferent electrolyte in the comparison cell. The substance 1 is now added to the comparison cell in the concentration which has just been determined; in the new curve, the effect of 1 is eliminated, and the concentration of 2 can easily be determined. The operation is now repeated with both 1 and 2 in the comparison cell, and so on. This differential method allows the concentrations of all the substances present in solution to be determined one by one. Two examples of this method are shown in Figs. 363 and 364.

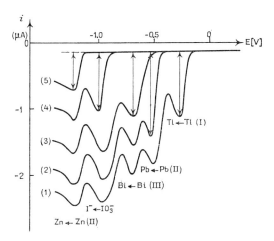

Fig. 364. Reduction of $2 \times 10^{-4} M$ Tl(I) $+ 10^{-4} M$ Pb(II) $+ 10^{-4} M$ Bi(III) $+ 0.33 \times 10^{-4} M$ IO$_3^-$ $+ 10^{-4} M$ Zn(II) in 0.1 M NaOH $+ 0.5 M$ tartrate. Rate of potential change $= 1.7$ V/min. Curve 1: direct curve. Curves 2 to 5: differential curves, compensated for:

(2) Tl(I)	(4) Tl(I) + Pb(II) + Bi(III)
(3) Tl(I) + Pb(II)	(5) Tl(I) + Pb(II) + Bi(III) + IO$_3^-$

(after MARTIN and SHAIN [20]).

Applications

The main advantage of this method is that fixed electrodes may be used, and the solution need not be stirred. It can be used with solid electrodes just as well as with the hanging mercury drop electrode.

The sensitivity is much higher than that of normal polarography, partly because the surface area of the electrode can be considerably bigger, which leads to a bigger current, and partly because the capacitive residual current is smaller than that found with the dropping mercury electrode. According to STREULI and COOKE [15, 16, 17], the method may be used to determine concentrations down to $5 \times 10^{-7} M$.

Fig. 361 shows the curves obtained for the reduction of $10^{-5} M$ Pb^{2+} at a mercury surface 1 cm^2 in area, for different voltage sweep rates [17].

It may be mentioned that the maximum current can be considerably reduced by the presence of substances which can be adsorbed on the surface of the electrode (e.g. gelatine) [15].

The method may also be used to study electrochemical reactions; comparison of the potentials at which the maxima of the oxidation curve and of the reduction curve (obtained by varying the potential in opposite directions: cyclic method) occur gives a measure of the rate of the reaction (Fig. 365).

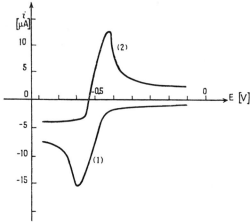

Fig. 365. Oxidation and reduction of 6×10^{-5} M anthraquinone-1,6-disulphonate in 0.1 M LiOH. Mercury electrode (3 cm²). Rate of potential change = 0.4 V/min. Curve 1: reduction, decreasing potentials; Curve 2: oxidation, increasing potentials (after STREULI and COOKE[16]).

The apparatus is not complicated, as it is simple to arrange to sweep the applied potential slowly.

II. CHRONOPOTENTIOMETRY

We will only consider here the case where the electrolysis current is kept *constant*.

The solution is not stirred, and the electrode is fixed. The effect of migration is made negligible by addition of an excess of an indifferent electrolyte.

Principle

Since the current is kept constant, the electrolysis proceeds at a constant rate. When the electrolysis circuit is closed, the concentrations of the substances taking part in the electrochemical reaction at the surface of the electrode start to vary. The electrode takes up the equilibrium potential of the solution in contact with it, which varies with time.

If the transport of the substances in solution is fast enough, the variations only occur for a certain period, after which a steady state is reached, and the electrode potential becomes constant.

But in the absence of convection, the transport is entirely due to diffusion, and

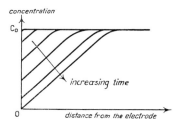

Fig. 366. Diffusion towards the electrode at constant current (after DELAHAY[1]).

we have already seen that in this case a real steady state is never reached. Since the transport is not enough to compensate for the decrease in concentration at the surface of the electrode, this concentration decreases until it reaches zero. The change in the concentration distribution throughout the solution with time is shown in Fig. 366. (All the curves have the same slope near the electrode: since the current is constant, the flow rate of the substance to the electrode, and hence $\dfrac{\partial C}{\partial x}$, is constant with time).

Let us consider a fast reaction. The electrode potential is given by the Nernst equation

$$E = E_0 + \frac{0.058}{n} \log \frac{|Ox|_{el}}{|Red|_{el}}$$

If a current i_0 is imposed and reduction occurs, $|Ox|_{el}$ decreases steadily from C_0 to zero, while $|Red|_{el}$ increases steadily from zero to C_0. The term $\log \dfrac{|Ox|_{el}}{|Red|_{el}}$ thus varies in theory from $+\infty$ to $-\infty$. The electrode potential changes abruptly when $|Ox|_{el}$ becomes zero. The rate at which Ox now arrives at the electrode is not enough to sustain the current i_0, so another substance is also reduced, and the electrode potential is now fixed by the new system. Finally, when no other reducible substance is left at the surface of the electrode, the solvent is reduced, and the potential remains constant.

The time at which the abrupt change in the potential occurs (*i.e.* the time when $|Ox|_{el} = 0$) is known as the *transition time*.

It may be shown that

$$|Ox|_{el} = C_0 - f(t) \qquad |Red|_{el} = f(t)$$

for initial concentrations $|Ox| = C_0$ and $|Red| = 0$. For a fast reaction and in total absence of convection movements (pure diffusion) the following holds

$$E = E_0 + \frac{0.058}{n} \log \frac{C_0 - Pt^{\frac{1}{2}}}{Pt^{\frac{1}{2}}}$$

where

$$P = \frac{2i_0}{\tau^{\frac{1}{2}} nFD_0^{\frac{1}{2}}}$$

if we suppose that the diffusion coefficients are equal.

If we set $\tau^{\frac{1}{2}} = C_0/P$ (τ has the dimensions of time)

$$E = E_0 + \frac{0.058}{n} \log \frac{\tau^{\frac{1}{2}} - t^{\frac{1}{2}}}{t^{\frac{1}{2}}}$$

The time τ is the transition time. It may be noted that the curve $E = f(t^{\frac{1}{2}})$ has the same form as the current–potential curves. The potential is equal to the standard potential after a time $\tau/4$ (Fig. 367).

The constant $\tau^{\frac{1}{2}}$, which plays the same role as the limiting diffusion current, is proportional to the concentration of the electrolyzed substance.

If the electrochemical reaction is slow, we obtain the equation

$$E = \text{constant} + \frac{0.058}{\alpha n} \log \left(1 - \frac{t^{\frac{1}{2}}}{\tau^{\frac{1}{2}}} \right)$$

The transition time is independent of the rate of the reaction, but the constant term, which is equal to the initial potential, depends on the concentration, the rate of the electrochemical reaction, its standard potential and the electrolysis current i_0. The curve can thus be displaced vertically by varying i_0.

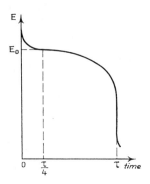

Fig. 367. Potential–time curve at constant current (reduction) (after DELAHAY[1]).

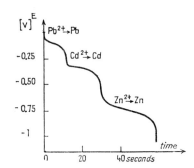

Fig. 368. Reduction of 10^{-4} M Pb²⁺ + 10^{-4} M Cd²⁺ + 10^{-4} M Zn²⁺ in 0.1 M KNO₃. Mercury electrode, electrolysis current 45 μA (after REILLEY et al.[35]).

Two successive electrochemical reactions

If the reactions $Ox_1 + n_1e \rightarrow Red_1$ and $Ox_2 + n_2e \rightarrow Red_2$ occur at sufficiently different potentials (*e.g.* Ox_1 reduced before Ox_2), two waves are observed, giving two transition times τ_1 and τ_2. The time τ_1 corresponds to the reduction of Ox_1, and is thus independent of the presence of Ox_2. The time τ_2 corresponds to the simultaneous reduction of Ox_2 and Ox_1; although the concentration of Ox_1 at the electrode is zero, Ox_1 still continues to diffuse towards the electrode and to be reduced there. The transition time τ_2 therefore depends not only on the concentration of Ox_2, but also on that of Ox_1, i.e. on τ_1 (Fig. 368).

Similarly, if an oxidant Ox_1 is reduced in several stages, *e.g.* $Ox_1 + n_1e \rightarrow Red_1$ and $Red_1 + n_2e \rightarrow Red_2$, two waves and thus two transition times τ_1 and τ_2 are observed. τ_2 is again a function of τ_1 (Fig. 369).

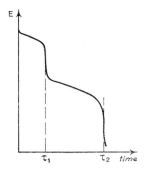

Fig. 369. Potential–time curve for the electrochemical reactions $Ox_1 + n_1e \rightarrow Red_1$, followed by $Red_1 + n_2e \rightarrow Red_2$ (after DELAHAY[1]).

Applications

This method has been widely used in analytical chemistry. Its sensitivity is excellent, since the electrolysis current may be chosen to give a transition time which may readily be measured. This time is limited by two factors: *a*) It must not exceed a few minutes, so that convection does not interfere with the diffusion. *b*) On the other hand, since the potential varies with time, part of the current is used in charging and discharging the electrical double layer. The transition time must be at least a thousandth of a second to ensure that this capacitive current is negligible compared to the total electrolysis current.

REILLEY et al.[35] claim that concentrations down to $10^{-6} M$ can be determined by this method. Its accuracy is greater than that of normal polarography. Its selectivity is more or less the same, but with the added advantage that the potential–time curve of a slow system may be changed by changing i_0.

It may be mentioned that the presence of adsorbable substances (*e.g.* gelatine) can reduce the value of the transition time considerably, which may be due to a decrease in the effective area of the electrode, so that the current density i_0 increases although the current remains constant.

The temperature must be kept constant to within 0.1° C for very precise determinations.

The experimental set-up is very simple.

Chronopotentiometric titrations

The determination of a concentration by measuring a transition time necessitates a preliminary calibration. In order to avoid this, REILLEY and SCRIBNER[37] have carried out chronopotentiometric titrations, by adding known quantities of a suitable reagent to the solution to be estimated, and measuring the transition time after each addition. The curve of $\tau^{\frac{1}{2}}$ as a function of v, the amount of titrant added, allows the end point of the titration to be determined.

Fig. 370 shows the chronopotentiometric titration curve of Fe^{2+} with Ce^{4+}. The dotted line represents the potentiometric titration.

Since the current–potential curves are similar in shape to the $E = f(t^{\frac{1}{2}})$ curves, these titration curves $\tau^{\frac{1}{2}} = f(v)$ are similar to amperometric titration curves $i = f(v)$. This method has one great disadvantage, however: after each addition of the titrant, the solution must be allowed to come to complete rest before the transition time is measured.

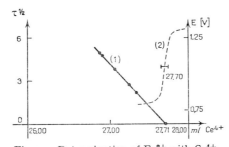

Fig. 370. Determination of Fe^{2+} with Ce^{4+}.
Curve 1: chronopotentiometric titration, electrolysis current = 40.1 μA. Curve 2: potentiometric titration at zero current (after REILLEY and SCRIBNER[37]).

Chronopotentiometry is also very useful for physico-chemical investigations[13]. It was first used for determining diffusion constants.

Standard potentials may be determined as with current–potential curves.

It is also possible to obtain some information about the rate of electrochemical reactions by following the oxidation reaction by the reduction reaction (or vice versa) by changing the sense of the electrolysis current after the first transition time. The potenti.il–time curve thus obtained has the shape shown in Fig. 371. Comparison of the potentials of the two flat portions gives a measure of the rate of the reaction.

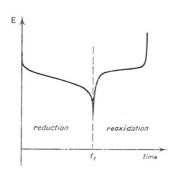

Fig. 371. Potential–time curve.
Until t_1, electrolysis current $= -i_0$; after t_1, electrolysis current $= i_0$ (after DELAHAY[1]).

III. OSCILLOGRAPHIC POLAROGRAPHY

The cathode-ray oscilloscope is very useful for observing and recording rapid electrical phenomena, and it is not therefore surprising that it has been used for the study of electrochemical reactions. Since the main advantage of the oscillograph is its low response time, it is particularly useful when the electrode potential or the electrolysis current varies abruptly with time. We will use the name *"oscillographic polarography"* to describe all electrochemical methods where the independent variable is varied periodically, and the cathode-ray oscilloscope is used as the measuring instrument.

Either the voltage or the current between the electrodes is made to vary periodically with respect to time, with an amplitude large enough to ensure that the whole range in which the reaction in question occurs is covered.

Oscillographic polarography with a controlled potential

Although the potential may in principle be any periodic function of time, only two types of function have been used in practice; the linear and sinusoidal variations with time.

Saw-tooth voltage

With the aid of a suitable circuit the voltage may be made to vary linearly with respect to time up to a certain value and then to return practically instantaneously to zero a large number of times per second (asymmetrical saw-tooth voltage, Fig. 372). The amplitude V may be adjusted so as to cover the whole potential range which is to be investigated, in practice from 0.5 V to 2 V.

The electrolysis current passes through a resistance and the amplified voltage is applied to the vertical plates of the oscilloscope, whilst the horizontal displacement is proportional to the time, *i.e.* to the potential, and has the same frequency as the saw-tooth voltage.

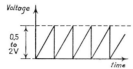

Fig. 372. Asymmetrical saw-tooth voltage.

MATHESON and NICHOLS[56] used this method with a frequency of 30 cycles per second and a dropping mercury electrode with a normal drop time (3 or 4 seconds). The trace obtained on the oscilloscope screen changes shape as the size of the drop increases (Fig. 373). In order to avoid this difficulty, the dropping mercury electrode was synchronized with the saw-tooth voltage (drop time $1/_{30}$ second). A stationary figure then appears on the screen, resembling the current–potential curves obtained in the steady state (Fig. 374). However, these curves are not of much practical interest: the step height is not proportional to the concentration, the capacitive residual current is large owing to the large rate of change of the voltage and the rapid flow of the mercury, and it is difficult to get the dropping mercury electrode properly synchronized.

In order to avoid as many of these troubles as possible, RANDLES[57,58] and SNOWDEN and PAGE[61] used the following set-up: drop time of about 7 seconds, applied

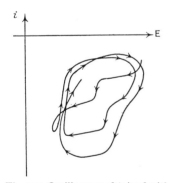

Fig. 373. Oscillogram obtained with a solution of 2×10^{-3} M Mn^{2+} in 0.1 M LiCl. Dropping mercury electrode (after MATHESON and NICHOLS[56]).

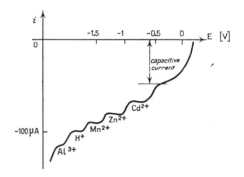

Fig. 374. Oscillogram obtained with a solution of 5×10^{-4} M Cd^{2+} + 10^{-3} M Zn^{2+} + 10^{-3} M Mn^{2+} + 5×10^{-4} M H^+ + 5×10^{-4} M Al^{3+} in 0.1 M LiCl. Dropping mercury electrode with drop time of $1/30$ second, synchronized with the saw-tooth voltage (after MATHESON and NICHOLS[56]).

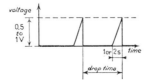

Fig. 375. Saw-tooth voltage with delay.

voltage = zero for from 5 to 6 seconds after the drop starts to form, then increasing to 0.5 or 1 V at a rate of 0.5 V/second and decreasing instantly to zero when the drop detaches itself from the capillary (Fig. 375). The dropping mercury electrode thus acts as an electrode of constant shape and size, since the phenomena are recorded during a small part of the drop time, at the end of the growth of the drop when the increase of the surface is slowest. The conditions are thus identical with those for linear chronoamperometry, as described above. The curves obtained on the screen have the same form and equation [51-55] as those for linear chronoamperometry, as may be seen from Figs. 376 and 377.

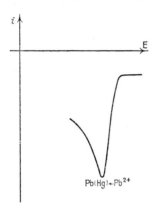

Fig. 376. Oscillogram for the reduction of 2.5×10^{-4} M Pb^{2+} in M KCl. Dropping mercury electrode (after RANDLES [57]).

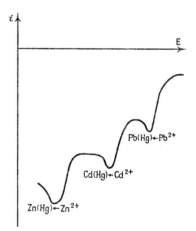

Fig. 377. Oscillogram for the reduction of $\frac{1}{16} \times 10^{-3}$ M $Pb^{2+} + \frac{1}{16} \times 10^{-3}$ M $Cd^{2+} + \frac{1}{16} \times 10^{-3}$ M Zn^{2+} in M KCl. Dropping mercury electrode (after RANDLES [58]).

SHAIN and CRITTENDEN [65] have recently used this method with electrodes other than the dropping mercury electrode. They applied a saw-tooth voltage increasing at the rate of 0.1 to 1 V/sec to a rotating platinum electrode (600 r.p.m.). They obtained the curves shown in Fig. 378.

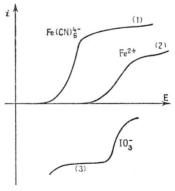

Fig. 378. Oscillograms for the oxidation of 2×10^{-3} M $Fe(CN)_6^{4-}$ and 3×10^{-3} M Fe^{2+}, and for the reduction of 2×10^{-4} M IO_3^-. Rotating platinum electrode (after SHAIN and CRITTENDEN [65]).

Applications

The original oscillographic polarographs were not very useful as analytical instruments, but the cathode-ray polarograph as developed by RANDLES has found wide application. According to SHINAGAWA *et al.*[68], who have studied the analysis of mixtures of Pb^{2+} and Tl^+, Cd^{2+} and In^{3+}, and Zn^{2+} and Ni^{2+} in this way, concentrations of 10^{-3} to $10^{-4} M$ can be determined with an accuracy of 2%. The cathode-ray polarograph has the advantage of a greater resolving power than the normal polarograph: it is enough if the potential difference between the peaks is about 40 mV, while a difference of 150 mV to 200 mV is needed between the half-wave potentials in the normal method[69].

Other advantages of oscillographic polarography are the great speed with which a determination can be carried out, and the simplicity of the equipment apart from the oscilloscope itself.

The method is of great interest for the study of chemical and electrochemical kinetics. It allows quite fast chemical reactions to be followed, since it is possible to record several curves per minute.

SEVČIK[52] and DELAHAY[54] used a symmetrical saw-tooth voltage for electrochemical kinetic studies, *i.e.* they increased the voltage from zero to V at a certain rate, and then decreased it from V to zero at the same rate instead of letting it fall very rapidly to zero (Fig. 379). This gives two current–potential curves corresponding to the in-

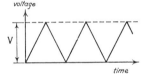

Fig. 379. Symmetrical saw-tooth voltage.

creasing and decreasing voltages, *i.e.* to the forward and back electrochemical reactions. The difference between the potentials of the two maxima gives a measure of the rate of the redox system (Fig. 380); the two potentials are the same for a fast system, and the difference between them increases as the system becomes slower.

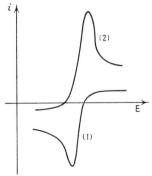

Fig. 380. Oscillogram obtained with a solution of $3 \times 10^{-4} M$ Pb^{2+} in N KOH. Mercury electrode Sweep frequency of potential $= 29.8$ c/s. Curve 1: reduction. Curve 2: re-oxidation (after SEVČIK[52])

Sinusoidal voltage

The first investigation of the use of varying potentials used a sinusoidal voltage of amplitude large enough to cover the whole potential range which was of interest[56]; but this technique was later abandoned for the use of either saw-tooth voltages of large amplitude or sinusoidal voltages of amplitude less than 100 mV.

If the electrode is given a constant mean potential on which is superimposed a sinusoidal voltage of amplitude between 10 mV and 100 mV, the sine-wave shown on the screen of the oscillograph is distorted owing to the electrochemical reaction. This distortion is minimum when the mean potential is equal to the half-wave potential: the current–time curve is then most nearly sinusoidal. This method allows half-wave potentials to be determined with great accuracy, as may be seen from Fig. 381.

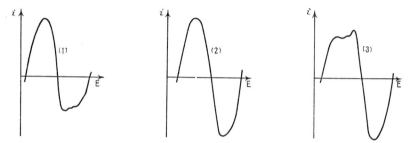

Fig. 381. Oscillograms obtained with 5×10^{-4} M phenosafranine in 0.1 M KCl at pH 4. Curve 1: $- 0.097$ V. Curve 2: $- 0.094$ V. Curve 3: $- 0.092$ V (after van CAKENBERGHE[71]).

Instead of determining the current–time curve, it is possible to form a Lissajous' figure on the screen by synchronizing the horizontal sweep with the vertical signal[70].

Oscillographic polarography with a controlled current

All the methods using a potential which varies with time can be transformed into methods using varying current, but in general this gives no advantages, and only complicates the interpretation of the curves obtained.

However, one such method was successfully used by HEYROVSKY and FOREJT[73,74] The electrode has initially a constant potential and a sinusoidal current is applied, whose amplitude is kept constant by means of a large series resistance. The alternating voltage which results is applied to the vertical deflection, and the potential–time curve is thus displayed on the screen. The frequency of the current is 50 c/s or more.

The curve changes shape when a dropping mercury electrode is used (Fig. 373), so HEYROVSKY used a mercury jet electrode which has a constant surface area.

It is also possible to display the derived curve $dE/dt = f(t)$ or $dE/dt = f(E)$ on the screen. In the latter case, the shape of the curve is independent of the surface area of the electrode and it is thus possible to use a dropping mercury electrode.

In the absence of an electroactive substance, the interface between the mercury and the solution acts as a simple electrical condenser, so the potential–time curve has more or less the same form as the applied current–time curve. In the presence of an electroactive substance, as long as the reaction is not proceeding at an appreciable rate the mercury-solution interface still acts like a simple condensor, so the potential–

time curve cannot be distinguished from that obtained in the absence of the substance. But when the electrochemical reaction occurs at an appreciable rate, current
can pass through the cell without the electrode potential varying much. The potential–
time curve thus shows a flat portion at the potential at which the electrochemical
reaction takes place, *i.e.* more or less at the half-wave potential

When the sign of the potential variation changes, the product of the electrochemical reaction gives rise to the same phenomenon at the potential at which the
reverse reaction occurs.

If the redox system is a fast one, the two flat portions of the curve occur at about
the same potential, since the two half-wave potentials are equal. The difference between the two half-wave potentials increases as the system becomes slower (Fig. 382).

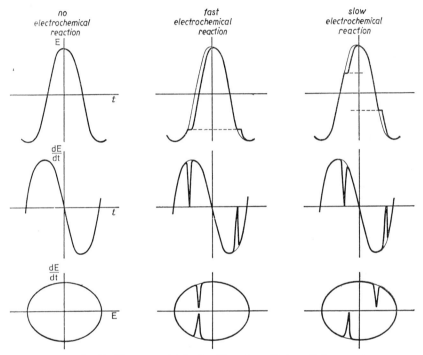

Fig. 382. Oscillograms obtained with a sinusoidal applied current.

The electrochemical reaction causes 'dents' (Fig. 382) in the derivative curves
$dE/dt = f(t)$ and $dE/dt = f(E)$.

FOURNIER and QUINTIN[80, 81] have showed that the width of the horizontal portions of the potential–time curve is inversely proportional to the square root of the
frequency of the a.c. current imposed. As the frequency is increased, a stage will
come when the break in the curve disappears, since the time during which the electrochemical reaction can happen has become too small to make any difference to the
curve. The frequency at which this happens is lower for a slow system: the rate of the
electrochemical reaction affects not only the position of the breaks in the curve, but
also their extent.

Applications

This method has been much used for the investigation of chemical and electro-chemical kinetics.

The width of the horizontal portions in the potential–time curves and the area of the peaks in the derivative curves depends on the concentration of the electroactive substance.

This method can therefore also be used for quantitative analysis. HEYROVSKY and FOREJT[74] recommend the derivative curves for this purpose (Fig. 383).

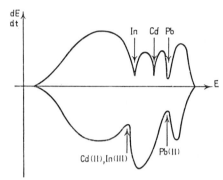

Fig. 383. Oscillogram obtained with traces of Pb(II), Cd(II) and In(III) in a zinc ore dissolved in 2 *N* KOH + 2 *N* KCN. Mercury electrode (after HEYROVSKY[79]).

Analyses have been carried out by a comparison method[86, 87, 88, 90, 91]. Two identical cells are used, with the same electrolysis conditions. One cell contains the element to be determined dissolved in a solution of an indifferent electrolyte, and the other contains only the solution of the indifferent electrolyte. The two curves obtained are displayed simultaneously on the screen of the same oscilloscope. A solution of a known concentration of the element to be determined is added slowly to the reference solution, until the peaks in the two curves coincide. The concentration of the unknown solution can then be deduced (*cf.* p. 196).

In practice, this method is neither as sensitive nor as accurate as the other electro-chemical methods of analysis. It allows concentrations of down to 10^{-4} *M* to be determined. But it has the advantage of being able to distinguish between substances which are indistinguishable by the usual methods, *e.g.* Cd^{2+} and In^{3+} or isomers. This method appears to have the best resolving power of all. Like all oscillographic methods, it also has the advantages of speed and simple equipment.

IV. ALTERNATING CURRENT POLAROGRAPHY

This methods seems to give the best precision and sensitivity. An alternating voltage of very small amplitude, about 5 mV, is superimposed on a constant voltage between the two electrodes. An alternating non-steady state is thus superimposed on the steady state due to the applied d.c. voltage, but without disturbing it to any appreciable extent.

The resultant electrolysis current may be resolved into two parts: a d.c. part *i*, related to the mean potential *E* of the electrode in a way determined by the steady-state conditions, and an alternating part of amplitude I. Either this amplitude or the mean value of the alternating part of the electrolysis current is measured for various values of the applied d.c. voltage. The latter may be varied discontinuously by hand, or slowly but continuously. We thus obtain a plot of I against the mean potential of the electrode.

Sine-wave modulation

Calculation shows that the amplitude I of the alternating current is proportional to the derivative of the d.c. electrolysis current, di/dE. The curve $I = f(E)$ thus has the same form as the derivative curve $di/dE = f(E)$.

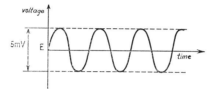

Fig. 384. Sine-wave modulation.

The maximum amplitude occurs at the half-wave potential, and its value is

$$I_{max} = kn^2 SD_0^{\frac{1}{2}} f^{\frac{1}{2}} V C_s$$

where n = number of electrons, S = area of electrode, D_0 = diffusion constant, f = frequency of alternating voltage, V = amplitude of alternating voltage, C_s = concentration, and k is the proportionality constant. I_{max} is thus proportional to the concentration of the electrolyzed substance (Fig. 385).

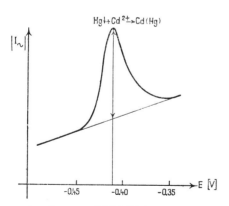

Fig. 385. Sine-wave polarography of 5×10^{-4} M Cd^{2+} in 0.5 M HCl. Dropping mercury electrode (drop time 10 to 12 seconds). Modulating voltage: 5 mV, 200 c/s. $I_\sim$ denotes the value of $i_\sim$ when the size of the drop is maximum (after BAUER and ELVING[125]).

Since I_{max} increases with the frequency of the alternating voltage, it might be thought that increasing this frequency would increase the sensitivity. In fact, the alternating current measured is composed of two parts: one due to the electrochemical reaction, and the other due to the capacitance of the electrode double layer. This alternating capacitive residual current increases rapidly with the frequency, and causes a serious error in the determination of I_{max}. It appears on the contrary that it is best to use very low frequencies (*e.g.* 5 to 10 c/s), unless the apparatus is modified so as to eliminate the capacitive current[108].

Square-wave polarography

BARKER and JENKINS[128] have shown that it is possible to eliminate the capacitive current, and thus to increase the sensitivity, by replacing the sinusoidal voltage by a square wave of about the same amplitude (Fig. 386). The principle of this method and the measuring technique are exactly analogous to those of the previous method.

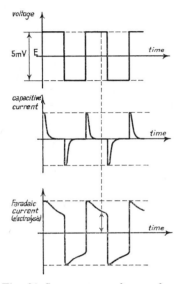

Fig. 386. Square-wave polarography.

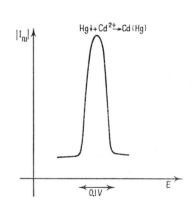

Fig. 387. Square-wave polarography of 10^{-4} M Cd^{2+} in M KCl. Dropping mercury electrode (after HANUN[141]).

This may be seen by examining the variations of the capacitive current and the electrolysis current with time, as shown in Fig. 386. These curves can be displayed on a cathode-ray oscillograph.

The electrical double layer can be charged and discharged very quickly (providing that the ohmic resistance of the solution is low), while the faradaic electrolysis current varies much more slowly. It is thus possible to correct for the capacitive current by only measuring the instantaneous value of the current towards the end of each half-cycle of the square wave, after the double layer has been discharged.

The curves of the alternating current as a function of the potential thus obtained are similar to those obtained with a sinusoidal voltage (Fig. 387). Frequencies of about 225 c/s appear to give the best results.

Application of a.c. polarography

This method offers great possibilities, both for quantitative analysis and for physico-chemical studies.

It has the same advantage as derivative polarography (*cf.* Chapter VIII) where analysis is concerned, *i.e.* a high resolving power for mixtures (Fig. 388). It is possible to determine the concentration of components of mixtures present in the ratio of 1 to 20 000. Moreover, when used with square-wave modulation, it seems to give the greatest sensitivity and accuracy. According to BARKER and JENKINS[128], it is possible to measure concentrations as low as $2 \times 10^{-7} M$ (fast systems) and even $4 \times 10^{-8} M$ by careful design of the electronics. The analytical applications of the method have recently been described by MILNER et al.[133, 134, 138, 139, 143].

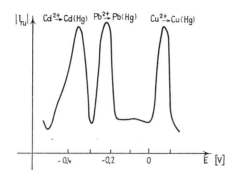

Fig. 388. Square-wave polarography of $10^{-4} M$ Cd^{2+} + $10^{-4} M$ Pb^{2+} + $10^{-4} M$ Cu^{2+} in M KCl. Dropping mercury electrode (after HANUN[141]).

Unfortunately, the experimental techniques of this method are without doubt most difficult to master.

This method also appears to be the most sensitive for electrochemical kinetic studies, and allows electrochemical reaction velocities to be measured which appear infinite with other methods[126].

Amperometric and potentiometric titrations by a.c.-polarography

Some workers have thought of using the fact that a.c. polarography gives indications proportional to di/dE to follow chemical or electrochemical reactions.

If an alternating voltage with a constant amplitude of a few millivolts is applied between two electrodes, it is possible to measure a current which is proportional to di/dE near $i = 0$; this current varies during the titration. The method is similar to that of amperometric titration with two indicator electrodes, where a small constant voltage ΔE is applied between the electrodes and the resultant current i is measured (see Chapter IX).

The method can also be transposed so as to make it analogous to a potentiometric titration with two indicator electrodes, where a very small current i is imposed and the potential difference between the electrodes is measured: an alternating current with a constant, very small, amplitude is applied and the resulting alternating voltage between the electrodes is measured.

FRANCK[126, 127] has recently described titrations carried out according to this principle, using a sinusoidal current of small constant amplitude; but this method is greatly limited by the size of the capacitive current. LAITINEN and HALL[140] have therefore described titrations using a square wave. Figs. 389 and 390 show characteristic titration curves obtained by these authors (*cf.* Chapters VII, VIII and IX).

This method has little advantage over normal amperometric and potentiometric titrations, because the experimental technique is so difficult; but LAITINEN and HALL estimate that end-points can be determined with 10 times the sensitivity of other methods.

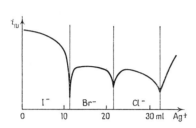

Fig. 389. Amperometric titration of $6.7 \times 10^{-3}\,M\ I^- + 6.7 \times 10^{-3}\,M\ Br^- + 6.7 \times 10^{-3}\,M\ Cl^-$ with $0.1\,M\ Ag^+$, by means of square-wave polarography. Amplitude of square wave 20 mV to 35 mV, frequency 20 c/s (after LAITINEN and HALL[140]).
Compare Fig. 237.

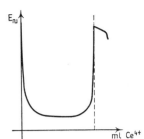

Fig. 390. Potentiometric titration of $0.1\,M\ Fe^{2+}$ with $0.0857\,M\ Ce^{4+}$, using square-wave current. Amplitude of square wave 2.4 μA, frequency 20 c/s (after LAITINEN and HALL[140]).

V. A.C. CHRONOPOTENTIOMETRY

TAKEMORI et al.[146] have recently described the use of an alternating current in chronopotentiometry. The electrolysis current consists of a constant part i_0, modulated by a sinusoidal current of amplitude i_1. The total current varies with the time with a frequency f

$$i = i_0 + i_1 \sin (2\pi f)t$$

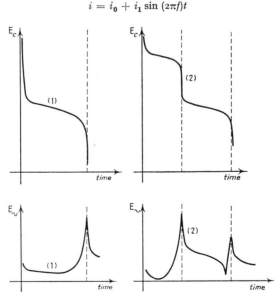

Fig. 391. a.c. chronopotentiometry.
Constant current $i_0 = -150$ μA. Alternating current of amplitude 15 μA and frequency 60 c/s. Curve 1: $1.2 \times 10^{-3}\,M\ Cd^{2+}$ in $0.2\,M$ KCl. Curves 2: $1.2 \times 10^{-3}\,M\ Cd^{2+} + 0.4 \times 10^{-3}\,M\ Zn^{2+}$ in $0.2\,M$ NH_3/NH_4Cl (after TAKEMORI et al.[146]).

The solution is not stirred and the electrode is fixed, as in normal chronopotentio-metry.

A periodic state of small amplitude is thus superimposed on a slowly varying non-steady state, which is hardly disturbed by it.

Calculation shows that the electrode potential (which varies with the time) is the sum of two terms: a non-periodic term E_c, which is the potential which the electrode would have if the alternating current were not present (chronopotentiometry with a current i_0), and an alternating part of the same frequency f as the imposed current. The amplitude of the alternating term is proportional to i_1/i_0, which is fixed by the operator, and also to $(dE_c/dt)t^{\frac{1}{2}}$, which is the term of main interest here. If this am-plitude is measured as a function of the time, the curve obtained has roughly the same shape as the derivative chronopotentiometric curve. Fig. 391 shows two curves obtained by the authors.

It seems clear that this method increases the accuracy of determination of the transition time without increasing the overall sensitivity of the normal chronopoten-tiometric method.

VI. ANODIC-STRIPPING POLAROGRAPHY

Electrochemical deposition at the surface of an electrode has often been used to con-centrate certain compounds. Subsequent stripping of the deposit can be used to de-termine the substance by a suitable method[147, 148], and this process of redissolution has often been used in coulometric determinations (see Chapter X).

One might think that the best electrode for this purpose would be made of an inert metal such as platinum, on which all solid compounds having oxidizing or re-ducing properties could be deposited, allowing a rapid coulometric determination. The sensitivity would also be excellent, were it not for several sources of error, espe-cially when dilute solutions are used. The main trouble is that it is sometimes difficult to get the last traces of the compound deposited on the electrode.

Other difficulties arise with a mercury electrode. The formation of amalgams gives rise to certain limitations, but the main trouble is that the metal tends to dif-fuse into the mercury so that it is difficult to carry out the redissolution quantitative-ly. This can be remedied by using a solid metallic electrode (e.g. silver or platinum) amalgamated on the surface. The metal is deposited in the same way on the surface film of mercury, but the metal cannot diffuse beyond the limits of this thin film. How-ever, the results obtained in this way are often not very reproducible.

Anodic-stripping polarography avoids both these inconveniences, since it is not necessary in this method to have quantitative deposition or quantitative redissolution.

Principle

A mercury electrode has been found to give the best results. The operation is carried out in two stages.

During a pre-electrolysis at controlled potential (corresponding to the limiting diffusion current) the mercury electrode acts as a cathode, and one or more metallic cations are reduced in the form of an amalgam at the surface of the mercury. The pre-electrolysis is carried out for a suitable length of time, which must be longer as the dilution of the substance to be determined increases. Only part of the substance in solution is deposited in a concentrated layer at the surface of the mercury.

The metal is then redissolved under suitable conditions, using a controlled potential or a controlled current. The mercury now acts as the anode. The characteristic curve produced on redissolution allows the determination of the concentration of the cation or cations in question, after calibration.

We will give some examples of methods of this type.

Stripping in the steady state

HICKLING, MAXWELL and SHENNAN[149] stirred the amalgam mechanically while stripping the metal. Thus they had steady state conditions, in which the concentration of the metal in the mercury only varied in the diffusion layer of constant thickness at the surface of the mercury.

The authors found the current–potential curves under these conditions to be similar to those obtained during cathodic deposition. For example, Fig. 392 shows the redissolution curves for a mixture of zinc and thallium.

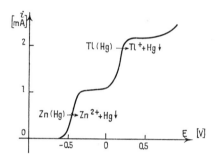

Fig. 392. Stripping in the steady state. (after HICKLING, MAXWELL and SHENNAN[149]).

The gain in sensitivity is slight, since it is difficult to use very small mercury electrodes. Since the stirring distributes the metal uniformly throughout the mercury, it is necessary in practice to deposit as much metal as possible during the pre-electrolysis, which takes a very long time. For example, one litre of a 10^{-6} M solution of Cd^{2+} in 0.1 N H_2SO_4 was pre-electrolyzed for 5 days, and then gave a limiting stripping current of 17 μA with a mercury electrode 1 ml in volume, with a surface area of 1 cm². The authors reckoned to be able to determine metallic cations in concentrations of 10^{-6} M within 1 %.

Furthemore the experimental technique of this method is not as simple as that of the normal method.

Anodic-stripping chronoamperometry

MAMANTOV, PAPOFF and DELAHAY[150] redissolve the metal at constant potential without stirring. After pre-electrolysis at a potential corresponding to the reduction of the metallic cation, the potential is suddenly increased to a more positive value, corresponding to the reoxidation of the metal. The current–time curves are then recorded. The pre-electrolysis is carried out for a very short time, a few seconds to a minute. The metal is thus deposited in a very concentrated layer at the surface of the mercury and does not have the time to diffuse into the body of the mercury. The current at the start of the redissolution is therefore very large. The form of the current–time curves allows the concentration of the original solution to be determined.

Fig. 393 shows the current–time curves obtained by these authors with 5×10^{-4} M Cd^{2+} in M KCl at a hanging mercury drop electrode (surface area 0.03 cm²), with various pre-electrolysis times.

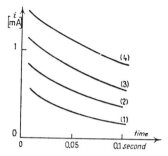

Fig. 393. Anodic-stripping chronoamperometry, 5×10^{-4} M Cd^{2+} in M KCl. Hanging mercury drop electrode (0.03 cm²). Potential = 0.00 V. Pre-electrolysis time: curve 1: 18 seconds; curve 2: 30 seconds; curve 3: 45 seconds; curve 4: 1 minute (after MAMANTOV, PAPOFF and DELAHAY[150]).

The authors estimated that the gain in sensitivity is about 100-fold, and that concentrations of the order of 10^{-7} M to 10^{-9} M can be determined. The experimental technique is simple, but the interpretation of the curves is difficult.

Anodic-stripping chronopotentiometry

The same authors[150] also used a different method of redissolution. After pre-electrolysis at controlled potential, they suddenly imposed a constant reoxidation current, and recorded the potential–time curve.

The pre-electrolysis conditions are the same. The authors waited 4 seconds before the reoxidation, to allow the solution to settle.

The potential increases sharply when the concentration of the metal in the mercury at the surface of the electrode becomes zero, *i.e.* at the end of the transition time (see p. 314) and a knowledge of the transition time allows the concentration of the original solution to be determined.

Fig. 394 shows the potential–time curves obtained under the same conditions as for Fig. 393 (5×10^{-4} M Cd^{2+} in M KCl, hanging mercury drop electrode).

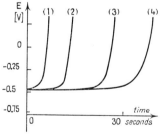

Fig. 394. Anodic-stripping chronopotentiometry 5×10^{-4} M Cd^{2+} in M KCl, hanging mercury drop electrode (0.03 cm²). Electrolysis current 45 μA. Pre-electrolysis time: curve 1: 10 seconds; curve 2: 25 seconds; curve 3: 50 seconds; curve 4: 75 seconds (after MAMANTOV, PAPOFF and DELAHAY[150]).

The gain in sensitivity is nearly as large as in the previous method, but the interpretation of the curves (by determination of the transition time) is simpler, and this method is to be preferred.

Anodic-stripping linear chronoamperometry

NIKELLY and COOKE[17] have carried out the anodic stripping according to the technique of linear chronoamperometry. After the pre-electrolysis the potential is increased at a constant rate. The current–time (or current–potential) curve is recorded.

The phenomena observed during reoxidation are identical with those observed during reduction according to this method (see p. 310). When the potential is high enough, reoxidation starts. The current passes through a maximum when the diffusion of the metal through the mercury towards the surface can no longer compensate for the losses by oxidation at the surface. The pre-electrolysis time is longer here, from 25 seconds to several minutes; but in general the results are more accurate when the time is shorter, since then diffusion of the metal away from the surface of the mercury is reduced. Under certain conditions the maximum values of the current are proportional to the initial concentrations of the solution, and thus allow the latter to be determined. Figs. 395 and 396 show the curves observed by the authors for solutions of $2.5 \times 10^{-5}\ M\ Pb^{2+}$ in $0.1\ M\ KNO_3$, and of $8.5 \times 10^{-6}\ M\ Cd^{2+} + 10^{-5}\ M\ Tl^+$ in $0.05\ M\ NH_3 + 0.05\ M\ NH_4Cl$, with a mercury electrode $0.05\ cm^2$ in area, a pre-electrolysis time of 5 minutes and a rate of increase of the potential of $0.2\ V/min$.

The gain in sensitivity is of the same order of magnitude as for the two previous methods. NIKELLY and COOKE estimate that a concentration of $10^{-8}\ M$ can be determined to within 3 or 4 %.

DE MARS and SHAIN[151] have used the same method with a hanging mercury drop electrode. Their results agree with those of NIKELLY and COOKE. With a pre-electrolysis time of an hour, they determined $10^{-9}\ M\ Cd^{2+}$ in $0.1\ M\ KCl$ to within 3 %.

KEMULA and KUBLIK[92] have obtained identical results.

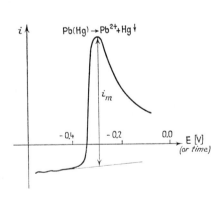

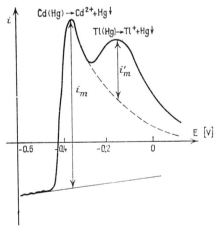

Fig. 395. Anodic-stripping linear chronoamperometry, $2.5 \times 10^{-5}\ M\ Pb^{2+}$ in $0.1\ M\ KNO_3$, mercury electrode ($0.05\ cm^2$). Pre-electrolysis time 5 minutes, rate of potential change 0.2 V/min (after NIKELLY and COOKE[17]).

Fig. 396. Anodic stripping linear chronoamperometry, $8.5 \times 10^{-6}\ M\ Cd^{2+} + 10^{-5}\ M\ Tl^+$ in $0.05\ M\ NH_3/NH_4Cl$, mercury electrode ($0.05\ cm^2$), Pre-electrolysis time 5 minutes, rate of potential change 0.2 V/min (after NIKELLY and COOKE[17]).

Other methods using anodic stripping

KALVODA[91, 152] has described the use of oscillographic polarography with a sinus-oidal current in conjunction with anodic stripping. The sensitivity of this method is also 10^{-9} M, but the accuracy seems to be considerably worse.

BARKER[130, 142] has described the use of square-wave polarography for anodic stripping. Thanks to the great sensitivity of this method, it is possible to determine concentrations of less than 10^{-9} M. In fact, the sensitivity seems to be limited by the poisoning of the surface of the electrode by impurities. Fig. 397 shows a curve obtained by BARKER with a solution of 1.4×10^{-7} M $Cu^{2+} + 6.4 \times 10^{-9}$ M $Cd^{2+} + Pb^{2+} + Zn^{2+}$ in M KCl $+ 0.1$ M HCl, after electrolysis for 30 minutes.

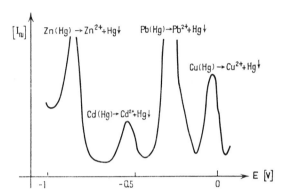

Fig. 397. Anodic-stripping square-wave polarography,
$Zn^{2+} + Pb^{2+} + 1.4 \times 10^{-7}$ M $Cu^{2+} + 6.4 \times 10^{-9}$ M Cd^{2+} (after BARKER[142]).

It is in principle possible to use any indicator method to follow the reoxidation of the amalgam. The overall sensitivity of the different anodic-stripping methods is usually of the same order as that of the indicator methods used.

Advantages of the method

The great advantage of this method is that it allows very dilute solutions to be analyzed with greater accuracy, without introducing troubles connected with coulo-metric determinations. If the cathodic curve is not very different from that of the residual current, the metal may be accumulated at the surface of the electrode by pre-electrolysis. The anodic curve, which is determined immediately after, is then considerably different from that of the residual current. From the examples given above, it can be seen that the gain in sensitivity should be of the order of 100.

The method has some further advantages: a certain latitude in choosing the sensitivity, since the current and time of pre-electrolysis can be varied within limits; and a certain selectivity, since on the one hand only the metals which form amalgams can be determined in this way, and on the other hand it is possible to deposit the metals selectively during the pre-electrolysis by operating at a suitable potential.

The fact that only metals which form amalgams can be determined is of course a disadvantage at times.

The mercury electrode has the further advantage that it is easily reproducible without any sort of pretreatment.

REFERENCES

Recent electrochemical methods

1 P. DELAHAY, *New Instrumental Methods in Electrochemistry*, Interscience Publishers, Inc., New York, 1954.
2 I. M. KOLTHOFF and J. J. LINGANE, *Polarography*, Interscience Publishers, Inc., New York, 2nd Edn., 1952.
3 G. W. C. MILNER, *The Principles and Applications of Polarography and other Electroanalytical Processes*, Longmans, Green and Co., London, 1957, pp. 119–134.
4 W. D. COOKE in W. G. BERL, *Physical Methods in Chemical Analysis*, Vol. III, Academic Press, New York, 1956, Chapt. III, pp. 71–107.
5 P. DELAHAY, in J. H. YOE and H. J. KOCH JR., *Trace analysis*, John Wiley and Sons, New York, 1957, Chapt. II, pp. 283–316.
6 J. HEYROVSKY, *Polarography*, Springer, Vienna, 1941, pp. 234–240.
7 J. HEYROVSKY and J. FOREJT, *Oscillographic Polarography*, Statni Nakladatelstvi Technike Literatury, Prague, 1953.
8 G. CHARLOT, *Modern Electroanalytical Methods*, Elsevier Publishing Company, Amsterdam, 1959.

Chronoamperometry at constant potential

9 H. GERISCHER and W. VIELSTICH, *Z. phys. Chem.*, 3 (1955) 16.
10 H. GERISCHER and W. VIELSTICH, *Z. phys. Chem.*, 4 (1955) 12.
11 W. VIELSTICH and P. DELAHAY, *J. Am. Chem. Soc.*, 79 (1957) 1874.
12 P. DELAHAY, *Ann. Rev. Phys. Chem.*, 8 (1957) 229.
13 P. DELAHAY, *J. Chim. phys.*, 54 (1957) 369.
14 A. V. GORODYSKY and YU. K. DELIMARSKY, *Dokl. Akad. Nauk SSSR*, 114 (1957) 1261.

Linear chronoamperometry (chronoamperometry with linearly varying potential)

15 C. A. STREULI and W. D. COOKE, *Anal. Chem.*, 25 (1953) 1691.
16 C. A. STREULI and W. D. COOKE, *Anal. Chem.*, 26 (1954) 963.
17 C. A. STREULI and W. D. COOKE, *J. Phys. Chem.*, 57 (1953) 824.
18 J. G. NIKELLY and W. D. COOKE, *Anal. Chem.*, 29 (1957) 933.
19 J. W. ROSS, R. D. DE MARS and I. SHAIN, *Anal. Chem.*, 28 (1956) 1768.
20 K. J. MARTIN and I. SHAIN, *Anal. Chem.*, 30 (1958) 1808.

Chronopotentiometry

21 H. F. WEBER, *Physik Ann.*, 7 (1879) 536.
22 H. J. S. SAND, *Phil. Mag.*, 1 (1901) 45.
23 Z. KARAOGLANOFF, *Z. Elektrochem.*, 12 (1906) 5.
24 J. A. V. BUTLER and G. ARMSTRONG, *Proc. Roy, Soc.*, A 139 (1933) 406.
25 J. A. V. BUTLER and G. ARMSTRONG, *Trans. Faraday Soc.*, 30 (1934) 1173.
26 A. RIUS, J. LLOPIS and S. POLO, *Anales fis. quim. Esp.*, 45 B (1949) 469, 1029.
27 L. GIERST and A. L. JULIARD, *Proc. Intern. Comm. Electrochem. Thermodyn. and Kinet.*, 2nd Meeting, Tamburini, Milan, 1951, pp. 117–179.
28 L. GIERST, *Thèse*, Brussels, 1952.
29 L. GIERST and A. L. JULIARD, *J. Phys. Chem.*, 57 (1953) 701.
30 P. DELAHAY and T. BERZINS, *J. Am. Chem. Soc.*, 75 (1953) 2486.
31 T. BERZINS and P. DELAHAY, *J. Am. Chem. Soc.*, 75 (1953) 4205.
32 P. DELAHAY and C. C. MATTAX, *J. Am. Chem. Soc.*, 76 (1954) 874.
33 L. GIERST and P. H. MECHELYNCK, *Anal. Chim. Acta*, 12 (1955) 79.
34 P. DELAHAY and G. MAMANTOV, *Anal. Chem.*, 27 (1955) 478.
35 C. N. REILLEY, G. W. EVERETT and R. H. JOHNS, *Anal. Chem.*, 27 (1955) 483.
36 M. M. NICHOLSON and J. H. KARCHMER, *Anal. Chem.*, 27 (1955) 1095.
37 C. N. REILLEY and W. G. SCRIBNER, *Anal. Chem.*, 27 (1955) 1210.
38 L. GIERST, *Anal. Chim. Acta*, 15 (1956) 262.
39 P. DELAHAY and C. C. MATTAX, *Anal. Chem.*, 28 (1956) 635.
40 H. A. LAITINEN and W. S. FERGUSON, *Anal. Chem.*, 29 (1957) 4.
41 F. C. ANSON and J. J. LINGANE, *J. Am. Chem. Soc.*, 79 (1957) 1015.
42 L. GIERST, *Proc. Intern. Comm. Electrochem. Thermodyn. and Kinet.*, 7th Meeting, Lindau,1955, Butterworths, London, 1957, p. 49.
43 L. GIERST, *Contributi Teorici E Sperimentali di Polorografia*, Vol. III, 1957, p. 11.
44 T. KAMBARA and I. TACHI, *J. Phys. Chem.*, 61 (1957) 1405.
45 H. A. LAITINEN and H. C. GAUR, *Anal. Chim. Acta*, 18 (1958) 1.
46 R. N. ADAMS, J. H. MCCLURE and J. B. MORRIS, *Anal. Chem.*, 30 (1958) 471.

[47] N. TANAKA and T. MURAYAMA, *Z. physik. Chem.*, 14 (1958) 370.
[48] P. J. ELVING and A. F. KRIVIS, *Anal. Chem.*, 30 (1958) 1648.
[49] J. D. VOORHIES and N. H. FURMAN, *Anal. Chem.*, 30 (1958) 1656.
[50] J. J. LINGANE, *Electroanalytical Chemistry*, Interscience Publishers Inc., New York, 2nd Edn., 1958, Chapt. XXII.

Oscillographic polarography with a controlled potential

—, *general theory*
[51] J. E. B. RANDLES, *Trans. Faraday Soc.*, 44 (1948) 327.
[52] A. SEVČIK, *Collection Czechoslov. Chem. Communs.*, 13 (1948) 349.
[53] T. BERZINS and P. DELAHAY, *J. Am. Chem. Soc.*, 75 (1953) 555.
[54] P. DELAHAY, *J. Am. Chem. Soc.*, 75 (1953) 1190.
[55] M. M. NICHOLSON, *J. Am. Chem. Soc.*, 76 (1954) 2539.

—, *applications*
[56] L. A. MATHESON and N. NICHOLS, *Trans. Am. Electrochem. Soc.*, 73 (1938) 193.
[57] J. E. B. RANDLES, *Analyst*, 72 (1947) 301.
[58] J. E. B. RANDLES, *Trans. Faraday Soc.*, 44 (1948) 322.
[59] P. DELAHAY, *J. Phys. Colloid. Chem.*, 53 (1949) 1279.
[60] P. DELAHAY, *J. Phys. Colloid. Chem.*, 54 (1950) 402, 630.
[61] F. C. SNOWDEN and H. T. PAGE, *Anal. Chem.*, 22 (1950) 969.
[62] P. DELAHAY, *Anal. Chim. Acta*, 5 (1951) 129.
[63] P. DELAHAY and G. L. STIEHL, *J. Phys. Colloid. Chem.*, 55 (1951) 570.
[64] P. DELAHAY and G. PERKINS, *J. Phys. Colloid. Chem.*, 55 (1951) 586.
[65] I. SHAIN and A. L. CRITTENDEN, *Anal. Chem.*, 26 (1954) 281.
[66] H. MATSUDA and Y. AYABE, *Z. Elektrochem.*, 59 (1955) 494.
[67] J. W. MARTIN and J. V. WESTWOOD, *Metallurgia*, 54 (1956) 305.
[68] M. SHINAGAWA, H. IMAI and H. SUNAHARA, *Nippon Kagaku Zashi*, 77 (1956) 1482, 1487.
[69] G. F. REYNOLDS and T. J. WEBBER, *Anal. Chim. Acta*, 19 (1958) 293, 406.

—, *sinusoidal voltage* (see also reference 56)
[70] R. H. MÜLLER, R. L. GARMAN, M. E. DROZ and J. PETRAS, *Ind. Eng. Chem., Anal. Ed.*, 10 (1938) 339.
[71] J. VAN CAKENBERGHE, *Bull. soc. chim. Belg.*, 60 (1951) 3.
[72] J. HEYROVSKY and R. KALVODA, *Oszillographische Polarographie*, Akad. Verlag, Berlin.
[73] J. HEYROVSKY, *Chem. listy*, 35 (1941) 155.
[74] J. HEYROVSKY and J. FOREJT, *Z. physik. Chem.*, 193 (1943) 77.
[75] J. HEYROVSKY, *Chem. listy*, 40 (1946) 61.
[76] J. HEYROVSKY, *Disc. Faraday Soc.*, 1 (1947) 212.
[77] J. HEYROVSKY, F. SORM and J. FOREJT, *Collection Czechoslov. Chem. Communs.*, 12 (1947) 11.
[78] R. BIEBER and G. TRÜMPLER, *Helv. Chim. Acta*, 30 (1947) 971.
[79] J. HEYROVSKY, *Anal. Chim. Acta*, 2 (1948) 533.
[80] M. FOURNIER and M. QUINTIN, *Compt. rend.*, 232 (1951) 834.
[81] M. FOURNIER, *J. Chim. phys.*, 49 (1952) C 183.
[82] J. W. LOVELAND and P. J. ELVING, *Chem. Revs.*, 51 (1952) 67.
[83] J. HEYROVSKY, *Anal. Chim. Acta*, 8 (1953) 283.
[84] J. HEYROVSKY, *Z. Elektrochem.*, 59 (1955) 803.
[85] W. HANS, *Z. Elektrochem.*, 59 (1955) 623.
[86] R. KALVODA and J. MACKŮ, *Collection Czechoslov. Chem. Communs.*, 20 (1955) 254, 257.
[87] R. KALVODA, *Collection Czechoslov. Chem. Communs.*, 20 (1955) 1503.
[88] R. KALVODA, *Collection Czechoslov. Chem. Communs.*, 22 (1957) 1390.
[89] J. HEYROVSKY, *Acta Chim. Acad. Sci. Hung.*, 9 (1956) 4, 73.
[90] R. KALVODA, *Acta Chim. Acad. Sci. Hung.*, 9 (1956) 93.
[91] R. KALVODA, *Anal. Chim. Acta*, 18 (1958) 132.
[92] W. KEMULA and Z. KUBLIK, *Anal. Chim. Acta*, 18 (1958) 104.
[93] J. DOLEZAL, *Chemie*, 9 (1957) 184.
[94] P. BERAN and J. DOLEZAL, *Chem. listy*, 51 (1957) 2243.
[95] P. BERAN and J. DOLEZAL, *Collection Czechoslov. Chem. Communs.*, 23 (1958) 1481
[96] J. MACKŮ, *Chem. listy*, 52 (1958) 980.
[97] J. HEYROVSKY, *Österr. Chem. Ztg.*, 58 (1957) 94.
[98] J. HEYROVSKY, *Zavodskaya Lab.*, 23 (1957) 399.
[99] J. HEYROVSKY, *Proc. Polarog. Conf., Warsaw, 1956*, p. 17.
[100] W. KEMULA and Z. KUBLIK, *Proc. Polarog. Conf., Warsaw, 1956*, p. 177.
[101] T. KAMBARA, *Rev. polarog.*, 5 (1957) 85.

[102] H. Matsuda, *Z. Elektrochem.*, 61 (1957) 489.
[103] K. Micka, *Z. anal. Chem.*, 206 (1957) 345.
[104] R. A. Schreiber, *Dissert. Abstr.*, 17 (1957) 1884.

Alternating current polarography

—, *sine-wave current*

[105] J. Boeke and H. van Suchtelen, *Z. Elektrochem.*, 45 (1939) 753.
[106] J. E. B. Randles, *Disc. Faraday Soc.*, 1 (1947) 11.
[107] P. Delahay, *Rec. trav. chim.*, 67 (1948) 165.
[108] G. Jessop, British Patent No. 640 (1948) 768.
[109] D. C. Grahame, *J. Am. Chem. Soc.*, 71 (1949) 2975.
[110] B. Breyer and F. Gutmann, *Austr. J. Sci. Research*, A 3 (1950) 558.
[111] B. Breyer, F. Gutmann and S. Hacobian, *Austr. J. Sci. Research*, A 3 (1950) 567.
[112] M. Fournier, *Compt. rend.*, 232 (1951) 1673.
[113] M. Fournier, *J. Chim. phys.*, 49 (1952) C 183.
[114] G. F. Reynolds, *Anal. Chim. Acta*, 6 (1952) 567.
[115] J. E. B. Randles and K. W. Somerton, *Trans. Faraday Soc.*, 48 (1952) 628, 937, 951.
[116] P. Delahay and T. J. Adams, *J. Am. Chem. Soc.*, 75 (1952) 5740.
[117] H. Gerischer, *Z. Elektrochem.*, 59 (1945) 604.
[118] H. Gerischer, *Angew. Chem.*, 68 (1956) 20.
[119] B. Breyer, F. Gutmann and H. H. Bauer, *Österr. Chem. Ztg.*, 1956, p. 57–67.
[120] I. Tachi and T. Kambara, *Bull. Chem. Soc. Japan*, 28 (1957) 25.
[121] M. Senda, M. Okuda and I. Tachi, *Bull. Chem. Soc. Japan*, 28 (1957) 31.
[122] M. Okuda and I. Tachi, *Bull. Chem. Soc. Japan*, 28 (1957) 37.
[123] M. Senda and I. Tachi, *Bull. Chem. Soc. Japan*, 28 (1957) 632.
[124] N. Tanaka, T. Koizumi, T. Murayama, M. Kodama and Y. Sakuma, *Anal. Chim. Acta*, 18 (1958) 97.
[125] H. H. Bauer and P. J. Elving, *Anal. Chem.*, 30 (1958) 334, 341.
[126] U. F. Franck, *Z. Elektrochem.*, 58 (1954) 348.
[127] U. F. Franck, *Z. Elektrochem.*, 62 (1958) 245.

Square-wave current

[128] G. C. Barker and I. L. Jenkins, *Analyst*, 77 (1952) 685.
[129] G. C. Barker and D. R. Cockbaine, *Atomic Energy Research Establ.*, C/R-1404, 1954.
[130] G. C. Barker, *Atomic Energy Research Establ.*, C/R-1563, 1954.
[131] D. J. Ferrett, G. W. C. Milner and A. A. Smales, *Analyst*, 79 (1954) 731.
[132] T. Kambara, *Bull. Chem. Soc. Japan*, 27 (1954) 523.
[133] D. J. Ferrett and G. W. C. Milner, *Analyst*, 80 (1955) 132.
[134] D. J. Ferrett, G. W. C. Milner, H. I. Shalgosky and S. J. Slee, *Analyst*, 81 (1956) 506.
[135] G. C. Barker, R. L. Faircloth and A. W. Gardner, *Atomic Energy Research Establ.*, C/R-1786, 1956.
[136] G. C. Barker, *Atomic Energy Research Establ.*, C/R-1553, 1957.
[137] G. C. Barker and A. W. Gardner, *Atomic Energy Research Establ.*, C/R-1606, 1957.
[136] G. W. C. Milner and S. J. Slee, *Analyst*, 82 (1957) 139.
[139] G. W. C. Milner and S. J. Slee, *Proc. XV Intern. Congr. Pure Applied Chem.*, Lisbon 1956, Vol. I, p. 791.
[140] H. A. Laitinen and L. C. Hall, *Anal. Chem.*, 29 (1957) 1390.
[141] R. E. Hanun, *Anal. Chem.*, 30 (1958) 350.
[142] G. C. Barker, *Anal. Chim. Acta*, 18 (1958) 118.
[143] G. C. Barker, G. W. C. Milner and H. I. Shalgosky, *Modern Analytical Chemistry in Industry*, W. Heffer and Sons, Cambridge, 1958, p. 199.
[144] R. L. Faircloth and D. J. Ferrett, *J. Brit. Inst. Radio Engrs*, 18 (1958) 143.
[145] G. C. Barker and R. L. Faircloth, *J. Polarog. Soc.*, (1958) 11.

A.c. chronopotentiometry

[146] Y. Takemori, T. Kambara, M. Senda and I. Tachi, *J. Phys. Chem.*, 61 (1957) 968.

Anodic-stripping polarography

[147] J. A. Maxwell and R. P. Graham, *Chem. Revs.*, 46 (1950) 471.
[148] J. K. Taylor and G. W. Smith, *J. Research Natl. Bur. Standards*, 56 (1956) 301.
[149] A. Hickling, J. A. Maxwell and J. V. Shennan, *Anal. Chim. Acta*, 14 (1956) 287.
[150] G. Mamantov, P. Papoff and P. Delahay, *J. Am. Chem. Soc.*, 79 (1957) 4034.
[151] R. D. De Mars and I. Shain, *Anal. Chem.*, 29 (1957) 1825.
[152] R. Kalvoda, *Chem. listy*, 51 (1957) 696.

Chapter XIII

NON-AQUEOUS SOLVENTS

The use of non-aqueous solvents offers a wide range of possibilities, since in principle all the properties of the system may change if the solvent is changed. The number of pure solvents is limited, but mixed solvents may also be used, thus allowing the properties of the system to be varied continuously.

The choice of solvents is limited by the fact that electrochemical reactions have to be carried out in them. Ions must be able to exist in solution in order that current can pass, and this is not the case with non-polar solvents with a low dielectric constant, such as carbon tetrachloride, chloroform, benzene, saturated hydrocarbons, etc.

The properties which depend on the solvent are:

1. *Chemical properties.* The nature of the solvent has a considerable effect on the equilibrium constants of acid–base reactions, on complex-formation and precipitation reactions. In particular, the choice of solvent may often be determined by considerations of solubility.

These chemical effects depend on the chemical properties of the solvent as an acceptor or donor, and also on its polarity and dielectric constant. This subject is discussed in some of the references.

2. *The electrochemical properties.* The electrochemical redox reactions at the electrodes and their kinetics also depend on the factors mentioned above. We will now examine this question in some greater detail.

Electrochemical properties of the solvent. Limitations on the range of electroactivity

We have seen in Chapter I that the range of electrochemical reactions is limited by the solvent, in that case water. The current–potential curves for the oxidation and reduction of the solvent constitute barriers which prevent electrochemical reactions from being carried out at very high potentials and at very low ones. It is not possible to electrolyze a substance if the solvent is electrolyzed more easily. A suitable choice of solvent thus allows electrochemical reactions to be carried out which are not possible in aqueous solution. The following simple rules may be stated:

a) If it is desired to reduce a substance which is very difficultly reducible, the solvent chosen must be even more difficult to reduce.

b) Similarly for oxidations.

c) If a mixed solvent is used, the most easily reducible component limits the range of reduction, and the most easily oxidizable component limits the range of oxidation.

It is only possible to give a qualitative indication of the limits of electroactivity in one solvent compared to those in another, for reasons which we will discuss further below (reference potential). We will give here some details of the electrochemical reactions which may limit the range of electroactivity in the most commonly used solvents.

Reduction

1. All those solvents which possess an acidic hydrogen can be reduced according to the equation

$$HA + e \rightarrow \tfrac{1}{2}H_2 + A^-$$

and, if free hydrogen ions are formed by the reaction $HA \rightleftharpoons A^- + H^+$, also according to the equation $2\,H^+ + 2e \rightarrow H_2$.

This is for example the case with

$$H_2O \rightleftharpoons H^+ + OH^-$$

$$CH_3CO_2H \rightleftharpoons H^+ + CH_3CO_2^-$$

$$H_2SO_4 \rightleftharpoons H^+ + HSO_4^-$$

In these solvents, the following reactions may limit the range of reduction

$$H^+ + e \rightarrow \tfrac{1}{2}H_2 \tag{1}$$

and

$$H_2O + e \rightarrow \tfrac{1}{2}H_2 + OH^-$$

or

$$CH_3CO_2H + e \rightarrow \tfrac{1}{2}H_2 + CH_3CO_2^- \tag{2}$$

or

$$H_2SO_4 + e \rightarrow \tfrac{1}{2}H_2 + HSO_4^-$$

It is thus to be expected that all solvents which, like water, can yield up a proton will limit the reduction range by the same reaction; but the reduction is easier if the acid HA is more dissociated, *i.e.* stronger. It is therefore theoretically possible to realize more vigorous reductions in water than in acetic acid, which is a stronger acid.

In fact, the effect of this chemical reaction is not the only thing to be considered: the effect of the solvent on the rate of the electrochemical reaction must also be taken into account. This effect, which may be great or small, will be discussed further below.

2. Salts which act as solvents can also be reduced.

Thus in ionized fused salts like the alkali chlorides, the reduction of the cations limits the reduction

$$Na^+ + e \rightarrow Na\downarrow$$

3. The "indifferent" electrolyte, present in large concentrations, may limit the reduction range, especially if the solvent is difficult to reduce. If it is desired to remove this barrier to as low a voltage as possible, it should be remembered that the quaternary ammonium ions, R_4N^+, are the most difficult to reduce.

All the water must be removed from a solvent if it is to be used at very low potentials. It is also always necessary to remove all dissolved oxygen, especially as this gas is more soluble in many non-aqueous solvents.

Oxidation

1. It is sometimes possible to extend the range of electroactivity considerably on the oxidation side with respect to that found with water (see Fig. 398).

2. The indifferent electrolyte may be a salt of an anion which is difficult to oxidize, *e.g.* F^- or a suitable organic anion.

3. The oxidation of the anode itself may also constitute a barrier (*e.g.* Hg, Pt, Ag).

Graphite generally allows very vigorous oxidations to be carried out.

Liquid ammonia presents a special case. In this solvent, the limit of electroactivity is determined by the passage of electrons from the electrode to the solution, or vice versa, without an electrochemical reaction[36].

The ranges of electroactivity given by various solvents are of considerable interest. Unfortunately, as yet little is known on this subject.

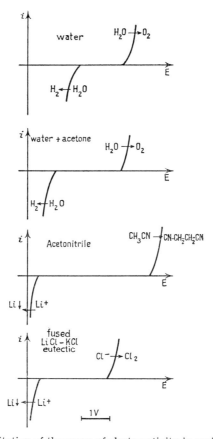

Fig. 398. Limitation of the range of electroactivity in various solvents.

Influence of the solvent on electrochemical reactions

The nature of the solvent has a more or less profound effect on the electrochemical reactions, altering both the relative values of the standard potentials and the rates of the reactions.

The changes in the standard potentials are mainly due to differences in the solvation of the electroactive species. In fact, the relative values of the standard potentials for the reduction of the metallic cations are roughly the same for all solvents, except for those cations which show unusual solvation. For example, Co^{2+} and Ni^{2+} are less solvated in acetonitrile than in water, and are therefore more easily reducible in the former solvent, compared to the other cations. The same is true for Ni^{2+}, Zn^{2+} and Cd^{2+} in anhydrous formic acid, in which they are less solvated than in water. On the other hand, Ag^+ and Cu^+ are strongly solvated in acetonitrile, and are therefore relatively more difficult to reduce than in water. This is also the case in ethylenediamine.

The influence of the solvent on the chemical reactions which may accompany the electrochemical reactions must also be taken into account.

The properties of the solvent also change the rates of the electrochemical reactions (*i.e.* the values of i_0 and of the transfer coefficients α and β). Experimental data on this subject are only available for the reduction of H^+ ions. For example, at mercury, copper or nickel cathodes, α is practically unchanged and i_0 is up to 100 times larger in methanol than in water, while at tungsten or tantalum cathodes, α is considerably larger and i_0 is about 10^5 times smaller in methanol than in water[45]. Both in ethanol and in acetonitrile, the overvoltage of hydrogen at a mercury electrode is lower than in water.

Influence of the solvent on the rate of diffusion

The limiting current in non-aqueous solvents is generally different from that found in water at the same solute concentration. This is partly due to differences in viscosity between the solvents, and partly due to more specific solvent effects such as the nature (*i.e.* the size) of the solvated species.

The Stokes-Einstein equation predicts that the diffusion constant D_0 should be inversely proportional to the viscosity η of the medium[6, 18].

TABLE I

DIFFUSION CONSTANTS
given in cm^2/sec

		Solvent		
Ion reduced	*Water*	*Ethylene diamine*	*Fused eutectic mixture of $LiNO_3$ $NaNO_3$ and KNO_3*	*Fused eutectic mixture of $LiCl$ and KCl*
	(1)	(2)	(3)	(4)
Ag^+	1.69×10^{-5}			2.6×10^{-5}
Tl^+	2.00×10^{-5}	1.85×10^{-5}		
Cu^+				3.5×10^{-5}
Cu^{2+}	0.72×10^{-5}	1.00×10^{-5}		
Pb^{2+}	0.98×10^{-5}	1.52×10^{-5}	0.18×10^{-5}	
Zn^{2+}	0.72×10^{-5}		0.15×10^{-5}	
Cd^{2+}	0.72×10^{-5}		0.15×10^{-5}	1.7×10^{-5}
Ni^{2+}	0.69×10^{-5}		0.12×10^{-5}	
Sr^{2+}	0.80×10^{-5}	0.80×10^{-5}		
Ba^{2+}	0.86×10^{-5}	0.80×10^{-5}		
Au^{3+}		2.23×10^{-5}		
Bi^{3+}				0.6×10^{-5}

After
(1) I. M. KOLTHOFF and J. J. LINGANE, *Polarography*, Interscience, New York, 1952.
(2) V. GUTMANN and G. SCHÖBER, *Monatsh. Chem.*, 88 (1957) 206.
(3) M. NACHTRIEB and M. STEINBERG, *J. Am. Chem. Soc.*, 72 (1950) 558.
(4) H. A. LAITINEN and W. S. FERGUSON, *Anal. Chem.*, 29 (1957) 4.

The effect of the temperature

An increase in the temperature causes reaction rates to increase considerably. This is especially true of electrochemical reactions.

Certain solvents allow very high temperatures to be used. Nearly all electrochemical systems are fast, for example, in fused salts such as the alkali chlorides.

One consequence of this is a reduction of the range of electroactivity at high temperatures, since the oxidation and reduction reactions of the solvent are usually slow at normal temperatures.

An increase in the temperature generally decreases the viscosity and thus leads to a higher limiting current. Thus glycerine, which is useless as a solvent at normal temperatures, can be used between 70 and 120° C [46, 47].

Problems peculiar to the use of non-aqueous solvents

a) Conductivity

We have seen in Chapter V that the solution must have a sufficiently large conductivity. Otherwise, the ohmic resistance of the cell is high and if the applied voltage is not very large, the current i is very small (see p. 117). Also, in order to suppress the effect of the migration of the electroactive ions, the solution must contain a relatively large concentration of an indifferent electrolyte. For both these reasons, the ionic strength of the solution must not be too small.

The conductivity of the solution is related to the ionizing power of the solvent, *i.e.* to its dielectric constant and polarity. The number of organic solvents with a sufficiently high dielectric constant (> 30) is unfortunately limited (see the table below). It is therefore often difficult to find a suitable indifferent electrolyte, especially since most inorganic salts are not very soluble in organic solvents.

The alkali perchlorates, nitrates and chlorides are still sufficiently soluble in mixed solvents containing water, because of the presence of the water. Lithium salts (especially the chloride and the perchlorate) and the tetraalkylammonium salts are among the most soluble and most ionized in anhydrous solvents. Here are some indications for suitable indifferent electrolytes which have been used in various solvents: 0.1 M tetraethylammonium perchlorate, 0.1 M tetrabutylammonium perchlorate or iodide, saturated sodium perchlorate and saturated (0.118 M) trimethylethylammonium chloride in acetonitrile; 0.1 M sodium nitrate in ethylenediamine; saturated lithium chloride in ethanol, methanol, acetone, acetic acid; M ammonium chloride in ethanol and methanol; 0.1 M lithium chloride and 2 M magnesium chloride in glycerol; sodium and potassium chloride, bromide and iodide up to 0.5 M in amides; saturated tetrabutylammonium iodide (only 0.0057 M) in liquid ammonia; and finally, the hydrides, boro-hydrides and organometallic compounds of aluminium, zirconium and titanium for ethers. With certain of these solvents, it is impossible to get a high conductivity (acetic acid, acetone, etc.).

Fused salts are especially interesting in this connection, since certain of them (alkali chlorides and nitrates, etc.) are still appreciably ionized in the liquid state, so that no indifferent electrolyte is needed to make the solution conducting.

TABLE II

DIELECTRIC CONSTANTS OF THE MORE COMMON SOLVENTS

After: G. Kortüm and J. O'M. Bockris; J. A. Riddick and E. E. Toops Jr.; A. Weissberger ed.;
L. R. Dawson, R. H. Graves and P. G. Sears.

Solvent	Dielectric constant	Temperature	Solvent	Dielectric constant	Temperature
N-methyl acetamide	165	40°	1-pentanol	13.9	25°
N-methyl propionamide	164	30°	Isopropanol	13.8	18°
N-methyl butyramide	128	25°	Sulphur dioxide	13.8	15°
Hydrocyanic acid	123	16°	Benzyl alcohol	13.1	
Formamide	109	20°	Pyridine	12.3	25°
Sulphuric acid	84		Hydrogen sulphide	10.2	−60°
Hydrofluoric acid	83	0°	1-1'-dichloroethane	10	25°
Water	80	20°	Phenol	9.8	60°
Fused acetamide	59		Methylamine	9.4	25°
Formic acid	57	20°	Ethylamine	6.9	10°
Hydrazine	53	20°	Aniline	6.9	20°
Selenium (IV) oxychloride	46	20°	Acetic acid	6.1	25°
Glycerol	42.5	25°	Ethyl benzoate	6.0	20°
Furfural	42		Ethyl acetate	6.0	25°
Ethylene glycol	41	20°	2-methyl 2-butanol	5.8	25°
Ethanolamine	37.7	25°	Chlorobenzene	5.6	25°
Acetonitrile	37.5	25°	Chloroform	4.8	20°
Nitromethane	36	25°	Bromoform	4.4	20°
Nitrobenzene	35	25°	Ethyl ether	4.3	20°
Methanol	32.6	25°	Diethylamine	3.6	25°
Propionitrile	27.2	25°	Trichlorethylene	3.4	25°
Benzonitrile	25.2	25°	Phosphorus trichloride	3.4	25°
Ethanol	24.3	25°	Propionic acid	3.4	40°
n-Propanol	22.2	20°	Butyric acid	3.0	20°
Liquid ammonia	22	−33°	Tin tetrachloride	2.9	20°
Acetone	21.5	20°	Carbon disulphide	2.6	20°
Acetaldehyde	21.1	25°	Triethylamine	2.4	25°
Acetic anhydride	20.7	18.5°	Toluene	2.4	25°
Propionaldehyde	18.5	17°	Benzene	2.3	15°
Cyclohexanone	18.3	25°	1,4-dioxane	2.2	25°
2-Butanone	18	25°	Carbon tetrachloride	2.2	25°
Isobutanol	18	25°	Cyclohexane	2.0	25°
Benzaldehyde	17.8	20°	n-nonane	1.97	20°
n-Butanol	17.7	17°	n-heptane	1.97	20°
Acetophenone	17.4	25°	n-octane	1.96	20°
Cyclohexanol	15	25°	n-hexane	1.90	15°
Ethylenediamine	14.2	25°	n-pentane	1.85	20°

b) *Reference electrodes and junction potentials*

As we have seen in Chapter VI, reference electrodes are of two types: with and without liquid junctions.

When a liquid junction is used, it may be possible to use aqueous reference electrodes (*e.g.* Hg/Hg_2Cl_2/saturated KCl) whose potential is known very precisely; but then the junction potential between the two solvents may be large, is practically impossible to measure accurately, and is not always reproducible. Moreover, such a reference electrode cannot be used if the electrolysis solution must be kept anhydrous.

It is better to use a reference electrode with the same solvent which is used in the electrolysis cell. The junction potential is then much smaller, and more reproducible. The potentials must then be referred to an arbitrary zero.

This is also true for reference electrodes without a liquid junction. Each solvent has therefore its own scale of potentials, which can only be qualitatively related to each other.

In practice, any fast system whose components are sufficiently soluble in the solvent in question, and whose activities remain constant, can be used for the reference electrode.

The following systems have been used as reference electrodes:
silver/saturated silver chloride/chloride, in the following solvents: water–dioxane (with HCl), methanol, glycerol (0.1 M LiCl), acetone (HCl), acetonitrile (saturated trimethylethylammonium chloride, 0.118 M), acetic acid (saturated KCl or LiCl), arsenic trichloride (tetramethylammonium chloride), fused eutectic mixture of LiCl–KCl, fused NaCl;
silver/10^{-2} M silver nitrate, in acetonitrile;
silver/5 % silver bromide, in fused mixture of aluminium bromide and sodium bromide, at 226° C;
mercury/saturated calomel/chloride, in acetone (saturated LiCl), acetic acid (saturated LiCl), fused eutectic mixture of lithium nitrate, sodium nitrate and potassium nitrate (0.5 % KCl);
cadmium/cadmium chloride, in formamide;
lead/0.01 M lead nitrate, in liquid ammonia;
platinum/M PtCl$_2$, in fused eutectic mixture of lithium chloride and potassium chloride.

Many authors have simply used a metallic electrode of large surface area, *e.g.* a mercury surface, as the constant-potential electrode (see p. 149).

Types of non-aqueous solvents

We may distinguish three types of solvents other than water.

A mixture of water with an organic solvent

The first thing a solvent has to do is to dissolve the chemical species under investigation. Many organic substances are not very soluble in water, and therefore cannot often be electrolyzed in aqueous solution. The addition of an organic solvent which is miscible with water allows many more organic substances to be dissolved.

The most commonly used solvents for this purpose are methanol, ethanol, butanol, glycerol, acetone, ethylene glycol, dioxane, pyridine, etc. (see the table below for references to the use of these solvents).

Anhydrous solvents

It is sometimes desirable to avoid the use of water, perhaps in order to dissolve a certain substance, perhaps because the electrochemical properties of water limit the oxidation or reduction.

But the use of anhydrous solvents presents certain problems:

1) It is often difficult to remove the last traces of some electroactive impurity which might affect the results. Water is a particular problem in this respect; it can

usually cause trouble at concentrations as low as $10^{-5} M$ (*i.e.* about $10^{-4}\%$ for a solvent of density 1).

2) The anhydrous solvent must be able to dissolve electrolytes, so as to allow current to pass.

3) Finally, some difficulties may be encountered with the use of reference electrodes.

The most common anhydrous solvents used at room temperature are alcohols (*e.g.* methanol, ethanol, isopropanol, butanol, glycol, glycerol), acids (*e.g.* formic, acetic, sulphuric), ethers, acetone, formamide, dimethylformamide, ethylenediamine, acetonitrile, liquid ammonia, etc.

It is also possible to use as solvents substances which are solid at normal temperatures, by heating them above their melting points. Amides, such as acetamide (m.p. $81°$ C), N-methyl propionamide, N-methyl butyramide, and urea have been used in this way. Glycerol, which is too viscous to use at normal temperatures, has been used between 70 and $120°$ C.

These latter solvents are more easily dehydrated.

Fused salts

Fused salts have also been used as solvents, because salts and oxides are soluble in them. In general, a pure salt with a sufficiently low melting point, or an eutectic mixture with a low melting point, is used. The salt or mixture of salts must be stable above the melting point, easy to purify and to dehydrate, and be strongly ionized.

A large number of salts which have a low melting point are unstable above the melting point, and give electroactive decomposition products; nevertheless, the following may be used:

ammonium formate (m.p. $116°$ C, used at $125°$ C);

eutectic mixture of ammonium nitrate, lithium nitrate and ammonium chloride (m.p. $86°$ C, used at $125°$ C);

eutectic mixture of lithium nitrate, sodium nitrate and potassium nitrate (m.p. $120°$ C, used at $160°$ C).

The use of the dropping mercury electrode in fused salts is limited to the above three systems.

Systems which melt above $200°$ C are on the whole easier to purify and more stable:

potassium nitrate (m.p. $334°$ C, used at $360°$ C);

eutectic mixture of potassium nitrate and potassium bisulphate (used between $360°$ C and $520°$ C);

eutectic mixture of potassium nitrate and potassium chloride (used between $360°$ C and $520°$ C);

eutectic mixture of lithium chloride and potassium chloride (used between $380°$ C and $450°$ C);

eutectic mixture of aluminium bromide and sodium bromide ($225-300°$ C);

eutectic mixture of aluminium chloride and sodium chloride ($234°$ C);

eutectic mixture of aluminium chloride and potassium chloride ($300°$ C);

potassium chloride (m.p. $776°$ C, used at $800°$ C);

carnallite (KCl, $MgCl_2$, 6 H_2O) (at $735°$ C);

sodium chloride (m.p. $801°$ C).

TABLE III

REFERENCES TO THE MOST COMMONLY USED SOLVENTS

Mixtures of water with organic solvents

water–acetone	2, 16, 17, 18, 21.
water–butanol	16.
water–dioxane	1, 2, 22, 23.
water–ethanol	2, 6, 10, 11, 12, 13, 15, 16.
water–ethyleneglycol	73.
water–glycerol	8, 9, 11.
water–isopropanol	19.
water–methanol	2, 11, 16, 20, 24.
water–pyridine	3, 14.

Anhydrous solvents

Acetamide	50, 59, 79, 81.
Acetone	43, 59, 65, 131.
Acetonitrile	44, 51, 52, 53, 59, 60, 67, 68, 69, 72, 94, 95, 96, 98.
Acetic acid	33, 34, 39, 42, 59, 64, 74, 82, 84, 99, 100, 101, 104, 105, 112, 113, 115, 121, 122, 123, 127, 130, 135, 137, 138, 139.
Formic acid	45, 58, 59, 129, 131, 132.
Methanesulphonic acid	63.
Sulphuric acid	40, 41, 59.
Liquid ammonia	36, 37, 38, 45, 59, 78.
Acetic anhydride	87.
Dimethylformamide	27, 49, 53, 54, 59, 60, 61, 70, 71, 75, 76.
Dioxane	65.
Ethanol	30, 45, 55, 59, 65, 116, 118, 119.
Ethers	45, 89, 90, 91, 92, 93, 114.
Ethylenediamine	56, 59, 66, 86, 124, 140.
Ethyleneglycol	35, 45, 59, 73.
Formamide	26, 48, 50, 59, 77, 81, 103, 109, 117.
Glycerol	46, 47, 59.
Hexone (methylisobutylcetone)	59, 141.
Hydrocarbons	65, 88, 130.
Isopropanol	59, 108.
Methanol	45, 59, 104, 108, 118, 119, 126.
Nitrobenzene	121, 122, 128, 130.
Pyridine	59, 97, 106, 127, 131.
Arsenic trichloride	107.
Fused urea	57.

Mixtures of organic solvents

Formic acid + acetic acid	142.
Acetic acid + pyridine	136.
Ethyleneglycol + butanol or chloroform	120.
Ethyleneglycol + dioxane	73.
Formamide + acetamide	50.

Fused salts

Borax	172, 173, 174, 177.
Chlorides	148, 153, 161, 162, 175, 179, 181, 184, 187, 191, 198, 199, 201, 206, 207, 208.
Lithium chloride–potassium chloride	156, 163, 167, 169, 170, 171, 181, 182, 197, 203, 211, 213, 214.
Sodium chloride–calcium chloride	212.
Potassium chloride–magnesium chloride	149.
Aluminium halides–alkali halides	145, 151, 158, 160, 168, 191.
Fluorides	176, 183, 185, 186.
Ammonium formate	164.
Ammonium and lithium nitrate + ammonium chloride	143.
Lithium, sodium and potassium nitrates	146.
Perchlorates	210.
Sulphates, bisulphates	147, 210.

References p. 355–359

EXAMPLES

Voltammetry

The system H_2/H^+ in water-acetone mixtures [18]

At a platinized platinum electrode, hydrogen ions, weak acids and water can be reduced as follows

$$2\,H^+ + 2e \to H_2$$

$$2\,HA + 2e \to H_2 + 2\,A^-$$

$$2\,H_2O + 2e \to H_2 + 2\,OH^-$$

If the solution contains dissolved hydrogen, this can be oxidized by the reverse reactions

$$H_2 - 2e \to 2\,H^+$$

$$H_2 + 2\,A^- - 2e \to 2\,HA$$

$$H_2 + 2\,OH^- - 2e \to 2\,H_2O$$

in the presence of a weak base A^- or of a strong base.

The current–potential curves for these systems in aqueous medium are shown in Figs. 73 and 74 (Chapter III).

The change in the shape of these curves when acetone is added to the solution gives an indication of the effect of a decrease in the dielectric constant on the strength of acids and bases. Figs. 399, 400 and 401 show the current–potential curves for solutions of perchloric and acetic acids, with or without hydrogen. It is assumed that perchloric acid remains a strong (completely dissociated) acid even when the solution contains a large amount of acetone.

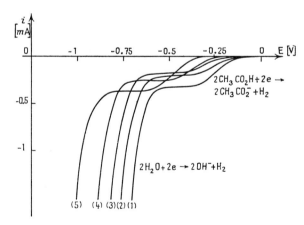

Fig. 399. Current–potential curves of $2 \times 10^{-3}\ M$ acetic acid in water–acetone mixtures. Nitrogen atmosphere. Platinized platinum electrode. Solution contains 0.5 M NaClO$_4$.

Curve 1: no acetone.   Curve 4: 75% acetone.
Curve 2: 25% acetone.   Curve 5: 90% acetone.
Curve 3: 50% acetone.

(after ROSSET and TRÉMILLON [18]).

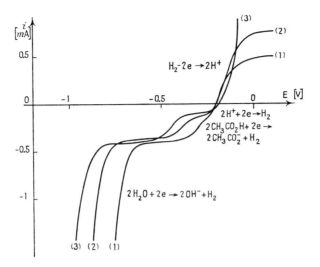

Fig. 400. Current–potential curves of 7×10^{-4} M perchloric acid $+ 2 \times 10^{-3}$ M acetic acid in water–acetone mixtures saturated with hydrogen. Platinized platinum electrode. Solution contains 0.5 M NaClO$_4$.

Curve 1: 20 % acetone.   Curve 3: 85 % acetone.
Curve 2: 60 % acetone.

(after ROSSET and TRÉMILLON[18]).

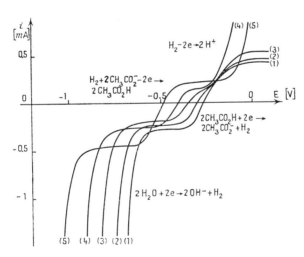

Fig. 401. Current–potential curves of 2×10^{-3} M acetic acid $+ 2 \times 10^{-3}$ M sodium acetate in water–acetone mixtures saturated with hydrogen. Platinized platinum electrode. Solution contains 0.5 M NaClO$_4$.

Curve 1: no acetone.   Curve 4: 75 % acetone.
Curve 2: 25 % acetone.   Curve 5: 95 % acetone.
Curve 3: 50 % acetone.

(after ROSSET and TRÉMILLON[18]).

The ionization constant of water, $K_{H_2O} = |H^+|\,|OH^-|$, is lowered by the addition of acetone, *i.e.* water becomes a weaker acid as acetone is added to it. This is reflected in the fact that the voltage gap between the reduction curves of H^+ ions and of water itself increases from 400 mV in pure water to 650 mV in a medium containing 85 % acetone.

Acetic acid, which is a weak acid of the same type as water, also becomes weaker as acetone is added to the solution. Its reduction curve is therefore displaced in much the same way as that of water. The reduction wave of perchloric acid is practically indistinguishable from that of dilute acetic acid in aqueous solution, but they are separated by about 200 mV in 85 % acetone.

The solubility of hydrogen increases with the proportion of acetone, leading to the rapid increase of the limiting diffusion for the oxidation of H_2 to H^+, such that the step for this reaction can no longer be recorded.

The reduction of hydrogen ions in acetonitrile[51, 52, 68]

Acetonitrile is less basic than water. We may represent the solvation of a proton in this solvent by the equation

$$CH_3CN + H^+ \rightleftharpoons HCH_3CN^+$$

which is analogous to

$$H_2O + H^+ \rightleftharpoons H_3O^+$$

Acid–base equilibria in acetonitrile

$$HA + CH_3CN \rightleftharpoons HCH_3CN^+ + A^-$$

are therefore not so far over to the right-hand side as the corresponding equilibria in water. However, perchloric acid still acts as a strong acid (completely dissociated) in acetonitrile, *i.e.* the equilibrium

$$CH_3CN + HClO_4 \rightleftharpoons HCH_3CN^+ + ClO_4^-$$

(or in a more general form $HClO_4 \rightleftharpoons H^+$ solvated $+ ClO_4^-$) is still right over to the right hand side.

The reduction of a solution of perchloric acid in acetonitrile at a dropping mercury electrode has a half-wave potential which is much less negative than that in water (the potentials being referred to a saturated calomel electrode with water as the solvent in both cases). This is partly due to the fact that hydrogen ions are much less solvated, and partly because the overvoltage of hydrogen at the mercury electrode is much less in acetonitrile than in water (about 0.8 V).

Water acts like a base in acetonitrile, *i.e.* the equilibrium

$$HCH_3CN^+ + H_2O \rightleftharpoons H_3O^+ + CH_3CN \tag{1}$$

(or in a more general form $H^+ + H_2O \rightleftharpoons H_3O^+$) is practically right over to the right-hand side.

The reduction wave of perchloride acid (solvated H^+) is rapidly displaced towards more negative potentials by the addition of water (Fig. 402). This is partly due to the displacement of the current–potential curves by the chemical reaction (1) (see Chapter III), and partly to the rapid increase in the overvoltage of hydrogen at the mercury electrode as water is added.

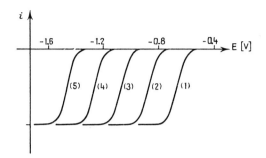

Fig. 402. Reduction of 10^{-3} N perchloric acid in acetonitrile, in the presence of an increasing excess of water. Reference electrode: $Hg\downarrow/Hg_2Cl_2\downarrow/$saturated KCl in water.

Curve 1: no water;   Curve 4: $|H_2O| = 1.0\ M$;
Curve 2: $|H_2O| = 10^{-2}\ M$;   Curve 5: $|H_2O| = 3.0$ M.
Curve 3: $|H_2O| = 0.1\ M$;

(after COETZEE and KOLTHOFF[68]).

The limiting current is proportional to the concentration between 5×10^{-4} and $5 \times 10^{-3}\ M$, and is about half of that in water, since the diffusion constant D_0 of solvated hydrogen ions is about $\frac{1}{4}$ of that in water. The limiting current does not increase, however, as water is added up to a concentration of 2%, since the mobilities of the ions HCH_3CN^+ and H_3O^+ are practically equal. When the concentration of water exceeds 5% the limiting current decreases, mainly owing to an increase in the viscosity of the solution.

Perchloric acid is the only substance which remains a strong acid in acetonitrile. The reduction waves of perchloric acid and acetic acid are separated by about 1.6 V. Anionic acids (HSO_4^-, $H_2PO_4^-$, $HC_2O_4^-$) give no reduction waves, and must thus be assumed to be extremely weak.

Coulometry

Coulometry of acids in water–acetone mixtures[21]

The current–potential curves shown in Figs. 399 to 401 indicate that perchloric acid and acetic acid are reduced at different potentials independently of each other in media containing a high concentration of acetone. The possibility thus arises of determining small amount of these two acids separately:

Coulometry at constant current has been used to determine acids and bases in aqueous solution (see Chapter X). In a mixture of water and a solvent which is not reducible before water (*e.g.* acetone), the reduction of water gives rise to OH^- ions

$$2\ H_2O + 2e \rightarrow H_2 + 2\ OH^-$$

Part of the current goes to reduce H^+ ions (perchloric acid) and acetic acid

$$2\ CH_3CO_2H + 2e \rightarrow H_2 + CH_3CO_2^-$$
$$2\ H^+ + 2e \rightarrow H_2$$

but the $CH_3CO_2^-$ and OH^- ions formed react quantitatively with H^+ ions, so the overall effect is as if only perchloric acid was reduced at a current equal to the imposed current. When all the perchloric acid has been consumed, the acetic acid is reduced with the same current, and then the water is reduced to give an excess of hydroxyl ions.

The phenomena at a bright platinum electrode are the same as those at a platinized platinum electrode.

Dissolved oxygen does not interfere with the determination, since its reduction leads to the disappearance of one hydrogen ion per electron, just like the reduction of the acids

$$O_2 + 4\,H^+ + 4e \rightarrow 2\,H_2O$$

Coulometry of acids in acetonitrile[96]

Acids can also be titrated by electrochemical reduction in this solvent. When enough water is added, the reduction reaction

$$2\,H_2O + 2e \rightarrow H_2 + 2\,OH^-$$

takes place, and the hydroxyl ions react quantitatively with the acids in solution. The current yield for the reduction of the acids is thus 100 %.

It is not possible to differentiate between those acids which are stronger than H_3O^+ by this method, since they all react with water to give H_3O^+.

Potentiometry and amperometry

A titration may be followed by potentiometry or amperometry in non-aqueous media as well as in water. It is advisable to use two indicator electrodes, so that there is no need for a reference electrode.

Potentiometric and amperometric titrations of acids in water–acetone mixtures[21]

The use of potentiometry to follow acid–base titrations in solvents other than water is well established, and has been described in many publications. We will only give one example here, to illustrate how the current–potential curves may be used in the setting up of a method of determining the end point.

The curves of Figs. 400 and 401 allow the shape of the titration curves of a mixture of 10^{-3} N perchloric acid and 10^{-3} N acetic acid in a solution containing 85 % acetone and saturated with hydrogen, with platinized platinum electrodes, to be predicted.

Fig. 403 shows the amperometric titration curves for potential differences of 100 mV and 15 mV between the electrodes, and the potentiometric titration curve for a constant current of 5.4 μA. These titrations were carried out coulometrically.

Potentiometric and amperometric titrations in a fused eutectic mixture of lithium chloride and potassium chloride[214]

Here are the standard potentials of certain systems in LiCl–KCl at 450° C

$$\text{Fe(III)} + e \rightleftharpoons \text{Fe(II)} \qquad E_0 = 0.09 \text{ V}$$
$$\text{Cr(III)} + e \rightleftharpoons \text{Cr(II)} \qquad E_0 = -0.52 \text{ V}$$
$$\text{V(III)} + e \rightleftharpoons \text{V(II)} \qquad E_0 = -0.75 \text{ V}$$

(with respect to the reference electrode Pt/0.05 M Pt(II)). Fe(III) thus oxidizes Cr(II) and V(II).

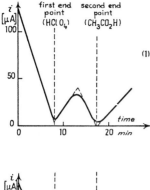

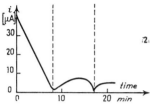

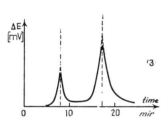

Fig. 403. Coulometric titrations of 10^{-3} M perchloric acid + 10^{-3} M acetic acid in water + 85 % acetone. Two platinized platinum indicator electrodes. (1) Amperometric titration curve at constant voltage (100 mV). (2) Amperometric titration curve at constant voltage (15 mV). (3) Potentiometric titration curve at constant current (5.4 μA).
(after Rosset and Trémillon [21]).

Fig. 404. Coulometric titration at constant current (1.059 mA) of 4.7×10^{-4} M Cr(II) with Fe(III). Curve 1: potentiometry with a graphite electrode. Curve 2: amperometry with a platinum electrode at $E = -0.1$ V (with respect to Pt/Pt(II)). Curve 3: amperometry with two platinum electrodes, $\Delta E = 0.25$ V.
(after Laitinen and Bhatia [214]).

Fig. 404 shows the titration curves of Cr(II) with Fe(III). The titrations have been followed potentiometrically (curve 1), amperometrically with one platinum indicator electrode (curve 2), and amperometrically with two platinum indicator electrodes (curve 3). The titration curves of V(II) with Fe(III) are similar.

These titrations were realized coulometrically at constant current by the oxidation of Fe(II) at a graphite electrode.

Recent electrochemical methods

Chronopotentiometry in fused salts[211],[213]

The current–potential curves at a fixed platinum micro-electrode for solutions of bismuth(III) chloride, cadmium(II) chloride, silver(I) chloride and copper(I) chloride in an eutectic mixture of lithium chloride and potassium chloride at 450° C confirm the theoretical relationship between the transition time, the electrolysis current and the concentration (see Chapter XII, p. 315).

Fig. 405 shows a curve obtained with a solution of cadmium chloride.

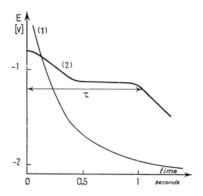

Fig. 405. Chronopotentiometry in fused LiCl + KCl. Pt/M Pt^{2+} reference electrode; platinum indicator electrode. Curve 1: solvent only, I_0 = 1.16 × 10^{-2} A/cm^2. Curve 2: 2.08 × 10^{-3} M CdCl$_2$, I_0 = 15.8 μA/cm^2 (after LAITINEN and GAUR[213]).

The diffusion constants determined from the transition times are considerably greater than in water. D_0 is found to decrease with the charge on the ion, which is characteristic of solvation by chloride ions; the number of solvating Cl$^-$ ions, and thus the effective size of the ion, increases with the charge.

Electrolytic deposition of metals in non-aqueous media

Certain metals (the alkali metals, alkaline earth metals, beryllium, aluminium, zirconium, titanium, uranium, etc.) cannot be deposited electrochemically from aqueous solutions, since water is reduced before the metallic cations or corresponding compounds. The use of non-aqueous solvents where the limit of electroactivity is shifted to considerably lower potentials should in principle allow such metals to be deposited.

The oldest industrial application of this principle consists in the electrolysis of a fused salt of the metal which it is wished to prepare[180], e.g. sodium chloride or sodium hydroxide in the preparation of sodium. It is sometimes possible to add other salts which form a eutectic mixture with a lower melting point, as long as the added cations are not reduced until the potential is considerably lower that that used. For example, a mixture of magnesium chloride, calcium and sodium chloride is used in the electrolytic preparation of magnesium.

The most important example of electrolysis in fused salts is the preparation of aluminium. The electrolysis medium consists of a mixture of fused alumina, Al$_2$O$_3$, cryolite, Na$_3$AlF$_6$, and fluorspar, CaF$_2$. The fluorspar is used mainly as flux. Na$^+$ and AlF$_6$$^{3-}$ ions produced by the dissociation of the cryolite have been found in the melt, and the alumina can dissociate to give solvated Al^{3+} and AlO$_3$$^{3-}$ ions. The oxidizable components of the mixture are oxygen (oxidation state = − 2) in the form of AlO$_3$$^{3-}$ ions, and fluorine (oxidation state = − 1) in the form of AlF$_6$$^{3-}$ ions. At a graphite electrode, the former ionic species is sometimes oxidized to give oxygen; but more often the graphite is "burnt", and carbon monoxide is evolved. The voltage required for electrolysis is thereby considerably reduced. The oxidation curve of graphite in the presence of AlO_3^{3-} ions is probably situated at lower potentials than that of oxygen ions.

The reducible components are: aluminium (oxidation state $= +3$), calcium (oxidation state $= +2$), and sodium (oxidation state $= +1$). The first of these is the main substance to be reduced at the cathode, giving the molten metal. The overall result is thus the disappearance of alumina by electrolysis, and the melt may be considered as a solution of alumina in a mixture of fused cryolite and fluorspar, even though the solvent also contains the metal which is to be prepared.

It is also possible to dissolve a compound of the metal to be prepared in a melt of the salts of other metals, as long as these are not deposited at the potentials used (alkali metal salts are generally used for this purpose). This method has become of considerable interest recently. For example, beryllium chloride, titanium chloride and uranyl chloride have been electrolyzed in mixtures of fused alkali chlorides (LiCl + KCl, NaCl + KCl)[181]. The solvated (by Cl⁻) metal ions are reduced at the cathode, while chlorine is evolved at the anode. Other metallic compounds such as oxides can also be dissolved in fused alkali chlorides, in which case the chloride may only act as solvent, without participating in the electrochemical reactions.

Attempts have also been made to deposit metals from solution in various organic solvents[77-94], e.g. acetic acid, ethylenediamine, formamide, acetamide, acetonitrile, and ethers. It is then necessary to find compounds of the metals which are sufficiently soluble in the organic solvent, and at the same time to find compounds which are sufficiently ionized to allow a current to pass.

For example, BRENNER et al.[89-92] have electrolyzed ethereal solutions of compounds like the halides, hydrides, borohydrides and organometallic compounds of aluminium, beryllium, magnesium, titanium and zirconium. These compounds must not contain oxygen or nitrogen, which are too firmly bound to these metals; and they must be solvated, but not too much, which is why ethers are used as solvents. The authors generally used a mixture of two such compounds; for example, $AlCl_3$ dissolved in ether does not conduct electricity, and neither does $LiNH_4$, but a mixture of the two does, and can be used to deposit aluminium. The authors have succeeded in depositing alloys in this way: Mg–B from $MgBr_2 + LiBH_4$, Mg–Al from $MgBr_2 + AlBr_3 + LiAlH_4$, Be–B, Be–Al, Ti–Al and Zr–Al. These deposits usually adhere well to the electrode, unlike those obtained with fused salts; but unfortunately metals deposited from organic solution are often contaminated with carbon, and it may therefore be better to deposit them from a fused salt medium.

The table given below lists certain metals in the order of their electrolytic deposition in a number of solvents, according to the values of their half-wave potentials given in the literature. The solvents and electrodes which are listed are the following: water, mercury and platinum electrodes; liquid ammonia, mercury electrode[36,37,38]; acetonitrile, mercury and platinum electrodes[67]; N,N'-dimethylformamide, mercury electrode[71]; formamide-acetamide, mercury electrode[50]; ethylene diamine, mercury electrode[66]; eutectic mixture of alkali nitrates, mercury electrode[146]; and eutectic mixture of alkali chlorides, platinum electrode[170,171].

SOLVENT	ELECTRODE		
WATER	Mercury	{ Reduction of water } Li-Ca-K-Sr-Na-Rb-Ba-Al—Mn—Cr/Fe-Co—Ni-Zn—Cd—Pb—Cu—Ag—‖ Oxidation of mercury / Oxidation of water	
	Platinum	{ Reduction of water } Tl—Pb—Cu—Ag-Hg—‖ Oxidation of water ←→ 500 mV	
LIQUID AMMONIA (−36° C)	Mercury	---Li—Na-K-Rb-Cs————Cu————Tl----	
DIMETHYL FORMAMIDE	Mercury	{ Reduction of indifferent electrolyte (R_4N^+) } Li-Ca-Sr-K-Na-Ba-Rb-Co-Zn-Ni————Cu—‖ Oxidation of mercury	
FORMAMIDE ACETAMIDE	Mercury	{ Reduction of indifferent electrolyte } K————Zn————Pb-Tl—‖ Oxidation of mercury	
ETHYLENE DIAMINE	Mercury	{ Reduction of indifferent electrolyte or solvent? } Ag-Ba-Ca-Mg-Sr-Zn————Pb————Cd-Tl—‖ Oxidation of mercury	
ACETONITRILE	Mercury	{ Reduction of indifferent electrolyte } Li-Rb-Na-Mg-K-Ca-Sr-Ba-Be-Al—Mn-Cr-Fe—Zn-Co-Cd-Cu-Ni—Ag—‖ Oxidation of mercury	
	Platinum	{ Reduction of indifferent electrolyte } Li————Zn————Cd-Cu————Ag————Hg—‖ Oxidation of acetonitrile ←→ 2 V	
FUSED EUTECTIC LiNO₃-NaNO₃-KNO₃ (160° C)	Mercury	{ Reduction of nitrates } Zn————Cd-Pb-Ni—‖ Oxidation of mercury	
FUSED EUTECTIC LiCl-KCl (450° C)	Platinum	{ Reduction of solvent (deposition of K-Li) } Al-Cr—Zn-Tl—Cd—Cu-Pb-Co-Sn-Ga-In-Hg-Bi————‖ Oxidation of platinum	
	Graphite	{ Reduction of solvent } Pb—‖ Oxidation of chlorides	

1 volt

REFERENCES

Electrochemistry in non-aqueous solvents

G. KORTÜM and J. O'M. BOCKRIS, *Electrochemistry*, Elsevier Publ. Co., Amsterdam, 1951.
I. M. KOLTHOFF and J. J. LINGANE, *Polarography*, Interscience Publ., Inc., New York, 1952, Vol. I, p. 99.
T. MOELLER, *Inorganic Chemistry*, John Wiley and Sons, New York, 1952, p. 337.
L. F. AUDRIETH and J. KLEINBERG, *Non-Aqueous Solvents*, John Wiley and Sons, New York, 1953.
G. W. C. MILNER, *Polarography*, Longmans Green and Co., London, 1957, p. 140.

—, *review*

V. GUTMANN and G. SCHÖBER, *Angew. Chem.*, 70 (1958) 98.

Electrochemistry in mixtures of water and an organic solvent

—, *conductivity measurements*

[1] B. B. OWEN and G. W. WATERS, *J. Am. Chem. Soc.*, 60 (1938) 2371.
[2] C. BERTIN, *Anal. Chim. Acta*, 7 (1952) 105.
[3] H. WILSKI and G. KORTÜM, *Z. physik. Chem.*, 5 (1955) 333.

—, *influence of the viscosity on the diffusion current*

[4] D. M. BRASHER and F. R. JONES, *Trans. Faraday Soc.*, 42 (1946) 775.
[5] I. VAVRUCH, *Collection Czechoslov. Chem. Communs.*, 12 (1947) 429.
[6] G. MATSUYAMA, *Ph. D. Thesis*, University of Minnesota, 1948.
[7] H. A. MCKENZIE, *J. Council Sci. Ind. Research Australia*, 21 (1948) 210.
[8] YA. I. TUR'YAN and P. A. VYSOTSKII, *Doklady Akad. Nauk SSSR*, 103 (1955) 1053.
[9] J. JORDAN, E. A. ACKERMAN and R. L. BERGER, *J. Am. Chem. Soc.*, 78 (1956) 2979.

—, *voltammetry* (see also references 6, 8 and 9)

[10] E. S. PERACCHIO and V. W. MELOCHE, *J. Am. Chem. Soc.*, 60 (1938) 1770.
[11] A. M. ZAN'KO and F. A. MANUSAVA, *J. Gen. Chem. (U.S.S.R.)*, 10 (1940) 1171.
[12] I. ZLOTOWSKI and I. M. KOLTHOFF, *J. Am. Chem. Soc.*, 64 (1942) 1297.
[13] I. ZLOTOWSKI and I. M. KOLTHOFF, *Ind. Eng. Chem., Anal. Ed.*, 14 (1942) 473.
[14] M. CALVIN and R. H. BAILES, *J. Am. Chem. Soc.*, 68 (1946) 949.
[15] O. D. SHREVE and E. C. MARKHAM, *J. Am. Chem. Soc.*, 74 (1949) 2993.
[16] P. K. MIGAL, YA. I. TUR'YAN and N. I. BONDARENKO, *Zhur. Fiz. Khim.*, 71 (1956) 2003.
[17] T. ASAHARA and S. HAYANO, *Abura Kagaku*, 5 (1956) 952.
[18] R. ROSSET and B. TRÉMILLON, *Bull. soc. chim.*, (1959) 135.

—, *coulometry*

[19] W. N. CARSON JR. and R. KO, *Anal. Chem.*, 23 (1951) 1019.
[20] A. P. MADHAVAN NAVI and S. H. IBRAHIM, *J. Sci. Ind. Research*, 15 B (1956) 703.
[21] R. ROSSET and B. TRÉMILLON, *Bull. Soc. Chim.*, (1959) 139.

—, *potentiometric and amperometric acid–base titrations*

[22] C. C. LYNCH and V. K. LA MER, *J. Am. Chem. Soc.*, 60 (1938) 1252.
[23] H. S. HARNED, F. WALKER and C. CALMON, *J. Am. Chem. Soc.*, 61 (1939) 44.
[24] K. SCHWABE and S. ZIEGENBALG, *Z. Elektrochem.*, 62 (1958) 172.

Electrochemistry in anhydrous solvents

—, *conductivity measurements*

[25] V. K. LA MER and H. C. DOWNES, *J. Am. Chem. Soc.*, 53 (1931) 888.
[26] L. R. DAWSON, T. M. NEWELL and W. J. MCCREARY, *J. Am. Chem. Soc.*, 76 (1954) 6024.
[27] D. P. AMES and P. G. SEARS, *J. Phys. Chem.*, 59 (1955) 16.
[28] E. D. WILHOIT and P. G. SEARS, *Trans. Kentucky Acad. Sci.*, 17 (1956) 123.
[29] L. R. DAWSON, E. D. WILHOIT, R. R. HOLMES and P. G. SEARS, *J. Am. Chem. Soc.*, 79 (1957) 3004.
[30] A. M. EL-AGGAN and D. C. BRADLEY, *J. Chem. Soc.*, (1958) 2092.
[31] L. R. DAWSON, G. R. LESTER and P. G. SEARS, *J. Am. Chem. Soc.*, 80 (1958) 4233.

—, *a complete list of references up to 1950 is given in*

[32] G. KORTÜM and J. O'M. BOCKRIS, *Electrochemistry*, Elsevier Publ. Co., Amsterdam, 1951, Vol. II.

—, *voltammetry*

[33] D. MCGILLAVRY, *Trans. Faraday Soc.*, 32 (1936) 1447.

[34] G. B. BACHMAN and M. J. ASTLE, *J. Am. Chem. Soc.*, 64 (1942) 1303.
[35] C. H. R. GENTRY, *Nature*, 157 (1946) 479.
[36] H. A. LAITINEN and C. J. NYMAN, *J. Am. Chem. Soc.*, 70 (1948) 2241, 3002.
[37] C. J. NYMAN, *J. Am. Chem. Soc.*, 71 (1949) 3914.
[38] H. A. LAITINEN and C. E. SHOEMAKER, *J. Am. Chem. Soc.*, 72 (1950) 663, 4975.
[39] A. W. DAVIDSON and F. JIRIK, *J. Am. Chem. Soc.*, 72 (1950) 1700.
[40] J. C. JAMES, *Trans. Faraday Soc.*, 47 (1951) 1240.
[41] A. A. VLCEK, *Chem. listy*, 46 (1952) 258.
[42] I. BERGMAN and J. C. JAMES, *Trans. Faraday Soc.*, 48 (1952) 956.
[43] P. ARTHUR and H. LYONS, *Anal. Chem.*, 24 (1952) 1422.
[44] S. WAWZONEK and M. E. RUNNER, *J. Electrochem. Soc.*, 99 (1952) 457.
[45] J. O'M. BOCKRIS, *J. Chim. phys.*, 49 (1952) C 41.
[46] N. RADIN and T. DE VRIES, *Anal. Chem.*, 24 (1952), 971.
[47] T. DE VRIES and D. B. BRUSS, *J. Electrochem. Soc.*, 100 (1953) 445.
[48] H. LETAW JR. and A. H. GROPP, *J. Phys. Chem.*, 57 (1953) 964.
[49] R. L. EDSBERG, D. W. EICHLIN and J. J. GARIS, *Anal. Chem.*, 25 (1953) 798.
[50] J. H. HOOK, H. LETAW JR. and A. H. GROPP *J. Phys. Chem.*, 58 (1954) 81.
[51] A. A. VLCEK, *Chem. listy*, 48 (1954) 1741.
[52] A. A. VLCEK, *Collection Czechoslov. Chem. Communs.*, 20 (1955) 636.
[53] S. WAWZONEK, E. W. BLAHA, R. BERKEY and M. E. RUNNER, *J. Electrochem. Soc.*, 102 (1955) 235.
[54] R. BERKEY, *Dissert. Abstr.*, 15 (1955) 953.
[55] A. A. VLCEK, *Chem. listy*, 40 (1955) 28.
[56] W. B. SCHAAP, A. E. MESSNER and F. C. SCHMIDT, *J. Am. Chem. Soc.*, 77 (1955) 2683.
[57] E. VECCHI and G. ZULIANI, *Ricerca sci.*, 25 (1955) 2667.
[58] T. A. PINFOLD and F. SEBBA, *J. Am. Chem. Soc.*, 78 (1956) 2095, 5193.
[59] A. T. TOROPOV and A. M. YAKUBOV, *Zhur. Fiz. Khim.*, 30 (1956) 1702.
[60] S. WAWZONEK, R. BERKEY, E. W. BLAHA and M. E. RUNNER, *J. Electrochem. Soc.*, 103 (1956) 456.
[61] A. FINDEIS and T. DE VRIES, *Anal. Chem.*, 28 (1956) 209.
[62] E. Y. GORENBEIN, *J. Gen. Chem. (U.S.S.R.)*, 26 (1956) 2351.
[63] S. WAWZONEK, R. BERKEY and D. THOMSON, *J. Electrochem. Soc.*, 103 (1956) 513.
[64] J. CIHALIK and J. SIMEK, *Chem. listy*, 51 (1957) 1283.
[65] K. SCHWABE, *Z. Elektrochem.*, 61 (1957) 484.
[66] V. GUTMANN and G. SCHÖBER, *Monatsh. Chem.*, 88 (1957) 206.
[67] I. M. KOLTHOFF and J. F. COETZEE, *J. Am. Chem. Soc.*, 79 (1957) 870, 1852.
[68] J. F. COETZEE and I. M. KOLTHOFF, *J. Am. Chem. Soc.*, 79 (1957) 6110.
[69] A. I. POPOV and D. H. GESKE, *J. Am. Chem. Soc.*, 79 (1957) 2074.
[70] A. B. THOMAS and E. G. ROCHOW, *J. Am. Chem. Soc.*, 79 (1957) 1843.
[71] G. H. BROWN and R. AL-URFALI, *J. Am. Chem. Soc.*, 80 (1958) 2113.
[72] A. I. POPOV and D. H. GESKE, *J. Am. Chem. Soc.*, 80 (1958) 1340.
[73] M. EISENBERG and R. E. DE LA RUE, *J. Electrochem. Soc.*, 105 (1958) 162.
[74] L. STARKA, A. VYSTRCIL and B. STARKOVA, *Collection Czechoslov. Chem. Communs.*, 23 (1958) 206.
[75] P. H. GIVEN, M. E. PEOVER and J. SCHOEN, *J. Chem. Soc.*, (1958) 2674.
[76] F. L. LAMBERT, *Anal. Chem.*, 30 (1958) 1018.

—, *electrolytic deposition of metals*

[77] H. RÖHLER, *Z. Elektrochem.*, 16 (1940) 419.
[78] L. F. AUDRIETH and L. F. YNTEMA, *J. Phys. Chem.*, 34 (1930) 1903.
[79] L. F. YNTEMA and L. F. AUDRIETH, *J. Am. Chem. Soc.*, 52 (1930) 2693.
[80] L. F. AUDRIETH and H. W. NELSON, *Chem. Revs.*, 8 (1931) 335.
[81] L. F. AUDRIETH, L. F. YNTEMA and H. W. NELSON, *Trans, Illinois State Acad. Sci.*, 23 (1931) 302.
[82] L. F. AUDRIETH, R. E. MEINTS and E. E. JUKKOLA, *Trans. Illinois State Acad. Sci.*, 24 (1931) 248.
[83] L. F. AUDRIETH, E. E. JUKKOLA and R. E. MEINTS and B. S. HOPKINS, *J. Am. Chem. Soc.*, 53 (1931) 1805.
[84] C. W. STILLWELL and L. F. AUDRIETH, *J. Am. Chem. Soc.*, 54 (1932) 472.
[85] E. E. JUKKOLA, L. F. AUDRIETH, and B. S. HOPKINS, *J. Am. Chem. Soc.*, 56 (1934) 303.
[86] G. L. PUTNAM and K. A. KOBE, *Trans. Electrochem. Soc.*, 74 (1938) 15, 609.
[87] H. SCHMIDT, I. WITTKOPF and G. JANDER, *Z. anorg. u. allg. Chem.*, 256 (1948) 113.
[88] T. P. WIER and F. H. HURLEY, U. S. Patent 2446, 349, 1948.
[89] A. BRENNER, *J. Electrochem. Soc.*, 103 (1956) 652.

90 J. H. CONNOR and A. BRENNER, *J. Electrochem. Soc.*, 103 (1956) 657.
91 W. E. REID, J. M. BISH and A. BRENNER, *J. Electrochem. Soc.*, 104 (1957) 21.
92 G. B. WOOD and A. BRENNER, *J. Electrochem. Soc.*, 104 (1957) 29.
93 J. H. CONNOR, W. E. REID and G. B. WOOD, *J. Electrochem. Soc.*, 104 (1957) 38.
94 H. SCHMIDT and H. STANGE, *Z. anorg. u. allg. Chem.*, 293 (1957) 274.

—, *oxidation at controlled potential*

95 H. LUND, *Acta Chem. Scand.*, 11 (1957) 1323.

—, *coulometry*

96 C. A. STREULI, *Anal. Chem.*, 28 (1956) 130.

—, *potentiometry*

97 J. R. PARTINGTON and J. W. SKEEN, *Trans. Faraday Soc.*, 30 (1934), 1062.
98 V. A. PLESKOV, *J. Phys. Chem. (U.S.S.R.)*, 22 (1948) 351.
99 O. TOMICEK and M. ZUKRIEGELOVA, *Chem. listy*, 46 (1952) 263.
100 O. TOMICEK, A. STODOLOVA and M. HERMAN, *Chem. listy*, 47 (1953) 516.
101 R. A. GLENN, *Anal. Chem.*, 25 (1953) 1916.
102 G. J. JANZ and H. TANIGUCHI, *Chem. Revs.*, 53 (1953) 397.
103 T. PAVLOPOULOS and H. STRAHLOW, *Z. physik. Chem.*, 2 (1954) 89.
104 V. NOVAK, *Chem. listy*, 49 (1955) 848.
105 E. SCARANO and A. CEGLIE, *Anal. Chim. Acta*, 12 (1955) 292.
106 H. C. MANDEL JR., W. M. McNABB and J. F. HAZEL, *J. Electrochem. Soc.*, 102 (1955) 263.
107 I. LINDQVIST, *Acta Chem. Scand.*, 9 (1955) 73, 79.
108 K. SCHWABE, *Naturwissenschaften*, 44 (1957) 350.
109 M. MANDEL and P. DECROLY, *Nature*, 182 (1958) 794.

—, *reviews, potentiometry in non-aqueous media*

110 J. T. STOCK and W. C. PURDY, *Chem. Revs.*, 57 (1958) 1159.
111 L. FISCHER, G. WINKLER and G. JANDER, *Z. Elektrochem.*, 62 (1958) 1.

—, *potentiometric acid–base titrations*

112 N. F. HALL and T. H. WERNER, *J. Am. Chem. Soc.*, 50 (1928) 2367.
113 N. F. HALL, *J. Am. Chem. Soc.*, 52 (1930) 5115.
114 G. SCHWARZENBACH, *Helv. Chim. Acta*, 14 (1931) 1069.
115 J. B. CONANT and B. F. CHOW, *J. Am. Chem. Soc.*, 55 (1933) 3745.
116 L. D. GOODHUE and R. M. HIXON, *J. Am. Chem. Soc.*, 57 (1935) 1688.
117 F. H. VERHOEK, *J. Am. Chem. Soc.*, 58 (1936) 2577.
118 I. M. KOLTHOFF and L. S. GUSS, *J. Am. Chem. Soc.*, 60 (1938) 2516.
119 I. M. KOLTHOFF and L. S. GUSS, *J. Am. Chem. Soc.*, 62 (1940) 249.
120 S. R. PALIT, *Ind. Eng. Chem., Anal. Ed.*, 18 (1946) 246.
121 J. P. WOLFF, *Anal. Chim. Acta*, 1 (1947) 90.
122 J. P. WOLFF, *Thèse*, Paris, 1948.
123 O. TOMICEK, *Collection Czechoslov. Chem. Communs.*, 13 (1948) 116.
124 M. L. MOSS, J. H. ELLIOTT and R. T. HALL, *Anal. Chem.*, 20 (1948) 784.
125 W. BROSER, *Makromol. Chem.*, 2 (1948) 248.
126 A. KIRRMANN and T. YVERNAUT, *Bull. soc. chim.*, 16 (1949) 538.
127 T. YVERNAUT, J. MORÉ and M. DURAND, *Bull. soc. chim.*, 16 (1949) 542.
128 R. SCHALL and P. RUMPF, *Compt. rend.*, 228 (1949) 926.
129 A. M. SKODIN, N. A. IZMAILOV and N. P. DZYNBA, *Zhur. Obshchei Khim.*, 20 (1950) 1999.
130 J. S. FRITZ, *Anal. Chem.*, 22 (1950) 1028.
131 A. M. SKODIN, N. A. IZMAILOV and N. P. DZYNBA, *Zhur. Obshchei Khim.*, 23 (1953) 27.
132 O. TOMICEK and P. VIDNER, *Chem. listy*, 47 (1953) 521.
133 O. TOMICEK and S. KREPELKA, *Chem. listy*, 47 (1953) 526.
134 D. H. EVERETT and S. E. RASMUSSEN, *J. Chem. Soc.*, 2812, 1954.
135 G. JANDER and H. KLAUSS, *J. Inorg. Nuclear Chem.*, 1 (1955) 126.
136 P. S. TUTUNDZIC and P. PUTANOV, *Glasnik Khem. Drushtva, Beograd*, 20 (1955) 157.
137 S. BRUCKENSTEIN and I. M. KOLTHOFF, *J. Am. Chem. Soc.*, 78 (1956) 2974.
138 I. M. KOLTHOFF, *Proc. XV Intern. Congr. Pure Applied Chem., Lisbon 1956*, p. 33.
139 I. M. KOLTHOFF and S. BRUCKENSTEIN, *J. Am. Chem. Soc.*, 79 (1957) 1.
140 A. J. MARTIN, *Anal. Chem.*, 29 (1957) 79.
141 D. B. BRUSS and G. E. A. WYLD, *Anal. Chem.*, 29 (1957) 232.
142 A. M. SKODIN, L. I. KARKUSAKI and M. J. KHIMENKO, *Zhur. Obshchei Khim.*, 27 (1957) 29.

Electrochemistry in fused salts

—, *voltammetry*

143 M. NACHTRIEB and M. STEINBERG, *J. Am. Chem. Soc.*, 70 (1948) 613.
144 Y. S. LYALIKOV and V. I. KARMAZIN, *Zavodskaya Lab.*, 14 (1948) 144.
145 Y. K. DELIMARSKY, E. M. SKOBETS and L. S. BERENBLYUM, *J. Phys. Chem. (U.S.S.R.)*, 22 (1948) 1108.
146 M. NACHTRIEB and M. STEINBERG, *J. Am. Chem. Soc.*, 72 (1950) 518.
147 Y. S. LYALIKOV, *Zhur. Anal. Khim.*, 5 (1950) 323.
148 Y. K. DELIMARSKY, *Ukrain. Khim. Zhur.*, 16 (1950) 414.
149 S. I. REMPEL, *Doklady Akad. Nauk SSSR.*, 74 (1950) 331.
150 J. J. LINGANE, *Anal. Chem.*, 23 (1951) 96.
151 N. G. CHOVNYK, *Doklady Akad. Nauk SSSR.*, 87 (1952) 1033.
152 Y. S. LYALIKOV, *Zhur. Anal. Khim.*, 8 (1953) 38.
153 Y. K. DELIMARSKY, B. F. MARKOV and L. S. BERENBLYUM, *Zhur. Fiz. Khim.*, 27 (1953) 1848.
154 Y. K. DELIMARSKY and I. D. PANCHENKO, *Doklady Akad. Nauk SSSR.*, 91 (1953) 115.
155 Y. K. DELIMARSKY and I. D. PANCHENKO, *Ukrain. Khim. Zhur.*, 19 (1953) 47.
156 R. A. OSTERYOUNG, *Ph. D. Thesis*, University of Illinois, 1954.
157 P. DROSSBACH and P. PETRICK, *Z. Elektrochem.*, 58 (1954) 95.
158 N. G. CHOVNYK, *Doklady Akad. Nauk SSSR.*, 95 (1954) 599.
159 Y. K. DELIMARSKY, *Uspekhi Khim.*, 23 (1954) 766.
160 N. G. CHOVNYK, *Doklady Akad. Nauk SSSR.*, 100 (1955) 495.
161 Y. K. DELIMARSKY, *Ukrain. Khim. Zhur.*, 21 (1955) 449.
162 I. D. PANCHENKO, *Ukrain. Khim. Zhur.*, 21 (1955) 468.
163 E. BLACK and T. DE VRIES, *Anal. Chem.*, 27 (1955) 906.
164 E. L. COLICHMAN, *Anal. Chem.*, 27 (1955) 1559.
165 N. G. CHOVNYK, *Referat. Zhur. Khim.*, 2 (1955) 1882.
166 I. D. PANCHENKO, *Ukrain. Khim. Zhur.*, 22 (1956) 1953.
167 W. S. FERGUSON, *Ph. D. Thesis*, University of Illinois, 1956.
168 N. G. CHOVNYK, *Zhur. Fiz. Khim.*, 30 (1956) 277.
169 H. A. LAITINEN, W. S. FERGUSON and R. A. OSTERYOUNG, *J. Electrochem. Soc.*, 104 (1957) 516.
170 H. A. LAITINEN and H. C. GAUR, *J. Electrochem. Soc.*, 104 (1957) 730.
171 H. A. LAITINEN, C. H. LIU and W. S. FERGUSON, *Anal. Chem.*, 30 (1958) 1266.
172 K. M. KALABALINA and Y. K. DELIMARSKY, *Dopovidi Akad. Nauk Ukr. R.S.R.*, 1957, 562.
173 Y. K. DELIMARSKY and K. M. KALABALINA, *Ukrain. Khim. Zhur.*, 23 (1957) 584.
174 Y. K. DELIMARSKY and K. M. KALABALINA, *Doklady Akad. Nauk SSSR.*, 116 (1957) 433.
175 L. D. YUSHINA and M. V. SMIRNOV, *Doklady Akad. Nauk SSSR.*, 115 (1957) 949.
176 H. KIDO, O. MATSUMOTO and Y. HAYAKAWA, *Sci. Repts. Saitama Univ., Ser. A2*, (1957) 161.
177 K. M. KALABALINA and Y. K. DELIMARSKY, *Ukrain. Khim. Zhur.*, 24 (1958) 152.
178 Y. K. DELIMARSKY, *Zhur. Obshchei Khim.*, 28 (1958) 1112.
179 L. SUSKI, *Zhur. Fizit. Khim.*, 32 (1958) 1393.

—, *electrolytic deposition of metals in fused salts*

180 V. GAERTNER, *Electrochimie pratique*, Eyrolles and Gauthiers-Villars, Paris, 1955, p. 376–418.
181 S. SENDEROFF and A. BRENNER, *J. Electrochem. Soc.*, 101 (1954) 16.
182 L. W. NIEDRACH and G. R. FOUNTAIN, *U. S. Atomic Energy Comm.*, KAPL. 1693, 1957.
183 S. MARION, *Bull. soc. chim.*, 1957, 522.
184 J. L. ANDRIEUX and J. DAUPHIN, *Compt. rend.*, 245 (1957) 1359.
185 S. ALÉONARD, *Bull. soc. chim.*, 1958, 827.
186 L. W. NIEDRACH and B. E. DEARING, *J. Electrochem. Soc.*, 105 (1958) 353.
187 J. BURGESS, C. T. BROWN and C. W. ROBERTS, *J. Appl. Chem.*, 8 (1958) 6.
188 D. E. COUCH and S. SENDEROFF, *Trans. Metall. Soc.*, 212 (1958) 320.
189 R. PIONTELLI, G. STERNHEIM and F. FUMAGALLI, *Ricerca sci.*, 28 (1958) 160.
190 C. MARZANO, *Plating*, 45 (1958) 941.

—, *potentiometry and amperometry*

191 B. LENGYEL and A. SAMMT, *Z. physik. Chem.*, 181 A (1937) 55.
192 E. M. SKOBETS and R. S. KAVETZKY, *Zhur. Obshchei Khim.*, 10 (1940) 21, 1858.
193 R. G. VERDIECK and L. F. YNTEMA, *J. Phys. Chem.*, 46 (1942) 344.
194 H. FLOOD and T. FORLAND, *Acta Chem. Scand.*, 1 (1947) 592.
195 Y. K. DELIMARSKY and R. S. KHAIMOVITCH, *Ukrain. Khim. Zhur.*, 15 (1949) 77.
196 Y. K. DELIMARSKY, *Zhur. Fiz. Khim.*, 24 (1950) 7.
197 Y. K. DELIMARSKY and A. A. KOLOTTI, *Ukrain. Khim. Zhur.*, 16 (1950) 3, 438.
198 E. ROCHOW and R. DIDTSCHENKO, *J. Am. Chem. Soc.*, 76 (1954) 3291.
199 H. CORIOU, J. DIRIAN and J. HURÉ, *Comm. énergie atomique (France), Rappt. No. 478 (1955)*.

[200] H. Coriou, J. Dirian and J. Huré, *J. Chim. phys.*, 52 (1955) 479.

[201] S. N. Flengas, *J. Chem. Soc.*, (1956) 534.

[202] W. J. Hamer, M. S. Malmberg and B. Rubin, *J. Electrochem. Soc.*, 103 (1956) 8.

[203] B. Porter and M. Feinleib, *J. Electrochem. Soc.*, 103 (1956) 300.

[204] S. N. Flengas and T. R. Ingraham, *Can. J. Chem.*, 35 (1957) 1139.

[205] Y. K. Delimarsky, *Uspekhi Khim.*, 26 (1957) 494.

[206] S. N. Flengas and T. R. Ingraham, *Can. J. Chem.*, 36 (1958) 1103.

[207] M. V. Smirnov and V. A. Chemezov, *Doklady Akad. Nauk SSSR.*, 120 (1958) 122.

[208] M. V. Smirnov and L. E. Ivanovsky, *Doklady Akad. Nauk SSSR.*, 121 (1958) 685.

[209] H. A. Laitinen and C. H. Liu, *J. Am. Chem. Soc.*, 80 (1958) 1015.

—, *recent electrochemical methods*

[210] J. E. B. Randles and W. White, *Z. Elektrochem.*, 59 (1955) 666.

[211] H. A. Laitinen and W. S. Ferguson, *Anal. Chem.*, 29 (1957) 4.

[212] J. M. Wood, *3rd Congr. Electrochem. Soc.*, Washington, May 1957.

[213] H. A. Laitinen and H. C. Gaur, *Anal. Chim. Acta*, 18 (1958) 3.

—, *coulometry (with potentiometric and amperometric indicator methods)*

[214] H. A. Laitinen and B. B. Bhatia, *Anal. Chem.*, 30 (1958) 1995.

DEFINITIONS, SYMBOLS AND UNITS

This appendix contains:

a) the principal symbols, units and conventions used in this book, referred to international conventions wherever they exist;

b) definitions of terms which could not conveniently be given in the text, but which may aid in understanding this book, in particular some chemical concepts;

c) a classification of the electrochemical methods of analysis.

POTENTIAL

Potential of an electrode with respect to a reference electrode: E. The potential of the normal hydrogen electrode (platinized platinum electrode, activity of H^+ ions in solution equal to 1, solution saturated with hydrogen under 760 mm Hg) is taken as zero by convention. *All the potential values given in this book are referred to the normal hydrogen electrode.* The values of the potential increase as the conditions become more oxidizing. The unit is the volt (V), the secondary unit is the millivolt (mV).

Standard potential: E_0. The oxidation potential of the redox system

$$aA + bB + \ldots. + ne \rightleftharpoons mM + pP + \ldots.$$

is given by the equation

$$E = E_0 + \frac{RT}{nF} \ln \frac{|A|^a \ |B|^b \ldots.}{|M|^m \ |P|^p \ldots.}$$

where $|A|$, $|B|$, etc. represent the *activities* of the substances A, B, etc.; E_0 is the standard potential of the system, and is equal to the oxidation potential when all the components of the system are present in unit activity. R is the gas constant, T the absolute temperature and F the faraday ($= 96500$ coulombs).

If one or more of the components of the system exist in the solid state (indicated by $\downarrow$), their activities are taken as one (or absorbed into the constant), as the solution is assumed to be saturated with the substance or substances in question.

When certain components exist in the gaseous state (indicated by $\uparrow$), the activity of each of these substances is taken as one (or absorbed in the constant) when the solution is saturated with the gas under standard atmospheric pressure.

Apparent standard potential: E'_0. The influence of factors such as complex formation or ionic strengths modifies the oxidation potential. It is therefore sometimes replaced by an empirical quantity which is however of practical importance, the apparant standard potential. This is the potential when each component of the system is present in a *concentration* of 1. This value, E'_0, is only valid for the medium in which it was determined.

Equilibrium potential: E_{eq}. This is the potential assumed by an isolated electrode ($i = 0$) placed in the solution. If only one redox system is present, the equilibrium potential is theoretically equal to the oxidation potential of the system. In practice, this is not true for a number of cases (see Chapter VII).

Mixed potential: E_M. This is an equilibrium potential measured when several redox systems are present, such that it is determined by *e.g.* the oxidant of one system and the reductant of another (see Chapter VII).

Half-wave potential: $E_{\frac{1}{2}}$. The value of the electrode potential when the electrolysis current is equal to half the limiting current. In simple cases, $E_{\frac{1}{2}}$ is not much different from E_0.

    The half-wave potential of a reduction (cathodic) step is denoted by $E_{\frac{1}{2}\,cat}$, and that of an oxidation (anodic) step by $E_{\frac{1}{2}\,an}$.

Potential difference between two electrodes: $E_A - E_C$ or ΔE.

Voltage applied between two electrodes: $V = E_A - E_C + |i|\,R$.

RATE OF ELECTROCHEMICAL REACTIONS

Current: i or I. The current is counted positive if it is due to an oxidation (anodic: i_{an}), and negative if it is due to a reduction (cathodic: i_{cat}). The absolute value of the current is denoted by $|i|$. The unit is the ampere (A); also used are the milliampere (mA) and the microampere (μA).

Current density: J. This is the electrolysis current per unit area (S) of the electrode: $J = i/S$. The most commonly used units of current density are the milliampere per square decimetre (mA/dm²) and the milliampere per square centimetre (mA/cm²).

Rate constants of a redox system. J_0 = absolute value of the electrolysis current density at an electrode of potential E_0 (standard potential) when one of the constituents of the redox system is present at the surface of the electrode in unit activity, and the other constituent is present in zero activity. α, β = transfer coefficients.

Overvoltage: η, η_{an} and η_{cat}. If E is the oxidation potential of a redox system, then the overvoltage is equal to the difference $E' - E$, where E' is the potential which must be applied to the electrode to give a certain oxidation or reduction current.

SOLUTIONS

Dielectric constant of the solvent: ε. The table on p. 342 gives the values of ε for the commonly used solvents.

Ionic charge: z. For example, Na⁺ has the charge $+1$, Al³⁺ the charge $+3$, Cl⁻ the charge -1 and $Fe(CN)_6^{4-}$ the charge -4.

Conductance of the solution: $\varkappa$. This is the reciprocal of the resistance R (in ohms, Ω) and the unit is the mho (Ω^{-1}).

Equivalent conductivity of an ion: l. Expressed in mho/cm².

Ionic strength: I. Defined as $I = \frac{1}{2} \Sigma\, z_i^2 C_i$, where z_i is the charge of each ion in solution and C_i is its concentration.

Concentrations, activities. The concentrations are represented by C. The concentrations of the substances A, B, etc. are written C_A, C_B, etc. They are expressed in gram-molecules or gram-ions per litre of solution. A solution is said to be $10^{-3}\ M$, $10^{-2}\ M$, $0.1\ M$, $1\ M$ when it contains 10^{-3}, 10^{-2}, 0.1 or 1 gram-molecule or gram-ion of the substance per litre. This is the molarity of the solution.

   The activity of a substance A is represented by $|A|$. The activity coefficient f_A is the ratio of the activity to the concentration: $|A| = f_A C_A$. The activity coefficient tends to unity as the solution becomes infinitely dilute.

   When the value of f_A is not known exactly, concentrations are often used in the place of activities in expressions involving the latter. This is justified if the ionic strength of the solution is constant (f_A = constant). The values of constants thus derived are "apparent" values, which only hold for that value of the ionic strength.

   For the sake of simplicity, we have made no difference between concentrations and activities, and have often used the symbols $|A|$, $|A|_{el}$, $|A|_s$, etc. to represent the concentration of A, the concentration of A at the electrode, the concentration of A in the solution, etc.

   But it must not be forgotten that in some cases the concentrations are used as an approximation for the activities (expression for the oxidation potential, mass action law, etc.) while in other cases the concentrations are used in their own right (expression for diffusion currents, etc.).

Acids and bases. An acid is a substance which is capable of yielding up a proton H^+ : NH_4^+, HF, HCO_3^- and H_2O are acids.

   A base is a substance which is capable of accepting a proton: NH_3, F^-, CO_3^{2-} and OH^- are bases.

   Acid–base equilibrium

$$\text{Base} + H^+ \rightleftharpoons \text{Acid}$$
$$NH_3 + H^+ \rightleftharpoons NH_4^+$$
$$F^- + H^+ \rightleftharpoons HF$$
$$OH^- + H^+ \rightleftharpoons H_2O$$
$$K_A = \frac{|\text{Base}|\,|H^+|}{|\text{Acid}|}$$

Complexes. A complex-formation reaction is the fixation of a ligand (ion or molecule) by an acceptor

$$\text{acceptor} + \text{ligand} \rightleftharpoons \text{complex}$$
$$Fe^{3+} + SCN^- \rightleftharpoons FeSCN^{2+}$$
$$FeSCN^{2+} + SCN^- \rightleftharpoons Fe(SCN)_2^+$$
$$Cu^{2+} + Cl^- \rightleftharpoons CuCl^+$$
$$Cu^{2+} + NH_3 \rightleftharpoons Cu(NH_3)^{2+}$$
$$Hg^{2+} + Y^{4-} \rightleftharpoons HgY^{2-}$$

where H_4Y represents ethylenediaminetetracetic acid (EDTA). The stability of a complex is determined by the equilibrium constant (law of mass action). We have used the *dissociation constant*

$$K = \frac{|\text{acceptor}|\,|\text{ligand}|}{|\text{complex}|}$$

$$pK = -\log K$$

Precipitation, redissolution of a precipitate.

The solubility of a substance is expressed as the molarity of the saturated solution.

In general, the law of mass action can be applied to precipitation or redissolution reactions, taking the activities of the sparingly soluble substances equal to 1 (or absorbed into the constant) on the supposition that the solution is saturated. For example

$$Al(OH)_3\downarrow + OH^- \rightleftharpoons AlO_2^- + 2\,H_2O \qquad K = \frac{|AlO_2^-|}{|OH^-|}$$

$$BiCl_4^- + H_2O \rightleftharpoons BiOCl\downarrow + 3\,Cl^- + 2\,H^+ \qquad K = \frac{|Cl^-|^3\,|H^+|^2}{|BiCl_4^-|}$$

Solubility product: s. In the particular case where the equilibrium constant reduces to a product of activities, it is called the solubility product. For example

$$Ag^+ + Cl^- \rightleftharpoons AgCl\downarrow \qquad s = |Ag^+|\,|Cl^-|$$

Buffers, buffer solutions. pH buffer. A solution is said to be buffered with respect to the pH if hydrogen ions can be added or removed without appreciably affecting the pH. Such a buffer solution is a solution of a weak acid and the corresponding base, *e.g.* acetic acid and sodium acetate

$$CH_3COO^- + H^+ \rightleftharpoons CH_3COOH \qquad\qquad pK_A$$

$$pH = pK_A + \log\frac{|CH_3COO^-|}{|CH_3COOH|}$$

If the concentrations of CH_3COOH and CH_3COO^- are sufficiently large compared to the concentration of H^+ involved, the pH hardly varies.

A solution may similarly be buffered with respect to any component (ion or molecule). For example, a pCl^- buffer

$$HgCl^+ + Cl^- \rightleftharpoons HgCl_2 \qquad\qquad pK$$

$$pCl^- = -\log|Cl^-| = pK + \log\frac{|HgCl^+|}{|HgCl_2|}$$

Potential buffer: this may be realized in the same way, *e.g.*

$$Fe(CN)_6^{3-} + e \rightleftharpoons Fe(CN)_6^{4-} \qquad\qquad E_0$$

$$E = E_0 + 0.058 \log\frac{|Fe(CN)_6^{3-}|}{|Fe(CN)_6^{4-}|}$$

Normality. Number of equivalents per litre. A normal solution of an acid contains one gram-ion of exchangeable H^+ ions per litre, and a normal solution of an oxidizing agent contains one available gram-electron per litre. The normality is denoted by N.

Amalgam. The solution of a metal (or metal–mercury compound) in mercury. If the metal is denoted by M, the amalgam is denoted by M(Hg). The concentration of the metal in the amalgam is denoted by $|M(Hg)|$.

TRANSPORT PHENOMENA

Migration current: i_M. The part of the total current i which is due to the migration of ions.

Diffusion current: i_D. The part of the total current which is due to the diffusion of ions.

Transport number of an ion: t. This is the fraction of the migration current due to the migration of the ion in question

$$t = \frac{lzc}{\Sigma\, l_i z_i c_i}$$

where $\Sigma\, l_i z_i c_i$ denotes the sum of the terms lzc for all the ions present in solution.

Diffusion constant of an ion or a molecule: D_0. Unit: cm²/sec. The table on p. 129 gives the values of some diffusion constants in aqueous solution, and the table on p. 340 gives some values of D_0 in other solvents.

Limiting diffusion current (in the steady state): i_l. The limiting diffusion currents due to the substances A, B, etc. are denoted by i_A, i_B, etc.; k_A, k_B, etc. are the corresponding diffusion coefficients.

OTHER TERMS

Titrations. A titration consists in the progressive addition of a reactant to the substance to be determined. We have denoted the ratio of the amount of reactant added to the original amount of the substance to be titrated by x.

End point. This is the point at which the reactant has been added in an amount equivalent to the substance to be titrated, *i.e.* in the stoichiometric proportion. If the reaction is

$$A + nB \rightarrow AB_n$$

the end point occurs for $x = n$. The titration may be carried out volumetrically or coulometrically.

Measurements

1. Simple terms describing the measurement of one quantity.

Volumetry. The measurement of a volume (denoted by v). Volumetric analysis: determination of the amount of a substance by measurement of the volume of titrant needed to reach the end point.

Coulometry. The measurement of an amount of electricity (denoted by Q), *i.e.* of a number of coulombs. Coulometric titration: a titration in which the reactant is prepared electrochemically by the expenditure of a measured amount of electricity.

The coulomb is the amount of electricity carried by a current of one ampère in one second. The faraday is the amount of electricity corresponding to one gram-electron, *i.e.* 96 500 coulombs. If n is the number of electrons involved in an electrochemical reaction, n faradays are needed to electrolyze one gram-ion or one gram-molecule of the substance in question.

Gravimetry. The measurement of the mass of a compound. Gravimetric analysis: the weight of a definite compound is determined.

Potentiometry. The measurement of the potential of an electrode or the potential difference between two electrodes. In potentiometry at constant current, the value of the small imposed current is denoted by i_ε.

Amperometry. The measurement of a current i.

Chronometry. The measurement of a time t. Units: second (sec), minute (min) and hour (hr).

2. *Terms describing the measurement of two quantities.*

In this case a relationship between two of the variables v, Q, E, i and t is determined.

Potentiometric volumetry: $E = f(v)$.

Amperometric volumetry: $i = f(v)$.

Potentiometric coulometry: $E = f(Q)$.

Amperometric coulometry: $i = f(Q)$.

Voltammetry: $f(i, E) = 0$. This term is restricted to the determination of the current–potential curves and their properties in the steady state.

Chronopotentiometry: $E = f(t)$. $\tau =$ transition time.

Chronoamperometry: $i = f(t)$.

3. *More general terms.*

The words determination, electrolysis, polarization, polarized, depolarizing and polarography are less precise, and thus more general, than the above terms. They may be of use when the precise description of a method is too complicated, when it is not wished to coin a new term, and when it is wished to group several types of measurements under the same name. We have however avoided the use of such words whenever possible.

Example of their use are oscillographic polarography and a.c. polarography. We have used the more precise term "current–potential curve" in place of "polarization curve".

4. *Terms indicating the conditions under which the measurements are carried out.*

Constant potential, constant current. The potential (or the current) is kept constant during the measurement, *e.g.* constant-current coulometry, constant-current potentiometric volumetry, constant-potential amperometric volumetry, constant-current chronopotentiometry.

Imposed potential, imposed current. The variation of the potential (or current) during the measurement is imposed. For example, voltammetry may be carried out at imposed potential or at imposed current. In linear chronoamperometry, the potential is made to vary linearly with respect to time. Oscillographic polarography with a sinusoidal current: the current imposed is of constant amplitude and varies sinusoidally with respect to time.

Controlled potential. This term is similar in meaning to the previous ones, but less strict. Electrolysis at controlled potential: the potential is kept within certain limits.

Anodic stripping (see p. 329): Reduction followed by reoxidation. The measurement is carried out during the redissolution. Anodic stripping coulometry: an amount of electricity is measured. Anodic stripping polarography, chronopotentiometry, chronoamperometry, etc.

INSTRUMENTATION

Steady state (see p. 17): the electrolysis phenomena are independent of time.

Pseudo-steady state (see p. 144): the phenomena are independent of time if the average over a relatively short period of time is considered.

Non-steady state: the phenomena change with time.

Fixed and moving electrodes (see p. 140): mercury surface, hanging mercury drop electrode, rotating electrode, vibrating electrode, dropping mercury electrode, rotating dropping mercury electrode, mercury jet electrode, etc.

Indicator electrode, comparison electrode, reference electrode (see p. 148): the table on p. 150 gives the values of the potentials of some currently used comparison electrodes with respect to the normal hydrogen electrode.

Potentiostat, amperostat: apparatus which provides a constant potential difference or a constant current (see p. 134 and 135).

Coulometers: chemical or electronic (see p. 259).

Differentiating circuit: an electronic or electrochemical device which allows the derivative of a variable to be measured (see p. 196).

CLASSIFICATION OF THE ELECTROCHEMICAL INDICATOR METHODS

An indicator method is a method of following the concentration of a given substance. Coulometry and volumetry can only be used to determine a concentration in conjunction with an indicator method to detect the end point.

The table on p. 367 summarizes the electrochemical indicator methods. The variations of C can be effected either by volumetry or by coulometry, and are thus proportional either to a volume of solution, v, or to an amount of electricity Q.

For example, in potentiometric titrations $E = f(v)$ for a volumetric titration, and $E = f(Q)$ for a coulometric titration.

TABLE I

DEFINITION AND CLASSIFICATION OF ELECTROCHEMICAL INDICATOR METHODS

		Imposed	*Measured*	*Name*
	Steady state $[f(i,E,c) = 0]$	$c = $ const.	$i = f(E)$ or $E = f(i)$	Voltammetry
		$i = $ const. (o or i_ε)	$E = f(c)$ or $\Delta E = f(c)$	Potentiometric titrations (with one or two indicator electrodes)
		$E = $ const. or $\Delta E = $ const.	$i = f(c)$	Amperometric titrations (with one or two indicator electrodes)
	Steady state + periodic state of small amplitude	$c = $ const. $E + \Delta E\sim$	$i \sim$ *i.e.* $\dfrac{\mathrm{d}i}{\mathrm{d}E} = f(E)$	a. c. polarography: sine-wave polarography
		$c = $ const. $E + \Delta E \sqcap$	$i \sqcap$ *i.e.* $\dfrac{\mathrm{d}i}{\mathrm{d}E} = f(E)$	square-wave polarography
		$\Delta E\sim$ or $\Delta E \sqcap$	$\dfrac{\mathrm{d}i}{\mathrm{d}E} = f(c)$ $(i = 0)$	a. c. amperometric titrations
		$\Delta i\sim$ or $\Delta i \sqcap$	$\dfrac{\mathrm{d}E}{\mathrm{d}i} = f(c)$ $(i = 0)$	a. c. potentiometric titrations
Non-steady state $f(i,E,t,c) = 0$	not periodic	$c = $ const. $E = $ const.	$i = f(t)$	Chronoamperometry
		$c = $ const. $E = E_i + \nu t$	$i = f(t)$ or $i = f(E)$	Linear chronoamperometry
		$c = $ const. $i = $ const.	$E = f(t)$	Chronopotentiometry
		$i = $ const.	$E = f(t)$ $\tau = f(c)$	Chronopotentiometric titrations
	periodic (large amplitude)	$c = $ const. $E = $ const. $+ \nu t$ (saw-tooth)	$i = f(t)$ or $i = f(E)$	Oscillographic polarography: with saw-tooth voltage
		$c = $ const. $E = E\sim$	$i = f(t)$ or $i = f(E)$	with sine-wave voltage
		$c = $ const. $i = i\sim$	$E = f(t)$ or $\dfrac{\mathrm{d}E}{\mathrm{d}t} = f(t)$ or $\dfrac{\mathrm{d}E}{\mathrm{d}t} = f(E)$	with sine-wave current
Non-steady state + periodic state of small amplitude		$c = $ const. $i = i_0 + \Delta i\sim$	$E\sim$ *i.e.* $\dfrac{\mathrm{d}E}{\mathrm{d}t} = f(t)$	a. c. chronopotentiometry

References p. 371

TABLE II

STANDARD OXIDO-REDUCTION POTENTIALS OF SOME SYSTEMS

(at 25° C; ionic strength = 0)

Ag

$Ag^+ + e$	$\rightleftarrows Ag\downarrow$	$+ 0.80$ V
$AgCl\downarrow + e$	$\rightleftarrows Ag\downarrow + Cl^-$	$+ 0.22$ V
$Ag^{2+} + e$	$\rightleftarrows Ag^+$	$+ 2.00$ V

Al

$Al^{3+} + 3e$	$\rightleftarrows Al\downarrow$	$- 1.66$ V

As

$As\downarrow + 3\ H^+ + 3e$	$\rightleftarrows H_3As\uparrow$	$- 0.60$ V
$HAsO_2 + 3\ H^+ + 3e$	$\rightleftarrows As\downarrow + 2\ H_2O$	$+ 0.25$ V
$H_3AsO_4 + 2\ H^+ + 2e$	$\rightleftarrows HAsO_2 + 2\ H_2O$	$+ 0.56$ V

Au

$AuCl_4^- + 3e$	$\rightleftarrows Au\downarrow + 4\ Cl^-$	$+ 0.99$ V

Ba

$Ba^{2+} + 2e$	$\rightleftarrows Ba\downarrow$	$- 2.90$ V

Be

$Be^{2+} + 2e$	$\rightleftarrows Be\downarrow$	$- 1.85$ V

Bi

$BiO^+ + 2\ H^+ + 3e$	$\rightleftarrows Bi\downarrow + H_2O$	$+ 0.32$ V

Br

$Br_2 + 2e$	$\rightleftarrows 2\ Br^-$	$+ 1.09$ V
$2\ HBrO + 2\ H^+ + 2e$	$\rightleftarrows Br_2 + 2\ H_2O$	$+ 1.6$ V
$2\ BrO_3^- + 12\ H^+ + 10e$	$\rightleftarrows Br_2 + 6\ H_2O$	$+ 1.5$ V

Ca

$Ca^{2+} + 2e$	$\rightleftarrows Ca\downarrow$	$- 2.87$ V

Cd

$Cd^{2+} + 2e$	$\rightleftarrows Cd\downarrow$	$- 0.40$ V

Ce

$Ce^{3+} + 3e$	$\rightleftarrows Ce\downarrow$	$- 2.33$ V
$Ce^{IV} + e$	$\rightleftarrows Ce^{III}$	$+ 1.70$ V (N $HClO_4$)

Cl

$Cl_2 + 2e$	$\rightleftarrows 2\ Cl^-$	$+ 1.39$ V
$2\ HClO + 2\ H^+ + 2e$	$\rightleftarrows Cl_2\uparrow + 2\ H_2O$	$+ 1.63$ V
$ClO_4^- + 2\ H^+ + 2e$	$\rightleftarrows ClO_3^- + H_2O$	$+ 1.19$ V

Co

$Co^{2+} + 2e$	$\rightleftarrows Co\downarrow$	$- 0.28$ V
$Co^{III} + e$	$\rightleftarrows Co^{2+}$	$+ 1.80$ V (N HNO_3)

Cr

$Cr^{3+} + 3e$	$\rightleftarrows Cr\downarrow$	$- 0.74$ V
$Cr^{III} + e$	$\rightleftarrows Cr^{II}$	$- 0.38$ V (N HCl)
$Cr_2O_7^{2-} + 14\ H^+ + 6e$	$\rightleftarrows 2\ Cr^{3+} + 7\ H_2O$	$+ 1.33$ V

Cu

$Cu^{2+} + 2e$	$\rightleftarrows Cu\downarrow$	$+ 0.34$ V

F

$$F_2\uparrow + 2e \quad\rightleftarrows\quad 2\,F^- \qquad\qquad + 2.87\ V$$

Fe

$$Fe^{2+} + 2e \quad\rightleftarrows\quad Fe\downarrow \qquad\qquad - 0.44\ V$$

$$Fe^{3+} + e \quad\rightleftarrows\quad Fe^{2+} \qquad\qquad + 0.77\ V$$

$$(FeCN)_6{}^{3-} + e \quad\rightleftarrows\quad Fe(CN)_6{}^{4-} \qquad\qquad + 0.36\ V$$

Ga

$$Ga^{3+} + 3e \quad\rightleftarrows\quad Ga\downarrow \qquad\qquad - 0.56\ V$$

Ge

$$Ge^{2+} + 2e \quad\rightleftarrows\quad Ge\downarrow \qquad\qquad \infty\ 0.0\ \ V$$

$$GeO_2\downarrow + 4\,H^+ + 4e \quad\rightleftarrows\quad Ge\downarrow + 2\,H_2O \qquad\qquad - 0.15\ V$$

Hg

$$Hg_2{}^{2+} + 2e \quad\rightleftarrows\quad 2\,Hg\downarrow \qquad\qquad + 0.79\ V$$

$$Hg_2Cl_2\downarrow + 2e \quad\rightleftarrows\quad 2\,Hg\downarrow + 2\,Cl^- \qquad\qquad + 0.27\ V$$

$$2\,Hg^{2+} + 2e \quad\rightleftarrows\quad Hg_2{}^{2+} \qquad\qquad + 0.91\ V$$

I

$$I_2\downarrow + 2e \quad\rightleftarrows\quad 2\,I^- \qquad\qquad + 0.54\ V$$

$$I_2 + 2e \quad\rightleftarrows\quad 2\,I^- \qquad\qquad + 0.62\ V$$

$$I_3{}^- + 2e \quad\rightleftarrows\quad 3\,I^- \qquad\qquad + 0.54\ V$$

$$HIO + H^+ + 2e \quad\rightleftarrows\quad I^- + H_2O \qquad\qquad + 0.99\ V$$

$$2\,IO_3{}^- + 12\,H^+ + 10e \quad\rightleftarrows\quad I_2 + 6\,H_2O \qquad\qquad + 1.19\ V$$

$$H_5IO_6 + H^+ + 2e \quad\rightleftarrows\quad IO_3{}^- + 3\,H_2O \qquad \sim + 1.6\ \ V$$

In

$$In^{3+} + 3e \quad\rightleftarrows\quad In\downarrow \qquad\qquad - 0.33\ V$$

K

$$K^+ + e \quad\rightleftarrows\quad K\downarrow \qquad\qquad - 2.92\ V$$

Li

$$Li^+ + e \quad\rightleftarrows\quad Li\downarrow \qquad\qquad - 3.03\ V$$

Mg

$$Mg^{2+} + 2e \quad\rightleftarrows\quad Mg\downarrow \qquad\qquad - 2.37\ V$$

Mn

$$Mn^{2+} + 2e \quad\rightleftarrows\quad Mn\downarrow \qquad\qquad - 1.19\ V$$

$$MnO_2 + 4\,H^+ + 2e \quad\rightleftarrows\quad Mn^{2+} + 2\,H_2O \qquad\qquad + 1.23\ V$$

$$MnO_4{}^- + 4\,H^+ + 3e \quad\rightleftarrows\quad MnO_2\downarrow + 2\,H_2O \qquad\qquad + 1.69\ V$$

Mo

$$Mo^{3+} + 3e \quad\rightleftarrows\quad Mo\downarrow \qquad \sim - 0.2\ \ V$$

$$Mo^V + 2e \quad\rightleftarrows\quad Mo^{III} \qquad\qquad + 0.11\ V\ (N\ HCl)$$

$$\qquad\qquad\qquad\qquad\qquad\qquad\qquad\qquad - 0.01\ V\ (N\ H_2SO_4)$$

$$MoO_2{}^{2+} + 2\,H^+ + e \quad\rightleftarrows\quad MoO^{3+} + H_2O \qquad\qquad + 0.48\ V$$

N

$$HNO_2 + H^+ + e \quad\rightleftarrows\quad NO\uparrow + H_2O \qquad\qquad + 0.99\ V$$

$$NO_3{}^- + 3\,H^+ + 2e \quad\rightleftarrows\quad HNO_2 + H_2O \qquad\qquad + 0.94\ V$$

Na

$$Na^+ + e \quad\rightleftarrows\quad Na\downarrow \qquad\qquad - 2.70\ V$$

Ni

$$Ni^{2+} + 2e \quad\rightleftarrows\quad Ni\downarrow \qquad\qquad - 0.23\ V$$

References p. 371

O

$H_2O_2 + 2\ H^+ + 2e$	$\rightleftarrows 2\ H_2O$	$+ 1.77$ V
$O_2\uparrow + 4\ H^+ + 4e$	$\rightleftarrows 2\ H_2O$	$+ 1.23$ V
$O_2\uparrow + 2\ H^+ + 2e$	$\rightleftarrows H_2O_2$	$+ 0.69$ V
$O_3\uparrow + 2\ H^+ + 2e$	$\rightleftarrows O_2\uparrow + H_2O$	$+ 2.07$ V

P

$H_3PO_3 + 2\ H^+ + 2e$	$\rightleftarrows H_3PO_2 + H_2O$	$- 0.50$ V

Pb

$Pb^{2+} + 2e$	$\rightleftarrows Pb\downarrow$	$- 0.13$ V
$Pb^{4+} + 2e$	$\rightleftarrows Pb^{2+}$	$+ 1.8$ V

Pd

$Pd^{2+} + 2e$	$\rightleftarrows Pd\downarrow$	$+ 0.99$ V
$PdCl_4{}^{2-} + 2e$	$\rightleftarrows Pd\downarrow + 4\ Cl^-$	$+ 0.62$ V
$PdCl_6{}^{2-} + 2e$	$\rightleftarrows PdCl_4{}^{2-} + 2\ Cl^-$	$+ 1.29$ V

Pt

$PtCl_4{}^{2-} + 2e$	$\rightleftarrows Pt\downarrow + 4\ Cl^-$	$+ 0.73$ V
$PtCl_6{}^{2-} + 2e$	$\rightleftarrows PtCl_4{}^{2-} + 2\ Cl^-$	$+ 0.74$ V

Re

$ReO_4{}^- + 4\ H^+ + 3e$	$\rightleftarrows ReO_2\downarrow + 2\ H_2O$	$+ 0.51$ V

S

$S\downarrow + 2\ H^+ + 2e$	$\rightleftarrows H_2S$	$+ 0.14$ V
$S_{rhomb}\downarrow + 2e$	$\rightleftarrows S^{2-}$	$- 0.48$ V
$2\ H_2SO_3 + H^+ + 2e$	$\rightleftarrows HS_2O_4{}^- + 2\ H_2$	$- 0.08$ V
$SO_4{}^{2-} + 4\ H^+ + 2e$	$\rightleftarrows H_2SO_3 + H_2O$	$+ 0.17$ V
$S_2O_8{}^{2-} + 2e$	$\rightleftarrows 2\ SO_4{}^{2-}$	$+ 2.0$ V

Sb

$Sb\downarrow + 3\ H^+ + 3e$	$\rightleftarrows H_3Sb\uparrow$	$- 0.51$ V
$SbO^+ + 2\ H^+ + 3e$	$\rightleftarrows Sb\downarrow + H_2O$	$+ 0.21$ V
$Sb_2O_5\downarrow + 6\ H^+ + 4e$	$\rightleftarrows 2\ SbO^+ + 3\ H_2O$	$+ 0.58$ V

Se

$Se\downarrow + 2\ H^+ + 2e$	$\rightleftarrows H_2Se\uparrow$	$- 0.40$ V
$H_2SeO_3 + 4\ H^+ + 4e$	$\rightleftarrows Se\downarrow + 3\ H_2O$	$+ 0.74$ V
$SeO_4{}^{2-} + 4\ H^+ + 2e$	$\rightleftarrows H_2SeO_3 + H_2O$	$+ 1.15$ V

Si

$SiO_2\downarrow + 4\ H^+ + 4e$	$\rightleftarrows Si\downarrow + 2\ H_2O$	$- 0.86$ V

Sn

$Sn^{2+} + 2e$	$\rightleftarrows Sn\downarrow$	$- 0.14$ V
$Sn^{IV} + 2e$	$\rightleftarrows Sn^{II}$	$+ 0.14$ V (N HCl)

Sr

$Sr^{2+} + 2e$	$\rightleftarrows Sr\downarrow$	$- 2.89$ V

Te

$Te\downarrow + 2\ H^+ + 2e$	$\rightleftarrows H_2Te\uparrow$	$- 0.72$ V
$TeO_2\downarrow + 4\ H^+ + 4e$	$\rightleftarrows Te\downarrow + 2\ H_2O$	$+ 0.53$ V
$H_6TeO_6\downarrow + 2\ H^+ + 2e$	$\rightleftarrows TeO_2\downarrow + 4\ H_2O$	$+ 1.02$ V

Th

$Th^{4+} + 4e$	$\rightleftarrows Th\downarrow$	$- 1.90$ V

Ti

$Ti^{3+} + e$	$\rightleftarrows$	Ti^{2+}	$- 0.37$ V
$Ti^{IV} + e$	$\rightleftarrows$	Ti^{III}	$+ 0.12$ V ($2\,M\,H_2SO_4$)

Tl

$Tl^+ + e$	$\rightleftarrows$	$Tl\downarrow$	$- 0.34$ V
$Tl^{3+} + 2e$	$\rightleftarrows$	Tl^+	$+ 1.28$ V

U

$U^{3+} + 3e$	$\rightleftarrows$	$U\downarrow$	$- 1.8$ V
$U^{4+} + e$	$\rightleftarrows$	U^{3+}	$- 0.63$ V
$UO_2^{2+} + 4\,H^+ + 2e$	$\rightleftarrows$	$U^{4+} + 2\,H_2O$	$\sim + 0.31$ V

V

$V^{2+} + e$	$\rightleftarrows$	$V\downarrow$	$\sim - 1.2$ V
$V^{3+} + e$	$\rightleftarrows$	V^{2+}	$- 0.26$ V
$VO^{2+} + 2\,H^+ + e$	$\rightleftarrows$	$V^{3+} + H_2O$	$+ 0.36$ V
$VO_2^+ + 2\,H^+ + e$	$\rightleftarrows$	$VO^{2+} + H_2O$	$+ 1.00$ V

W

$2\,WO_3\downarrow + 2\,H^+ + 2e$	$\rightleftarrows$	$W_2O_5\downarrow + H_2O$	$- 0.03$ V
$WO_3\downarrow + 6\,H^+ + 6e$	$\rightleftarrows$	$W\downarrow + 3\,H_2O$	$- 0.09$ V

Zn

$Zn^{2+} + 2e$	$\rightleftarrows$	$Zn\downarrow$	$- 0.76$ V

Zr

$ZrO_2\downarrow + 4\,H^+ + 4e$	$\rightleftarrows$	$Zr\downarrow + 2\,H_2O$	$- 1.43$ V

See G. CHARLOT, D. BÉZIER and J. COURTOT, *Constantes sélectionnées-Potentiels d'oxydo-réduction. Tables de Constantes*, Pergamon Press, London, 1958.

Half-wave potentials: see references page 220.

J. BJERRUM, G. SCHWARZENBACH and L. G. SILLÉN, *Stability Constants of Metal-ion Complexes with Solubility Products of Inorganic Substances*, Part I: Organic Ligands, Part II: Inorganic Ligands, The Chemical Society, London, 1957 and 1958.

Diffusion constants
see p. 129 and 340.

Dielectric constants
see p. 342.

INDEX